W9-BLR-965

Motor Learning

Principles and Practices

Second Edition

John N. Drowatzky
The University of Toledo
Toledo, Ohio

Macmillan Publishing Company
New York
Collier Macmillan Publishers
London

Printed in the United States of America
Library of Congress Catalog Number 80-69551
ISBN 0-02-330740-4

Macmillan Publishing Company
866 Third Avenue
New York, N.Y. 10022
Collier Macmillan CANADA, Inc.

Printing 4 5 6 7 Year 7 8 9 0 1

Dedicated to

Minnie Louise
Linnea Louise
Kara Louise
Katrina Leigh

Contents

Preface

The physical education classroom is a dynamic ever-changing environment. Physical educators must mold and shape this environment to promote learning and facilitate performance. Not all factors that affect the teaching situation, however, are under an instructor's control. Therefore, the instructor must determine what factors can be controlled and what must be accepted. Levels of maturation and past experiences of pupils must be accepted, as teachers have little or no control over these factors. Principles of learning, on the other hand, can be applied by an instructor to produce optimal organization of practice situations.

This edition of *Motor Learning*, like the first edition, focuses on three central factors composing the learning situation in physical education: the learning process, the learner, and the task. The material dealing with the learning process describes the ways in which learning can occur and indicates the changes that occur within learners as skills are acquired. The changing nature of the learning process is emphasized and highlighted. Each learner is unique, bringing individual strengths and weaknesses to each situation. The material relating to the learner emphasizes the nature of individual differences and such characteristics as personality, perception, and motivation. The material relating to the task indicates techniques that an instructor can use to more effectively organize the instructional setting. Inasmuch as teaching remains an art, a knowledgeable and successful teacher blends the central foci of student, task, and learning process into a dynamic, powerful situation. It is indeed a joy to be part of stimulating teaching-learning situations.

The material in this edition has been updated, revised, and in some cases newly developed. One change that is immediately evident is the placement of pertinent principles at the end of each chapter. These "Guiding Principles for the Teacher" are brief statements of major concepts, which are explained in more detail in the chapter. The chapter dealing with personality has been completely revised to better describe how a student's personality plays a part in the learning process. Finally in keeping with current motor learning research, a chapter dealing with information processing has been added. Here the concept of motor programs and feedback-controlled movements are described and applied to motor activity. As much of the research in this area involves reaction time and movement time, the chapters have been rearranged so that timing and information processing are presented in sequence.

Once again, I would like to thank those who made it possible for me to write this text, my professors, colleagues, and students. Learning proves to be a two-way street; I gain as much from the process as my students do. I would also like to thank my wife, Linnea, and daughters, Kara and Katrina, for their support and understanding throughout the project.

February 1981 *J. N. D.*

1 Basic Concepts of Motor Learning

The study of motor learning—of how people learn physical skills and what factors enhance or detract from physical performance—provides important information for physical education teachers, coaches, and curriculum planners. Principles of motor learning can aid in the selection of activities, planning for instructional progression, development and use of drills, formulation of instructional strategies, and making provisions for individual differences among students.

Consider the following situations in which an understanding of motor learning could aid a teacher or coach. A common problem in athletic performance is described by Ernest L. Thayer (1964) in "Casey at the Bat":

> Then from the gladdened multitude went up a joyous
> yell,
> It bounded on the mountain top and rattled in the dell,
> It struck upon the hillside, and rebounded in the flat,
> For Casey, mighty Casey, was advancing to the bat.
>
> There was ease in Casey's manner as he stepped into
> his place,
> There was pride in Casey's bearing and a smile on
> Casey's face,

And when responding to the cheers he lightly doffed his hat,
No stranger in the crowd could doubt, 'twas Casey at the bat. . . .
Ten thousand eyes were on him as he rubbed his hands with dirt,
Five thousand tongues applauded as he wiped them on his shirt,
And while the writhing pitcher ground the ball into his hips—
Defiance gleamed from Casey's eye—a sneer curled Casey's lips. . . .

The sneer is gone from Casey's lip; his teeth are clenched with hate,
He pounds with cruel violence his bat upon the plate;
And now the pitcher holds the ball, and now he lets it go,
And now the air is shattered by the force of Casey's blow.

Oh! Somewhere in the favored land the sun is shining bright,
The band is playing somewhere, and somewhere hearts are light,
And somewhere men are laughing, and somewhere children shout;
But there is no joy in Mudville—mighty Casey has "Struck Out."

Similar frustrations can readily be observed in coaching and teaching situations. For example, a young softball player might perform well during practice and yet, on the day of the game, with his or her parents in the stands, muff easy fly balls. The same types of mistakes occur in the performing arts: young artists sometimes miscue during their dance or recital before an audience of their friends and relatives.

Do such mishaps indicate a lack of practice, or was the faulty performance the result of some other factor? Heightened levels of motivation might well explain failures such as Casey's. A teacher or coach who is aware of factors that affect motivation could help a performer keep the level of arousal within bounds so that it does not interfere with performance.

In the "old days," one learned to swim by being thrown into deep water, to sink or swim. Today, however, swimming is taught by breaking the instruction into small units following a carefully planned progression. Research on teaching has helped develop the distinction between whole instruction and part instruction. Teachers can devise the most advantageous form of presentation on the basis of the size of the instructional unit, the meaningfulness of the material, and the ability of the students. Some materials can be presented in large, complicated units, and some must be taught in small units to achieve the best teaching-learning situation.

Some time ago (so the story goes) a basketball coach required players to mentally rehearse their basketball skills every waking moment outside of practice. One day, the coach questioned the players to see whether they followed this instruction. The team's star forward admitted to not always thinking of basketball away from the court, and so the coach took that player off the team. Today, using studies about mental practice, we can determine whether the coach's actions were appropriate.

These examples illustrate teaching and coaching situations in which motor learning principles can be used to advantage. Typical topics for research in motor learning are suggested by the following questions:

Do beginning performers learn physical skills more quickly in front of interested spectators or in isolated practice sessions?

How can bulletin boards and other audiovisual aids be used as teaching devices?

How can a coach or teacher estimate the potential of a player or student who has not yet learned a particular sports skill?

Can the ability to hit curve balls be greatly improved by practice?

How does a young child learn a complex motor skill?

What major problems do beginners face when they learn to play tennis?

Should sports skills be taught by drilling individual movements?

Should players be taught how to self-analyze their sports performances?

How should a coach treat a team after a defeat or treat players after they make mistakes?

Should a performer focus attention on his or her own movements?

This text provides principles of motor learning that can be used for guidance in the teaching of motor skills. The studies that form the basis of this material vary in generality. Further, research is lacking in some areas. The most notable example is the absence of studies using female subjects, particularly in athletic situations. Although it is highly probable that boys and girls react the same in most situations, a need for such research exists. Likewise, research is needed to provide information that teachers and coaches can use to meet new classroom situations created by Title IX and the Education for All Handicapped Children Act.

MATURATION AND LEARNING

We plan, we move, we change the world around us. These are lifelong processes. Human motor activity is present at birth and continues throughout our lives. Movements that have been executed before birth begin to be extended and developed almost as soon as scientific observations of an infant can be made. From this early starting point, both maturation and learning affect an individual's development.

Maturation is the process of development through which an individual becomes more adult. It is a sensitive and intricate process, which depends on organic growth and developmental factors rather than practice or experience. That is, maturation involves variables that are internal to an individaul. It is not affected by the individual's activity, and it influences behavior even during periods of minimal exchange between the person and the environment.

Learning, in contrast, requires activity. It modifies an individual's behavior only during periods when the person interacts with the environment. Learning is reflected in behavior that is acquired in response to one's environment. Maturation, together with past experience, sets limits on an individual's behavioral repertoire and plasticity, so that one's level of maturation determines one's potential for learning. Although maturation and learning can be described separately, they are so closely interwoven in the total growth process that it is impossible to separate them completely.

Life can be described as a process of continual adaptation, both in physical structure and in behavior. Motor learning is the process of adaptation of behavior involving movement and muscular response.

Researchers have generally looked at behavioral adaptation in terms of mental, social, and physical development. Mental development is studied through changes in abstract reasoning abilities, social development through changes in relationships with others, and physical development through the expansion and elaboration of movement and muscular responses.

Motor behaviors depend on other factors besides learning, however. Our responses can vary greatly from place to place and from time to time. A particular motor behavior used under particular conditions is also determined by such factors as motivation, the nature of the external environment, and the organizational state of a person's responses.

Motivation commonly refers to internal and emotional states (Morgan and King, 1966). It reflects self-concept and one's view of his or her own abilities, the need to engage in a particular activity, and expectations about the outcome and long-range consequences of the activity.

Responses to the external environment depend on the stimulus patterns that are present and on physical conditions that affect performance, such as temperature (just observe the number of people participating in physical activity during the summer as opposed to the winter).

The organizational state of a person's behavior reflects his or her level of maturity and past experiences. Some behaviors develop in a regular sequence, regardless of training, and thus are results of maturation rather than learning.

CLASSIFICATION OF MOTOR RESPONSES

Postural, Transport, and Manipulative Movements

Movement is structured in response to temporal and spatial characteristics of the environment. Both of these characteristics must be taken into account if efficient, accurate motor behavior is to develop. Smith and Smith (1962) suggested that motor responses are composed of three types of movements: postural, transport, and manipulative movements (see Figure 1.1).

Postural movements tend to be gross adjustments of the body that regulate the body's position in response to gravity and acceleration. A posture can involve either a static contraction of fixator musculature, to maintain a position, or low-level simultaneous contractions of

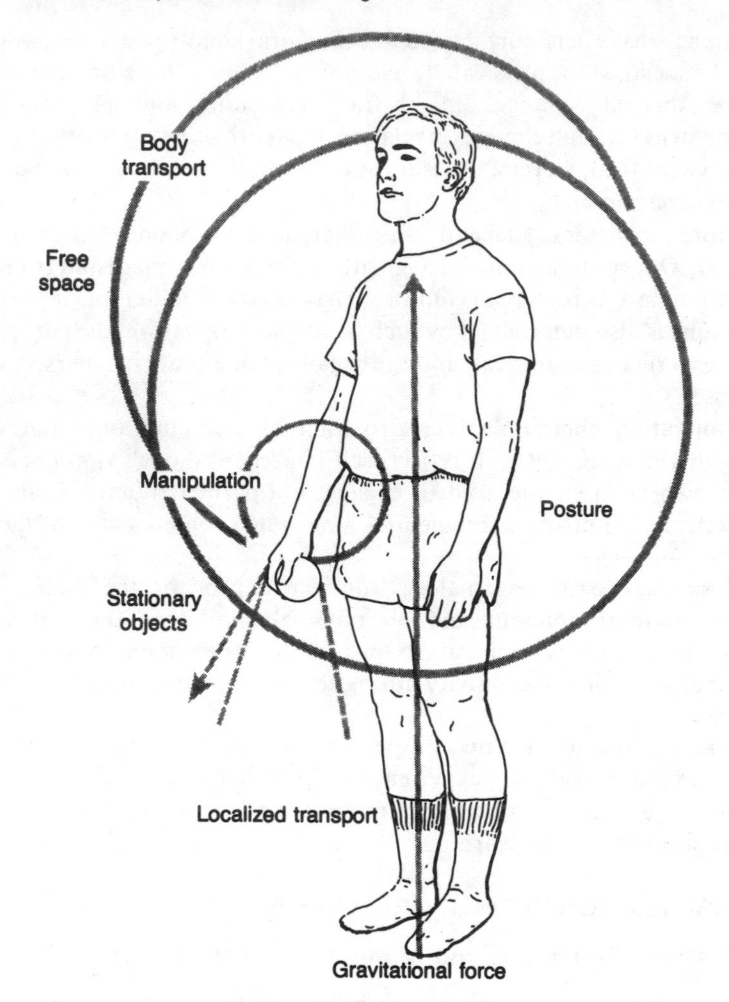

Figure 1.1. The three components of motor responses: posture, transport, and manipulation. (Adapted from Smith and Smith, 1962.)

antagonistic muscles, to maintain balance. Unstable equilibrium requires that the relative force of antagonistic muscle groups constantly fluctuate (Rasch and Burke, 1963). Postural movements, therefore, involve a wide variety of muscular responses.

Transport (locomotor) movements enable a person to move through space. They require the right and left sides of the body to move either together or in opposition. Locomotion can be serial, composed of an integrated sequence of movements that are continually controlled, or it can be discrete. In either case, these movements are important in assisting an individual to learn about the nature of the environment, of space, and of himself or herself. Smith and Smith have further classified transport movements as either generalized, involving the entire body and enabling a person to move through space, or localized, involving a particular member of the body, such as an arm or a leg.

Manipulative movements depend on the position and dimensions of objects involved in the response. Kephart (1964) proposed that manipulations can be distinguished into two types, *contact patterns* and *receipt and propulsion.* Through contact patterns, such as grasping, turning, and releasing—individuals learn about the characteristics of stationary objects and how to control them. Receipt and propulsion are movements used to manipulate objects that move through space, such as catching, throwing, kicking, trapping, pushing, and pulling.

In general, the development of motor behavior begins with the learning of postural movements. Once these have been acquired, basic transport movements begin, followed in turn by manipulative movements (Espenschade and Eckert, 1967). This progression of motor behavior is compatible with the observation that motor control develops from head to feet (cephalocaudally) and from the midline of the body to the extremities (proximodistally). Figures 1.2 and 1.3 illustrate this development during the early years of life.

Motor Patterns and Motor Skills

The immature movement skills of children evolve into motor patterns, which in turn lead to the development of motor skills. The latter develop from gross to fine skills. Motor patterns have broad purposes and are characterized by extensive use, whereas motor skills are formed to accomplish a specific end (Wickstrom, 1970; Godfrey and Kephart, 1969).

Motor patterns are composites of movements, characterized by their variability and their applicability to a wide range of diverse activities. Typically, for example, infants first learn to walk on hard, smooth surfaces, such as a kitchen floor. A child who has just acquired this elementary skill, however, is still unable to walk on a thick carpet or lawn. As the child masters walking in a variety of environments—on smooth surfaces, uneven surfaces, resilient surfaces, inclines, stairs, and so forth—these separate walking skills are merged into a composite, well-integrated walking pattern, which is adaptable for use in a range of situations.

Figure 1.2. Developmental sequence in bipedal locomotion. (Redrawn from M. M. Shirley, *The first two years. A study of twenty-five babies.* Volume II, Institute of Child Welfare Monograph Series No. 7, The University of Minnesota Press, Minneapolis, Copyright © 1933 by the University of Minnesota.)

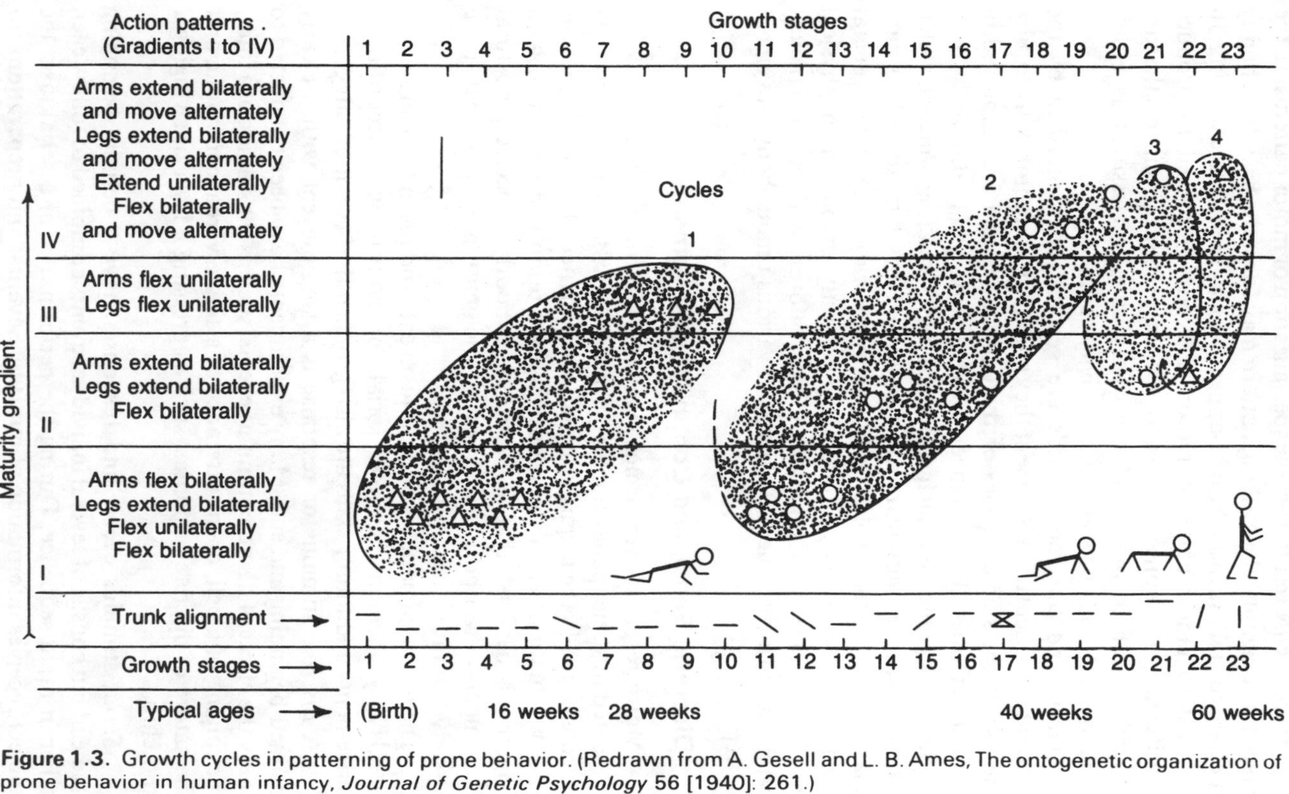

Figure 1.3. Growth cycles in patterning of prone behavior. (Redrawn from A. Gesell and L. B. Ames, The ontogenetic organization of prone behavior in human infancy, *Journal of Genetic Psychology* 56 [1940]: 261.)

Motor skills result from the specialization of motor patterns. In the preceding example, the walking pattern may form the basis for a highly specialized skill, such as the odd-appearing gait used in race walking. In contrast to motor patterns, motor skills are employed to produce specific motor responses, that is, to perform precise movements that are limited in extent and variability. They can be classified as either fundamental skills or sports and activity skills.

Gross and fine motor skills are generally distinguished by the amount of muscular involvement they require. Fine motor skills require the use of the small muscles of the extremities and are employed in limited activities. Performance of these skills has traditionally been studied with equipment such as pursuit rotors and finger mazes, which require limited muscular involvement. Gross motor skills are characterized by the involvement of many muscle groups and by general levels of body activity. They are commonly employed in physical education research. Examples of gross motor skills are balancing, catching, throwing, racquet skills, and various unique body movement patterns.

Discrete, Serial, and Continuous Movements

Motor responses are formed in relation to stimuli, which are always presented in some spatial and temporal context. Both dimensions must be considered in the acquisition and performance of a skill. Responses to new situations are always superimposed upon and integrated with ongoing behaviors, that is, with basic bodily processes, postural movements, transport movements, and manipulations that have already been initiated.

The temporal patterns of stimulus events and responses can be used to classify them as discrete, serial, or continuous. Accordingly, movements and motor skills are also grouped in these three categories.

A *discrete* stimulus or response is a single event with a clearly defined beginning and end. Many experiments have been conducted to study the effect of discrete stimulus events, such as the shining of a light, the ringing of a bell, or the utterance of a single verbal command, and the nature of discrete responses, such as pressing a lever or swinging a golf club.

Serial stimulus events and responses have a definite beginning and end but consist of several individual events combined to follow each other in rapid sequence. During the performance of a serial task, the subject receives information about future events, and preparations for

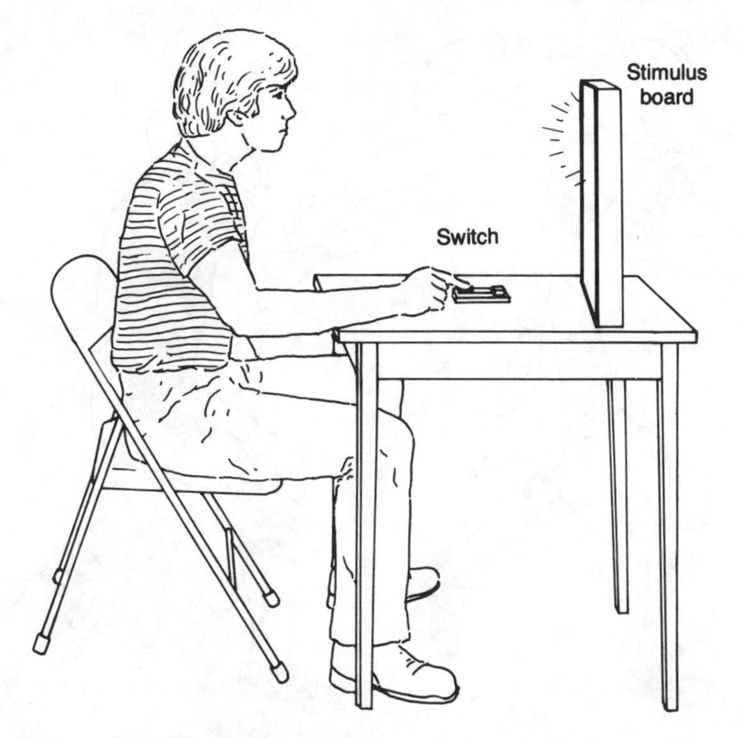

Figure 1.4. Discrete tasks, requiring a single movement in response to a single stimulus, are commonly used to measure reaction time.

the next movement are made while the current movement is being completed. Many sports, such as tennis, basketball, badminton, putting the shot, and football, involve serial events.

Stimulus events that present continuous information and responses that consist of repetitive, nearly identical movements are *continuous*. Most tracking tasks (catching a fly ball, driving an automobile, or keeping a stylus in contact with the pursuit rotor) present continuous stimulus information, and frequently the subject is required to correct his or her responses to keep a balanced system. Running, walking, and swimming are examples of continuous movements. Continuous stimulus events do not require continuous responses. In fact, humans are greatly limited in their ability to respond to signals that occur in rapid succession. Sports skills and tasks that present continuous information, such as batting a pitched ball, place severe demands on the ability to process continuous information.

Figure 1.5. A serial skill involves several skills connected into a sequence; the performer is required to make decisions at several points during the activity.

The spatial and temporal pattern of stimuli and responses in voluntary movements can never be regarded as automatic. Voluntary control is effected with the help of sensory feedback, and the first improvements in performance are attributable to feedback control. Initial feedbacks are generally visual in sports skills, but during learning the links between certain sequences in motor acts become dependent on other modalities (chiefly proprioception, or muscle sensation). With the development of feedback control, each part of the act triggers the next one.

The temporal aspect of motor responses is best understood in terms of *two-phase motor units* or *polyphase motor units* that occur in sequence under the control of feedback (Fitts, 1964). Two-phase motor units form the basis for spatially and temporally organized motor sequences. The first phase of movement is preparation, which enables the performer to place the body in proper alignment to carry out the task. The second phase, execution, is represented by completion of the act itself. For example, the act of jumping is a temporally and spatially unified sequence consisting of a preparatory phase (crouching) and the execution of the act (jumping into the air with leg extension). Striking skills are another good example of two-phase movements, with the backswing representing the preparatory phase. The pattern for a typical two-phase motor response is set up prior to its initiation (mental preparation) but can be influenced either by feedback or by new stimulus events during its execution.

Serial and continuous skills are polyphase units, which consist of sequences of two-phase units. Walking and running are examples in the simplest form, with each step having a preparatory phase (the ballistic movement and foot plant) and an execution phase (push-off with the foot).

PERCEPTION

Historically, sensations have been defined as simple experiences that result from the stimulation of sense organs. Common examples

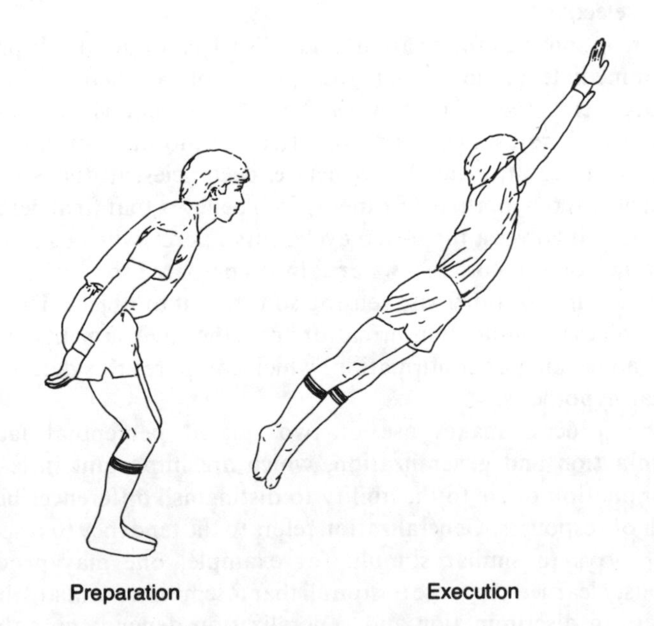

Figure 1.6. Two-phase motor units consist of a preparation phase and an execution phase.

include vision, hearing, pain, smell, touch, and warmth. Sensory information indicates only that some stimulation of a receptor has occurred. Perception, in contrast, is a more complex experience, which involves the combination or integration of several sensations and their interpretation on the basis of past experience. In other words, perceptions are sensations with meanings. One experiences objects and events, and thereby comes to know the world, by means of perception.

The important characteristics of perceptions are "that simple perceptions are in fact complex; that they are additive, that they depend partly on motor activity, and that their apparent simplicity is only the result of a long learning process" (Hebb, 1949, p. 17). As one acquires more experience and learning, one's perceptions also become more complex, better formed, and better integrated into behavior.

Perception allows objects in the external world to be conceived as having an identity. A stimulus has identity if it is recognized as falling into some categories and being excluded from others. Similarly, an object has identity if it can be readily associated with other objects or with some action. According to Hebb (1949, p. 27), "identity is a matter of degree, readiness of recognition, and the extent to which generalization is selective."

Perception thus forms an individual's basis for action. It provides both immediate and long-range foundations of experience. Stable and accurate perceptual contact with the environment is necessary for interpersonal adjustment and for effective motor responses. Final perceptual integration involves beliefs, expectancies, attitudes, selective tendencies, and hypothesis. Bruner (1951) believes that final perceptual integration involves a three-step cycle. First, perceiving begins with an expectancy or a hypothesis; we are always prepared to some extent for seeing, hearing, or otherwise sensing some event or object. The second step involves the input of information from the environment. The third step is a checking or confirmation, which compares this data with the original hypothesis.

This process makes use of two related perceptual faculties, discrimination and generalization, which are important in learning. Discrimination refers to the ability to distinguish differences between stimuli or responses. Generalization refers to the tendency to respond in similar ways to similar stimuli; for example, one may produce a previously learned response to stimuli that resemble a familiar stimulus. "Success in discrimination and generalization depends on either the location of a differentiating characteristic between two figures or one that is common to a previously learned pattern and the new pattern to be aquired" (Hebb, 1949, p. 22).

THEORIES OF LEARNING

The development of abstract abilities, social relationships, and physical skills all involve learning. For many years theories of learning have been divided into two broad categories, connectionist theories and cognitive theories.

The various connectionist theories, in spite of their differences, all agree in the belief that learning occurs with the formation of a bond or connection between a stimulus and a response or responses. Because of their emphasis on the formation of such connections, proponents of this view are also known as stimulus-response (S-R) theorists. Connectionists are concerned with learning and behavior patterns that are mechanical—for a given input, or stimulus, a predictable response follows. These theorists typically study trial-and-error learning, in which much random movement occurs and numerous errors are made during the initial trials, but which slowly and irregularly reduces the number of errors until the goal is obtained.

Cognitive theorists, in contrast, are concerned with the manner in which an individual's cognitions—perceptions, beliefs and attitudes—determine behavior. Cognitive approaches to learning deal with the modification of cognitions by experience. Cognitive theorists emphasize the fact that we can choose our responses and can select behaviors that are appropriate to different situations. We learn expectancies, ideas, and attitudes and use them to select responses. Many cognitive psychologists have studied the type of learning called insight, which occurs suddenly and is accompanied by a feeling of understanding.

As a general rule, connectionist theories emphasize the fact that behavior appears to be controlled by sensory stimuli. That is, they regard behavior as a series of reactions or responses to environmental events that have just occurred. The problem with this approach is that most connectionist theories completely overlook the fact that we can select our responses from a great variety of choices. This selection is made possible through such factors as attention, expectations, attitudes, needs, and hypotheses, in addition to the immediately preceding sensory stimulation. As Hebb (1949, p. 5) noted, the recognition of a choice in behaviors "does not deny the importance of immediate stimulus; it does deny that sensory stimulation is everything in behavior." The cognitive approach, however, is also not without problems. The recognition of choice in responses makes the prediction of behavior difficult. It is impossible to measure or account for an individual's cognitive processes.

At first glance, these two approaches to the study of learning would not appear reconcilable. Recently, however, the differences between them have been diminishing, and today a balanced view of learning requires that both approaches be considered. The remainder of this book addresses itself to the application of learning theories to teaching, factors that affect learning and performance, and other principles that physical educators can use to improve instruction.

GUIDING PRINCIPLES FOR THE TEACHER

1. Life is a continual process of adaptation, involving maturation and learning. Motor learning is the adaptation process in which movement and muscular responses are developed.

2. Motor responses can be placed into three categories: (*a*) postural movements, to regulate the body's position with respect to gravity; (*b*) locomotor or transport movements, which enable a person to move the body or its parts through space; and (*c*) manipulations, enabling one to learn about and control objects. Contact patterns (the manipulation of static objects) have been distinguished from receipt and propulsion (the manipulation of moving objects).

3. Motor patterns are general responses, with great variability and applicability to a range of diverse activities, which are used for broad purposes in movement. Motor skills are specific motor responses, limited in variability and applicability, which are developed to produce specific movements in a particular activity.

4. Fine motor skills involve the small muscles of the extremities and are used in limited tasks, such as activities with the pursuit rotor, finger mazes, and peg boards. Gross motor skills require the interaction of many muscle groups with general bodily activity, as in running, catching, throwing, and racquet skills.

5. Stimuli and responses can be classified as discrete, serial, or continuous, according to their temporal patterns. Discrete tasks are single events with a clearly defined beginning and end. Serial tasks have a definite beginning and end but combine several individual events, which follow each other in rapid sequence. Tasks with continuous

stimulus events (e.g., tracking a ball) and repetitive, nearly identical responses are continuous.

6. A physical response has two phases, preparation and execution. In the preparatory phase, a performer places the body in proper alignment to carry out a task. In the execution phase, the task itself is completed. For example, jumping is a temporally and spatially unified sequence consisting of preparation (crouching) and then execution (springing with extension of the legs). Striking skills are another good example, with the backswing representing the preparatory phase of the two-phase unit.

SUMMARY

Motor activity is constantly expanded and consolidated from birth reflexes by means of learning and maturation. Learning is behavioral adaptation that results from training procedures or from environmental conditions that act on an individual. Motor learning is learning that is concerned with movement and motor responses. Not all behavioral change is due to learning, however. If a change in behavior develops through a regular succession, regardless of practice, then maturation rather than learning underlies the change. Separation of these two factors is not easily accomplished, as most changes in behavior are due to an interaction of learning and maturation.

Motor responses must be evaluated with reference to the temporal and spatial requirements of the environment. Several classification systems have been devised to facilitate this analysis. Motor responses can be divided into three classes: postural, transport, and manipulative movements. Postural movements regulate body position in response to gravity. Transport movements enable a person to move the body or parts of it through space; they therefore assist an individual in learning about the environment, space, and himself or herself. Manipulative movements enable one to contact and interact with static objects and objects that move through space.

Motor responses are also classified as patterns or as skills, depending on the adaptability of the response. Motor skills are further distinguished into gross or fine skills, according to the amount of muscular involvement. The temporal patterns of stimulus events and responses allow motor skills to be described as discrete, serial, or continuous. Discrete skills are two-phase motor units: in the preparatory phase, the body is placed in the proper alignment, and in the execution phase, the response is completed. Serial and continuous skills are polyphase motor units, formed by the combination of two-phase motor units.

Sensations, arising from within us and from our environment, are developed into perceptions, which are higher-order processes that require a great deal of learning and practice. Perception occurs when sensations become integrated and acquire meaning. Our perceptions are used as we learn to recognize various stimuli through identity. They give our world some degree of consistency and form the basis for various judgments through discrimination and generalization.

Many researchers have studied the changes in behavior that occur through learning. Theories of learning tend to emphasize either the mechanistic (connectionist) or the voluntaristic (cognitive) aspects of learning and behavior. Both approaches have merit in particular situations, but an overall view requires that both be considered.

REFERENCES

Bruner, J. S. 1951. Personality dynamics and the process of perceiving. In *Perception: An approach to personality*, ed. R. R. Blake and G. V. Ramsey. New York: Ronald Press.

Espenschade, A. S., and Eckert, H. M. 1967. *Motor development*. Columbus, Ohio: Charles E. Merrill.

Fitts, P. M. 1964. Perceptual-motor skill learning. In *Categories of human learning*, ed. A. W. Melton. New York: Academic Press.

Godfrey, B. B., and Kephart, N. C. 1969. *Movement patterns and motor education*. New York: Appleton-Century-Crofts.

Hebb, D. O. 1949. *Organization of behavior*. New York: John Wiley and Sons.

Hill, W. F. 1963. *Learning: A survey of psychological interpretations*. San Francisco: Chandler.

Kephart, N. C. 1964. Perceptual-motor aspects of learning disabilities. *Exceptional Children* 31:201 206.

Morgan, C. T., and King, R. A. 1966. *Introduction to psychology*. 3d ed. New York: McGraw-Hill.

Paillard, J. 1960. The patterning of skilled movements. In *Handbook of physiology*. Sec. 1, vol. 3, ed. H. W. Magoun. Washington, D.C.: American Physiological Society.

Rasch, P. J., and Burke, R. K. 1963. *Kinesiology and applied anatomy*. Philadelphia: Lea & Febiger.

Smith, K. U., and Smith, W. M. 1962. *Perception and motion: An analysis of space-structured behavior*. Philadelphia: W. B. Saunders.

Thayer, E. L. 1964. *The first book edition of Casey at the bat*. New York: Watts.

Wickstrom, R. L. 1970. *Fundamental motor patterns*. Philadelphia: Lea & Febiger.

2 Development of Motor Responses

Learning, in this book, refers to the relatively permanent modification of behavior as a result of training and environmental conditons that act on an individual. This does not mean that the individual is only a passive receptor, but the definition emphasizes that the various environmental stimuli confronting a person cause him or her to react. Learning seems to occur during this reaction process, which may be either observable or covert.

When one reads about this subject, one can easily become confused by the variety of definitions encountered. This diversity results partly from the use of the term *learning* in a more specialized sense in psychology than in ordinary speech, and partly from the fact that different psychologists concentrate on different aspects of the phenomenon of learning. Regardless of the definition, what is learned need not be correct or adaptive (we learn improper techniques as well as correct skills), be conscious or deliberate (coaches often make athletes aware of mistakes that they have unconsciously learned to make), or involve any observable response (attitudes and emotions are learned). In short, most of our reactions, either mental or physical, are learned behavior. Learning plays a role in motor activities, academic pursuits, the formation of attitudes and prejudices, social interaction, and communication.

Training and environmental conditions, however, are not the only factors that contribute to behavioral changes. Growth, or maturation, is another important element. Behavior that develops through a regular sequence, irrespective of practice, may be caused by maturation rather than by learning. If training procedures do not modify or speed up certain behavioral changes, then training plays no important causal role, and therefore such changes are not cases of learned behavior.

The general pattern for the acquisition of motor responses, particularly in children, does not show such a clear-cut distinction between learning and maturation but presents a complex interaction of these and other elements. A better term to describe the progressive changes in a person's interactions with the environment is *psychological development.* Interaction between behavior and environment means that a particular response may or may not occur, depending on the stimulation that the environment provides. This is true whether one response or a series of responses are involved. For example, consider an outfielder playing baseball on a cloudy day. Suddenly, the sun is uncovered by the clouds—a change in the environmental stimulation. The bright light causes a response—squinting to reduce the glare—but squinting requires too much effort for comfort and reduces the field of vision. The response-produced changes in stimulation (the strain from squinting and the reduction in visual field) bring forth another response—lowering the sunglasses into place. Thus behavior is a continual reaction to the stimulus environment. All persons are constantly exposed to a variety of conditions that cause changes in responses.

Studies of motor responses typically are concerned with changes that occur over periods of time. For example, developmental aspects of motor responses might be investigated in a study of the modifications in posture and movement by which a toddler's first steps evolve into an adult running style. Coaches and teachers are concerned with changes that can take place over shorter time spans, in which erratic, unskilled responses can be transformed into consistent, highly skilled performances.

The following sections discuss learning that is produced under typical environmental conditions, by means of observations, experiences, social interactions, experimental and manipulative behavior, physical activity, and the satisfaction of biological needs.

MOTOR RESPONSES OF INFANTS

The point of departure for the anaysis of motor learning is motor responses of newborn infants. Infancy is the one stage at which people appear to be nearly homogeneous in their motor abilities. Casual observers might report that newborn infants cannot do anything but suck, cry, wave their arms and legs, and dirty their diapers, but that observation is grossly inaccurate. A child comes into the world with an amazingly extensive repertoire of motor responses. These responses are generally reflexive, but they involve all parts of the body—eyes, face and mouth, throat, head and neck, head and arms, trunk, organs, feet and legs—and the coordination of many body parts (Thompson, 1962).[1]

Piaget (1952) and others have recognized the importance of these reflexes in later psychological development. In Piaget's theory, infants' early reflexes are regarded as behavioral patterns for the formation of new responses, which are basic to the child's perception of space and, ultimately, intellectual development (Flavell, 1963; Piaget and Inhelder, 1967). These birth reflexes are extended into a broader behavioral repertoire by the process of learning, which accordingly raises the child's level of functioning.

CLASSICAL CONDITIONING

Psychologists have described three general processes by which learning takes place: classical conditioning, instrumental conditioning, and cognitive learning. *Classical conditioning* makes use of stimuli to which a subject responds by reflex; through conditioning, the subject learns to produce the same response to other stimuli. This type of learning involves little or no motivation on the part of the learner. The sequence of events is independent of the individual's behavior; that is, neither reward nor punishment is responsible for this type of behavioral change (Kimble, 1961).

Classical conditioning was discovered by chance during I. P. Pavlov's study of salivation and gastric juices during digestion. If meat powder is placed in a dog's mouth, saliva flows in response. Pavlov observed that if a unique, neutral stimulus, such as the sound of a bell,

[1]For more detailed treatment of motor responses in newborn infants, consult Dennis (1934) and Dewey (1935). A broad survey of motor development at all age levels was conducted by Espenschade and Eckert (1967).

was regularly presented just before the animal was given food, eventually the sound alone would cause the saliva to flow. He would ring a bell and then provide food almost immediately; this procedure was repeated for a number of trials, until the sound of the bell without the food would cause the dog to salivate. An example of the results obtained in this type of experiment is shown in Figure 2.1.

The stimulus (meat, in Pavlov's experiment) that orginally elicits a reflexive response (salivation) is called an *unconditioned stimulus* (UCS), and the reflexive response is an *unconditioned response* (UCR). There is an innate bond between the UCS and the UCR. The neutral stimulus (the sound of the bell, in the preceding example, which served as a signal for the food) is designated a *conditioned stimulus* (CS), and the original response, once it has been paired with the CS, becomes a *conditioned response* (CR). A model for this process is diagrammed in Figure 2.2.

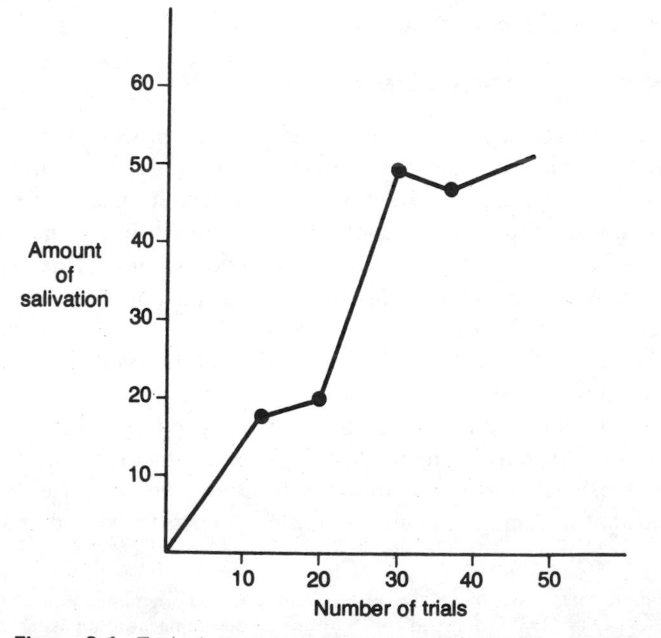

Figure 2.1. Typical conditioning pattern in the salivary response of a dog.

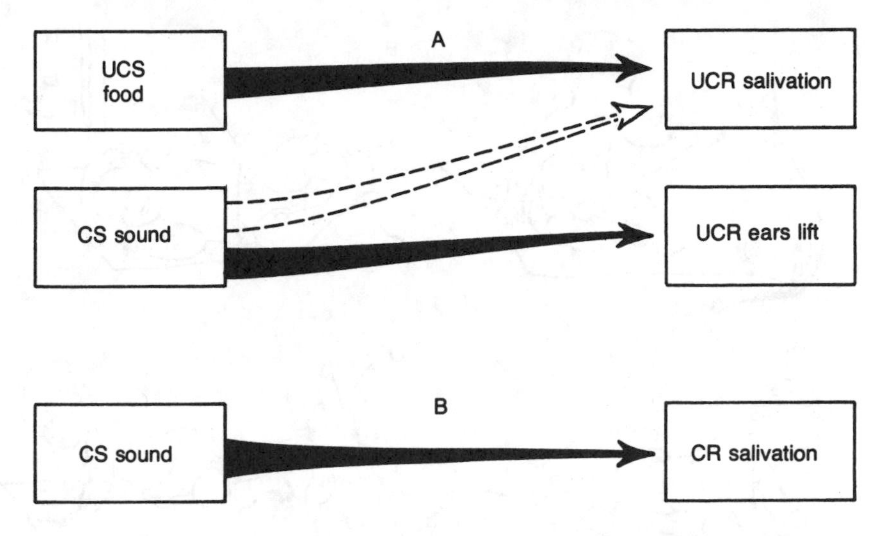

Figure 2.2. The classical conditioning model: (*A*) the pairing of an unconditioned stimulus with a neutral stimulus, which is to become conditioned; (*B*) after conditioning, the conditioned stimulus alone elicits the conditioned response. (Modified from Staats and Staats, 1963.)

By means of classical conditioning, the original birth reflexes are paired with environmental stimuli, so that the motor behavior of infants can become extended and useful in new situations. Classical conditioning applies not only to motor responses but also to emotional and sensory learning. For example, Watson and Rayner (1920) conditioned a fear response in a child by striking a metal bar with a hammer and simultaneously presenting a cat to the child (see Figure 2.3). Soon, not only did the cat cause the fear pattern, but so did similar furry objects, such as a rabbit. Other examples of classical conditioning can be observed in everyday situations. After a series of visits a physician's office for injections, a child begins to cry even before the needle is brought into view. Sensory conditioning can be observed in the child's reflexlike response, designed to avoid pain, after repeated pairings of a painful stimulus and a visual or auditory stimulus. Similarly, repeated painful experiences with physical activity can produce avoidance responses that create problems for both teacher and student.

Simultaneous presentation of the neutral stimulus and the original (unconditioned) stimulus is the initial requirement for classical conditioning. After the original reflex has become a conditioned response, however, it can be elicited by other stimuli that are similar to

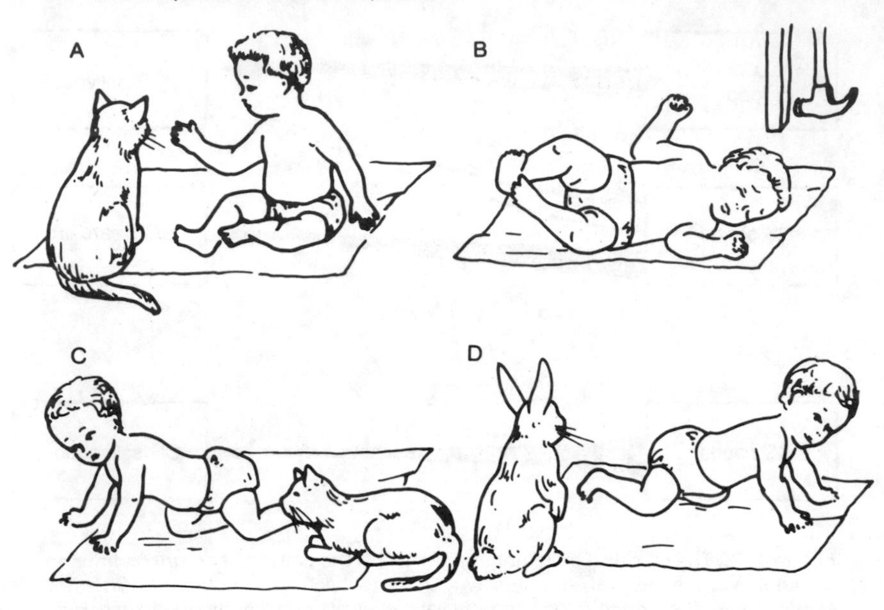

Figure 2.3 Conditioning a fear response: (*A*) the infant's response to a cat before conditioning; (*B*) the unconditioned stimulus, presented simultaneously with the cat on several occasions; (*C*) the infant's response to the cat after conditioning; (*D*) the generalization of conditioning to a rabbit.

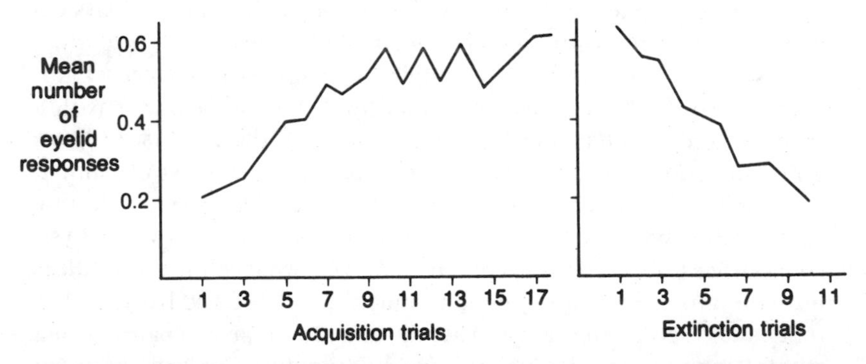

Figure 2.4. Acquisition and extinction curves obtained in the conditioning of an eyelid response. (Data from Lipman, 1963.)

the CS, in a phenomenon known as *generalization*. In the preceding example, the infant's conditioned fear of the cat was eventually evoked by other furry objects. Further learning takes place by higher-order conditioning, in which additional neutral stimuli are paired with a conditioned stimulus so that they also elicit the reflexlike response. Thus, a response elicited by one stimulus can be transferred to a series of new stimuli.

If the conditioned stimulus is not periodically paired with the original stimulus, it eventually loses its ability to elicit the conditioned response. The process by which stimulus-response bonds are weakened, called *extinction*, is illustrated in Figure 2.4. Through the combination of classical conditioning and extinction, a child's responses become more selective and appropriate.

INSTRUMENTAL CONDITIONING

Another learning process is *instrumental conditioning*, which involves the learning of voluntary responses. It differs from classical conditioning in two major respects. First, it does not require an initial reflexive S-R bond. Second, in instrumental conditioning, behavioral changes are determined by rewards and punishments given out as consequences of the subject's response, while reward and punishment have little effect in classical conditioning.

The typical laboratory demonstration of instrumental conditioning involves placing a hungry cat (or some other experimental animal) in a box with a bar mounted inside. Whenever the animal presses the bar, a pellet of food appears. Through trial and error, the hungry cat connects pushing the bar with food, and the response of pressing the bar becomes more and more prevalent. This behavior is repeated as long as the response brings some reward; that is, the cat presses the bar as long as it remains hungry and continues to receive food as a consequence of its actions. See Figure 2.5 for examples of instrumental learning curves. The learned response becomes extinguished if the reinforcement (reward or punishment) is discontinued. Instrumental responses can also become linked with new stimuli through higher-order conditioning.

Skinner (1938, 1953) has intensively studied instrumental conditioning. He has referred to classical conditioning as *respondent conditioning* to emphasize that it is largely reflexive—the subject simply responds to a stimulus and is not affected by any consequences of the response. For instrumental conditioning he coined the term *operant conditioning* to emphasize that a person can operate on the environment (including one's own body) either to produce a reward or to avoid a punishment.

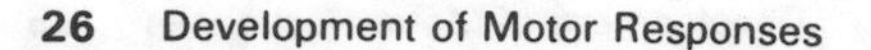

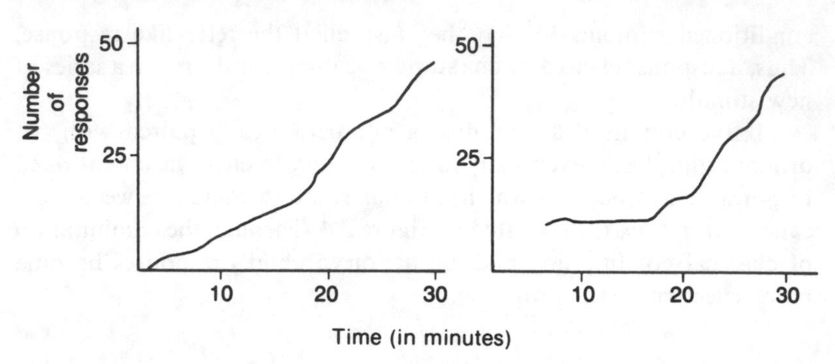

Figure 2.5. Typical instrumental conditioning acquisition curves.

Instrumental behavior involves trial and error during the learning process, and the response must be rewarded in some manner if it is to be repeated. Examples of responses that result from instrumental conditioning include shooting a basketball at a hoop, which is reinforced by making a goal; turning on a television set, which is rewarded with sound and picture; and lifting weights, which can result in a more pleasing physique, a feeling of accomplishment, or social acceptance. Instrumental behavior, for the most part, involves the use of skeletal muscles and the formation of voluntary responses, and its continuation depends on reinforcement (Bijou and Baer, 1961).

Instrumental conditioning plays an important role in broadening the behavioral repertoire of children. They learn to interpret and respond appropriately to various patterns of stimulation, which they receive from within their own bodies and from the environment. They learn to discriminate between similar stimulus patterns because their responses to the stimuli lead to different consequences. They also learn to generalize physically dissimilar stimuli and sensory modalities because of similarities in their behavioral consequences.

Learning to respond in ways that tend to maximize satisfaction and minimize frustration and pain is a major dimension of psychological development. It occurs in the classroom, on the playing field, and at home. Parents and teachers must be sensitive to and knowledgeable about factors that influence discrimination and generalization.

Reinforcement

The role of reinforcement in learning was largely ignored until Thorndike (1913) postulated the law of effect, which recognized that an

S-R connection can either be strengthened or be weakened by its consequences. If the S-R sequence were followed by a "satisfier," the S-R bond would be strengthened. Conversely, if the sequence were followed by an "annoyer," the connection would be weakened. This law is restated in the familiar principle that satisfying consequences reinforce S-R bonds.

It remained for Skinner (1938, 1953), however, to detail the powerful effect of reinforcement on learning. His studies show that either positive or negative reinforcement can strengthen an S-R bond and that reinforcement influences the rate of response, the vigor with which a response is performed, and the promptness with which it occurs. An instrumental response can have four kinds of consequences. It can

1. produce positive reinforcement,
2. remove or avoid negative reinforcement,
3. produce negative reinforcement, or
4. remove or avoid positive reinforcement.

If a response either produces positive reinforcement or removes negative reinforcement (e.g., eliminates fatigue or pain), the S-R bond is strengthened. If it produces negative reinforcement (e.g., fatigue or pain) or removes positive reinforcement, the S-R bond is weakened until it is extinguished, and the response is not repeated.

The behavior of an individual in a group and the actions of the group are responsive to the same principles of reinforcement (Staats and Staats, 1962). The reinforcement provided by one member of a group serves to shape the action of others, and that member's responses are determined in a reciprocal fashion by the reinforcement of others. This pattern of reciprocal reinforcement influences the development of competitive responses as well as cooperative ones. Teachers must be concerned with learners both as individuals and as members of a social group. The interaction of individual and group and its influence on the behavior of each party cannot be ignored.

Secondary Reinforcement. Any stimulus that becomes paired with a reinforcer of a particular response can also acquire the ability to reinforce that response. Gold stars placed on a football helmet, a score on a record board, and a kind word from a coach can reinforce athletic behavior because of their association with outstanding performance. Such stimuli, which acquire their effectiveness by association with other reinforcers, are known as *secondary reinforcers.* A pregame ritual and warm-up activities can provide reinforcement for coach and players, and similar preclass procedures can reinforce students' behaviors. Some preclass or pregame events might negatively reinforce the students or players and their tendency to respond. Therefore, coaches and teachers must always consider the effects of both positive and negative reinforcement in their work with students (Bugelski, 1956).

Schedules of Reinforcement. The extensive research of Ferster and Skinner (1957) demonstrated that learning occurs whether a response is reinforced each time it is produced or whether it is reinforced intermittently. If reinforcement is provided each time a response occurs, the training follows a *schedule of continuous reinforcement*. The initial phase of teaching can usually be accomplished most efficiently with the use of continuous schedules. This is not the typical manner in which people reinforce others, however. Because we tend to engage in several activities or interact with several people at the same time, we tend to provide reinforcement haphazardly. If reinforcement is provided only on selected occasions, not each time a response is made, the training follows an *intermittent schedule* of reinforcement.

Two classes of intermittent schedules—ratio schedules and interval schedules—have been studied in laboratory experiments. Under a *ratio schedule,* reinforcement is contingent upon the number of times a response is emitted. The schedule can follow either a fixed ratio, by which the response is reinforced every *n*th time it occurs, or a variable ratio, by which the number of responses between reinforcements varies. The success of slot machines in Las Vegas exemplifies the effectiveness of ratio schedules. Reinforcement according to the passage of time rather than the number of responses follows an *interval schedule*. In this case, reinforcement is given to the first response made after the lapse of a certain period of time since the previous reinforcement. A variable interval schedule is one in which the time between reinforcements is not constant. These intermittent schedules are summarized in Table 2.1.

In general, reinforcement schedules can be applied to achieve a high rate of response and to condition behavior that is difficult to extinguish. To make this procedure effective, schedules must be developed gradually, with responses being reinforced nearly every time they occur during the early period of learning.

The power of reinforcement to strengthen responses, the presence of secondary reinforcers, and the effects of schedules of reinforcement both aid and hinder teachers. Sometimes, teachers inadvertently reinforce responses they wish to extinguish. For example, a teacher who

Table 2.1. Intermittent Schedules of Reinforcement for Instrumental Conditioning

Ratio schedule	Reinforcement is given only after a certain number of responses have occurred.
Fixed ratio	The ratio of reinforced responses to unreinforced responses is constant (e.g., every third response is reinforced).
Variable ratio	The ratio of reinforced responses to unreinforced responses changes after every reinforcement (e.g., the first, third, seventh, etc., responses are reinforced). The variation in the ratio does not necessarily follow a regular pattern.
Interval schedule	Reinforcement is given only after a certain interval of time has elapsed, independently of the number of responses that have occurred.
Fixed interval	Reinforcement is given for the first response that occurs after the lapse of a certain interval of time and is repeated for the first response after the next interval (e.g., after every 3 minutes).
Variable interval	Reinforcement is given after different intervals of time (e.g., after 1 minute, 2 minutes, 5 minutes, etc.). The variation in the length of the interval does not necessarily follow a regular pattern.

continues to respond to a child's distracting behavior can strengthen that behavior, since attention is a form of reward. It might be more appropriate to ignore the distraction. The reinforcement of secondary aspects of the distraction also can strengthen the response. Finally, this behavior is likely to be reinforced on a variable ratio schedule; that is, the teacher might ignore the distraction for a while but then finally give in and respond to the child. Even one reinforcement during the extinction process can reestablish the response with considerable strength.

This example indicates how noxious behavior can persist for a long time, even with a minimal amount of reinforcement, because of a history of reinforcement. Teachers often describe children's behavioral patterns that are extremely durable and persistent but have no readily apparent source of reinforcement in the child's current environment. Nagging, teasing, temper tantrums, and whining are typical examples. The explanation of those behaviors may lie in a history of reinforcement on a variable schedule. Likewise, an extensive history of variable reinforcement can make it extremely difficult for a coach to teach advanced performers how to overcome consistent errors in skilled motor performance.

Shaping. *Shaping* is the process of changing behavior through the reinforcement of responses that approximate the desired response. When a training program begins, it is important to ensure that reinforcement is not too slow in coming and that each desired response receives positive reinforcement. Usually, even gross approximations of the desired outcome are rewarded at first, but slowly and regularly, rewards are given only to responses that more closely resemble the desired behavior. Shaping leads the learner to the final response through a chain of simpler responses, so that the desired behavior is gradually acquired in a series of steps. Hence the procedure is also called the method of successive approximations. The following example, involving the behavior of a seriously disturbed child, illustrates the technique (Wolf, Mees, and Risley, 1964, quoted in Morgan and King, 1966, p. 91).

> In addition to numerous other difficulties, this boy was practically blind after a series of operations for cataracts when he was two years old. It was extremely important for him to wear glasses, and this behavior was shaped by successive approximations to the desired final response of continously wearing the glasses. The child was placed in a room where several empty glasses frames were lying around. Whenever he picked up one of these, he was reinforced with small pieces of candy or fruit. Soon he touched the frames quite often, but it was extremely difficult to shape the next step in the chain, putting the glasses on in the proper way. The therapists then arranged to use more powerful reinforcers by making the bites of lunch contingent upon having the glasses closer and closer and closer to the proper wearing position. In a very short time, with this more powerful reinforcer, it was possible to shape both the behavior of putting on the glasses and the behavior of looking through them after they had been put on properly. The boy was soon wearing his glasses for 12 hours each day.

COGNITIVE LEARNING

It is generally recognized that learning can also occur in ways other than conditioning, with its gradual acquisition of new responses through trial and error. Learning is often discontinuous—error curves show sharp drops without warning, and different kinds of errors appear from one trial to the next (Hebb, 1949). An understanding of the moves and countermoves involved in sports strategy can be acquired without extensive conditioning. Such learning, or insight, often is accompanied by a feeling of understanding, and even though it occurs suddenly (after only one or a few trials), it is resistant to forgetting. Insight is based upon previously acquired conceptions and perceptions and therefore is a form of *cognitive learning.* It consists of an understanding of the causal relationships between ends and means. The better one's percepts and concepts are established, the more quickly cognitive learning occurs.

Human behavior is purposeful, or goal-directed. Many psychologists believe that behavior is not so much a response to stimuli as a striving toward goals. Stimuli guide us toward a goal and determine what responses we use to attain it, but the presence of the goal gives unity and meaning to our behavior. We can easily shift from one response to another, as circumstances require, without changing goals. A great variety of responses can be used to reach a single goal. If one response is not successful, various alternatives can be tried, or a sequence of different responses might be required. To explain this ability to shift responses in goal-directed behavior, it has been proposed that some hidden variable—a perception, learning, or motivation, perhaps occurring as activity in the nervous system—intervenes between a stimulus and a response (Hill, 1963). The intervening variable would determine the selection of a particular response from the range of responses that a person could produce. An individual's past experiences continually contribute to the development of cognitive learning.

Tolman (1942) postulated two basic principles of cognitive learning. The principle of sign-Gestalt expectation holds that an individual has expectations that the world is organized in certain ways and that certain objects or events lead to others. Second, the concept of place learning emphasizes that the learner does not need to approach a goal through a fixed sequence of responses; rather, one can vary one's responses according to changes in conditions. Without appropriate experience, these forms of learning would not occur. Experience, therefore, is the basis underlying insight and cognitive learning.

People generally use classical, instrumental, and cognitive learning styles according to their level of development. The manner in which these styles of learning merge and interrelate is best described by Hebb (1949). He believes that psychological development takes place in two periods, characterized respectively by primary learning and by later learning. Primary learning begins at birth and is predominant until an individual is about 12 years old. During this period, environmental control is established over behavior as sensory events continually impose new types of organization on the cortex, through classical and instrumental conditioning. Later learning is conceptual, involving patterns and events whose parts, at least, are already familiar and have acquired a number of reasonably well-formed associations. Prompt learning is possible if a stimulus triggers well-organized concepts. Without these, several trials are required. Consequently, adult learning typically takes the form of cognitive learning or insight, acquired suddenly after a single trial or a few trials, in contrast to the repetitive, trial-and-error nature of primary learning.

Trial-and-error learning does not occur exclusively before the age of 12, and cognitive learning does not occur exclusively thereafter. The kind of learning style that an individual uses depends on his or her past experiences. A person can shift back and forth between learning styles as required by his or her stage of psychological development. A young child who has accumulated sufficient experience with a situation can begin to learn about it cognitively. Likewise, adults require instrumental conditioning in situations with which they have had no past experience. The fact that different styles of learning are employed under different circumstances should be considered in determining an instructor's style of teaching (for examples, see Skinner, 1961, 1968).

DEVELOPMENTAL PATTERNS

All people are continually engaged in a process of development. Adults as well as children modify their responses and combine well-established responses into new sequences. The same kind of modification occurs with perceptions, as people come into contact with new situations and learn new activities. People actively engage their environments and continually modify their behavior. Development in young children is much more apparent because of the rapidity of changes at that stage.

Kephart's Perceptual-Motor Bases

The basic mechanism for the early development of children is motor experience. Kephart (1964) believes that symbolic (i.e., verbal or pictorial) abilities evolve directly from perceptual-motor abilities. In his view, all classroom experiences rest on the fundamental assumption "that the child has established an adequate orientation to the basic realities of the universe—space and time" (p. 201). Movements are a child's first interactions with the environment, and the first learning to occur is motor learning. A newborn child enters a world in which motor acts produce sensations. Gradually, as the child grows into an adult, motor acts acquire visual meanings and visual stimuli acquire motor meanings.

Kephart (1960) contrasts the value of generalized motor patterns with that of specialized motor skills (see chapter 1). The wide applicability and extensive variety of motor patterns make them essential to information gathering during a child's early stages of development. According to Kephart (1960, 1964) and Godfrey and Kephart (1969), four motor patterns are particularly significant in providing a perceptual-motor basis for future learning:

1. *Balance and maintenance of posture.* Through the development of balance and posture, a child acquires essential knowledge about gravity and the body's relationship to it. This knowledge develops into an understanding of spatial relationships (up-down, left-right, front-back). Also, because subsequent exploratory activities involve movement, posture and balance are prerequisite for further development.
2. *Locomotion.* A child uses locomotor patterns to investigate relationships in space. Transport movement enables the child to learn about the positions of objects and the spatial relationships between one object and another.
3. *Contact.* Contact patterns—reaching, grasping, and releasing—enable a child to manipulate objects and to learn about such characteristics as shape, form, and size constancy.[2]
4. *Receipt and propulsion.* A child explores movements in space through receipt patterns (such as catching and trapping) which allow contact with moving objects, and through propulsion, (such as throwing, kicking, and striking), by which motion is imparted to objects.

[2]Constancy refers the invariance of certain physical properties of objects despite changes in their sensory appearance. For example, a child learns that a solid object maintains a constant size whether it is near or far away, even though the number of receptor cells stimulated in the eye changes as the object becomes closer or farther. Similar learning occurs with the perception of colors in different levels of light.

The fundamental motor patterns develop into skills and abilities, which support future learning. Among these later developments are gross and fine motor skills, eye-hand coordination, laterality, directionality, ability to stop, dexterity, temporal-spatial translation, form perception, and body image. See Figure 2.6 for a schematic illustration of the necessary components of efficient movement.

Laterality is an awareness of spatial direction in relation to one's own body. Directionality develops as this understanding of direction is applied to external space and to motion. With the emergence of body image, a child can use his or her body as a point of reference to understand the body's position in space, how much space it occupies, and other physical characteristics.

An understanding of time as well as space is necessary. Kephart (1964) believes that motor activities teach the temporal relationships of

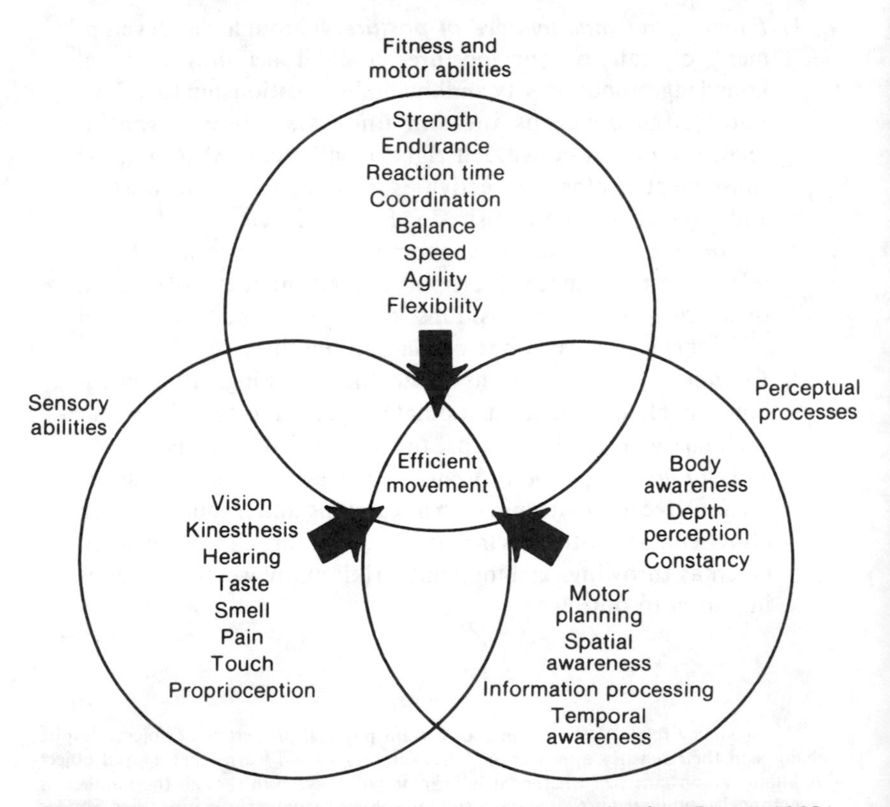

Figure 2.6. The components of efficient movement. (Modified from Barsch, 1968.)

synchrony (simultaneity of temporal origins), rhythm (stable, equal time intervals), and sequencing (ordering of events in time). This learned motor-temporal system is projected on objects in the environment.

Piaget's Developmental Psychology

The fundamental role of motor patterns and the progression observed in motor learning have also been emphasized by Piaget. In Flavell's (1963, p. 84) account of Piaget's theory, principles that are learned "become progressively more internalized and schematic by reducing perceptual and motor supports, e.g., moving from objects to symbols of objects, from motor action to speech, etc." Internalization is the process through which the environment acquires meaning. For example, spatial representation evolves from sensorimotor activity as a symbolic function that enables a child to act not only on objects that are real and physically present in the perceptual field but also on objects that are symbolized or mentally represented (Laurendeau and Pinard, 1970).

In Piaget's theory of development, the first period, and perhaps the most important, is the sensorimotor stage. It begins at birth, when behavior is characterized by reflexes and self-regulated physiological activities. From this rudimentary beginning, a child quickly develops sensorimotor patterns that parallel and assist the development of visual and auditory meanings. As this stage progresses, the child begins to generalize motor patterns and to coordinate simple individual patterns into new and more complex behaviors. This generalization and formation of new behaviors allows important new abilities to develop. For the first time, the child can make changes in the environment and learn relationships of objects to each other and to himself or herself. As the sensorimotor stage ends, the child has learned new means of action, first through physical experimentation and later through mental combinations. In this way, goal-directed behavior develops from early sensorimotor activities. The child is able to perform adaptive actions, indicating his or her awareness that the self is differentiated from objects "out there" (Furth, 1969).

Aside from the emergence and consolidation of sensorimotor patterns, six special capacities have been described by Piaget as products of a child's initial reflexive adaptation patterns. These include the abilities to imitate and to play, an understanding of the characteristics of objects, and the ability to use concepts of space, time, and causality. Each of these capacities is important to the child's future growth and development.

Although the sensorimotor stage persists for only the first 18 months after birth, sensorimotor activities continue to exert important influences throughout life. Their continuing importance in the second stage of development, the preoperational stage, has been noted by Flavel (1963, p. 121):

> With the advent of the capacity to represent actions rather than simply to perform them, the sensory-motor period draws to a close and the child is ready for an analogous but even more extended and tortuous apprenticeship in the use of symbols. The end of the sensory-motor period is thus synchronous with the beginning of the preoperational period. This does not, of course, mean that the child no longer continues to develop in the sensory-motor sphere. But it does mean that henceforth the most intellectual adaptations of which a given child is capable will take place in a conceptual-symbolic rather than purely sensory-motor area.

A child in the preoperational stage (from 18 months to 7 years of age), typically is conscious of existence in a world of permanent objects that are separate from himself or herself and have causal influences on each other. Behavior is directly linked to what the child perceives and does at a given instant. Next, in the stage of concrete operations (from 7 to 11 years), thinking is no longer restricted to physical objects that are present. Verbal information is meaningful, but the child is not yet able to make adequate inferences from verbal information alone, so that it must be combined with movement or other types of information. Finally, in the abstract operations stage (11 years and older), the child develops adult abilities and characteristics. "Hence Piaget's theory permits him to see adult logical operations as sensory-motor actions which have undergone a succession of transformations, rather than a different species of behavior entirely" (Flavell, 1963, p. 83).

Piaget's scheme of child development places strong emphasis on motor activities. Sensorimotor experience provides the foundation for later intellectual development. It is sensorimotor ability from which and in which perception develops and evolves (Flavell, 1963).

The work of Piaget describes a series of developmental stages through which a child progresses. Yet, without experience and learning, the child could not advance in his or her development. A blending of principles of learning and knowledge of development contributes to a teacher's effectiveness. Success in teaching occurs only if the learning principles that are applied are appropriate for the students in their particular developmental stages.

THE LEARNING OF SKILLS

Learning through practice involves changes in both the sensory cues that a performer uses and the responses that are produced. A performer becomes more selective and sophisticated in using different types of perceptual information to develop a response. Responses become more precisely adapted to the overall task requirements, and less attention is needed to integrate the individual actions composing a response (Welford, 1968). Successful performances must somehow be coded so that they can be placed into memory and retrieved later. Strategies, or plans of action, are also developed, tested, and coded in memory.

According to Welford (1976), a performer must learn to fit stimuli into a general outline, or schema, which is superimposed upon the incoming information, and which shapes both perception and recall. Details that do not fit the schema are either ignored or processed separately. The development of perceptual schema suggests that learning changes the perception of stimuli, not only in their individual characteristics, but also in their overall relationship to each other.

Learning also modifies responses on two levels. First, complex responses are formed from the integration of individual actions. Second, performers learn how much care must be exercised and how much effort is required by a task. Such learning enables a performer to respond correctly, with the required accuracy, and distribute effort to perform for the required length of time.

Finally, one must learn to identify important feedback and use it to correct errors in performance. This learning must be accomplished so that the performer can make appropriate modifications in responses to deal with changed task demands.

GUIDING PRINCIPLES FOR THE TEACHER

1. Learning is a relatively permanent change in behavior that results from experience or practice. Motor learning is learning that is evidenced through changes in muscular responses or movement. Sports

and occupational skills are the most common examples, but speaking and writing also rely on motor learning.

2. The acquisition of new behavior by children depends on an interaction of learning and maturation. Learning occurs as one responds to one's surroundings. Maturation is an innate process of development through which one becomes more adult.

3. Classical conditioning is a learning process that involves reflexive behavior. An unconditioned stimulus, which elicits a reflexive response, can be paired with a neutral stimulus, so that the neutral stimulus becomes conditioned; the subject learns to produce the same reflexlike behavior in response to this conditioned stimulus.

4. Instrumental conditioning is a learning process through which voluntary responses are acquired. This type of learning depends on the consequences of responses. We learn approach responses, or responses of repeating behaviors, if they have pleasant consequences, and we learn avoidance responses from behavior that has unpleasant consequences.

5. Cognitive learning can occur after concepts and perceptions have been established through classical and instrumental conditioning. Such learning, often called insight, occurs suddenly and with a feeling of understanding. It can be applied to a wide variety of situations, and it enables us to make choices among our responses.

6. Extinction is the process by which a stimulus-response bond is weakened, so that eventually the stimulus no longer elicits the response.

7. Voluntary (instrumental) behavior can have four kinds of consequences: it can (*a*) produce positive reinforcement, (*b*) remove or avoid negative reinforcement, (*c*) produce negative reinforcement, or (*d*) remove or avoid positive reinforcement. The first two types of consequences reinforce approach behaviors. The third and fourth reinforce avoidance responses.

8. Events and consequences associated with a response, but which are distinct from its primary consequences, also can acquire the ability to reinforce the response. These secondary reinforcers include such things as gold stars, pregame rituals, and smiles or frowns.

9. Responses that are conditioned on intermittent schedules of reinforcement are more difficult to extinguish than responses that have been reinforced continuously. Consequently, even one reinforcement during the extinction process can reestablish a response with considerable strength.

10. Shaping forms new behaviors by successive approximations. Responses are reinforced if they resemble a desired behavior, grossly at first but more and more closely as training proceeds.

11. Young children and adults who are acquiring new skills must initially learn through instrumental conditioning. After some background has been acquired, cognitive learning techniques can be used.

12. Several fundamental movement patterns facilitate future learning. These patterns include balance and the maintenance of posture, transport (locomotion), and manipulation (contact, receipt, and propulsion).

SUMMARY

A newborn child begins life in a vulnerable state, equipped only with birth reflexes and basic physiological functions. By the combined forces of learning and maturation, the child adapts and progresses through a general pattern of psychological development. Initially, classical conditioning provides the means through which the child extends and varies his or her responses. New responses are continually acquired through conditioning and extinguished if the unconditioned stimuli are withdrawn. The process of responding to stimuli that are similar to a conditioned stimulus is called generalization. The process of differentiating between stimuli is called discrimination. Generalization and discrimination of responses also occur.

Instrumental conditioning is concerned with voluntary responses. It relies on the presence of reinforcement, either positive or negative. Intermittent reinforcement has been shown to develop responses that strongly resist extinction. Consistency in reinforcement or nonreinforcement is the major criterion for the acquisition or extinction of voluntary responses. Shaping is a technique of forming new behaviors by successive approximations; reinforcement is awarded to responses that resemble a desired behavior, initially as crude approximations but progressively becoming more refined.

Classical and instrumental conditioning are the predominant styles of learning during the first 12 years of life. After concepts and perceptions have been formed through conditioning, however, cognitive learning becomes most prevalent. Responses are guided and selected according to cognitions, such as attitudes, expectancies, and motivations.

Styles of learning are merged and blended in a child's psychological development. Teachers must understand the principles of learning and must know which learning styles are appropriate for students in different stages of development. Fundamental movement patterns form the basis for all future learning—motor, perceptual, sensory, and cognitive. Teaching becomes the art of selecting appropriate principles for particular developmental levels, to maximize the acquisition of new skills and concepts.

REFERENCES

Barsch, R. H. 1968. *Enriching perception and cognition: Techniques for teachers.* Vol. 2. Seattle: Special Child Publications.

Bijou, S. W., and Baer, D. M. 1961. *Child development.* Vol. 1, *A systematic and empirical theory.* New York: Appleton-Century-Crofts.

Bugelski, B. R. 1956. *The psychology of learning.* New York: Holt, Rinehart and Winston.

Dennis, W. A. 1934. A description and classification of the responses of the newborn infant. *Psychological Bulletin* 31:5 22.

Dewey, E. 1935. *Behavior development in infants: A survey of the literature on prenatal and postnatal activity, 1920–1934.* New York: Columbia University Press.

Drowatzky, J. N. 1971. *Physical education for the mentally retarded.* Philadelphia: Lea & Febiger.

Espenschade, A. S., and Eckert, H. M. 1967. *Motor development.* Columbus, Ohio: Charles E. Merrill.

Ferster, C. B., and Skinner, B. F. 1957. *Schedules of reinforcement.* New York: Appleton-Century-Crofts.

Flavell, J. H. 1963. *The developmental psychology of Jean Piaget.* London: D. Van Nostrand.

Franks, V., and Franks, C. M. 1960. Conditioning in defectives and normals as related to intelligence and mental deficit: The application of a learning theory model to a study of the learning process in the mental defective. *Proceedings of the London Conference for the Scientific Study of Mental Deficiency.* Cited in *Handbook of mental deficiency: Psychological theory and research,* ed. N. R. Ellis. New York: McGraw-Hill, 1963.

Furth, H. G. 1969. *Piaget and knowledge: Theoretical foundations.* Englewood Cliffs, N.J.: Prentice-Hall.

Godfrey, B. B., and Kephart, N. C. 1969. *Movement patterns and motor education.* New York: Appleton-Century-Crofts.

Hebb, D. O. 1949. *Organization of behavior.* New York: John Wiley and Sons.

Hill, W. F. 1963. *Learning: A survey of psychological interpretations.* San Francisco: Chandler.

Kephart, N. C. 1960. *The slow learner in the classroom.* Columbus, Ohio: Charles E. Merrill.

. 1964. Perceptual-motor aspects of learning disabilities. *Exceptional Child* 31:201-206.

Kimble, G. A. 1961. *Hilgard and Marquis' conditioning and learning.* New York: Appleton-Century-Crofts.

Laurendeau, M., and Pinard, A. 1970. *The development of the concepts of space in the child.* New York: International Universities Press.

Lipman, R. S. 1963. Learning: Verbal, perceptual-motor and classical conditioning. In *Handbook of mental deficiency: Psychological theory and research,* ed. N. R. Ellis. New York: McGraw-Hill.

Morgan, C. T., and King, R. A. 1966. *Introduction to psychology.* 3d ed. New York: McGraw-Hill.

Piaget, J. 1952. *The origins of intelligence in children.* New York: International Universities Press.

Piaget, J., and Inhelder, B. 1967. *The child's conception of space.* New York: W. W. Norton.

Skinner, B. F. 1938. *The behavior of organisms.* New York: Appleton-Century-Crofts.

———. 1953. *Science and human behavior.* New York: Macmillan.

———. 1961. Teaching machines. *Scientific American* 205 (November): 91–102.

———. 1968. *The technology of teaching.* New York: Appleton-Century-Crofts.

Staats, A. W., and Staats, C. K. 1963. *Complex human behavior: A systematic extension of learning principles.* New York: Holt, Rinehart and Winston.

Thompson, G. G. 1962. *Child psychology: Growth trends in psychological adjustment.* 2d ed. Boston: Houghton Mifflin.

Thorndike, E. L. 1913. *The psychology of learning.* New York: Teachers College.

Tolman, E. C. 1942. *Purposive behavior in animals and man.* New York: Appleton-Century-Crofts.

Watson, J. B., and Rayner, R. 1920. Conditioned emotional reactions. *Journal of Experimental Psychology* 3:1–14.

Welford, A. T. 1968. *Fundamentals of skill.* London: Methuen.

———. 1976. *Skilled performance: Perceptual and motor skills.* Glenview, Ill.: Scott, Foresman.

Wolf, M., Mees, H., and Risley, T. 1964. Application of operant conditioning procedures to the behaviour problems of an autistic child. *Behaviour Research and Therapy* 1:305–312.

3 The Nature of Motor Learning

Learning has been described as the key process through which teachers have some control over behavior. In one way or another, learning influences every aspect of our lives—our language, games, attitudes and beliefs, goals, personality, and even perceptions that are used for new learning. Chapter 2 indicated that learning occurs in different processes, depending on an individual's past experiences and maturation level as well as environmental factors. Heredity might determine one's ultimate potential, but learning determines how much of that potential will be realized.

Learning is a relatively permanent change in behavior that results from experience or practice; it is a process of adaptation. Motor learning is learning that is evidenced through muscular responses, which are generally expressed in movement of the body or one of its parts. Sports skills and occupational skills are the most frequently noted examples, but activities such as writing and speaking also require learned muscular responses. Motor learning is determined partly by the types of skills to be learned, but it is also subject to some of the same principles that govern verbal learning and forms of problem solving.

When does learning occur? What kinds of changes occur during learning? How does one know when learning has occurred? These questions express typical concerns of teachers and researchers alike. This chapter examines information that is pertinent to these questions to help teachers to evaluate behavioral change and guide the learning process more effectively. This information should help in the structuring of classroom situations and in the organization of teaching materials.

LEARNING AND PERFORMANCE

Learning cannot be observed directly, although many people speak as though it is. Its occurrence can only be inferred from observable changes in performance. Learning is a construct, an intervening variable, which links performance and practice. Teachers must remember this difference between learning and performance. What is measured is performance, and this is sometimes identified with learning or lack of learning, although it may not represent either.

When parents (who sometimes exhibit more pride or ignorance than common sense) demand a public display of their child's artistic or athletic talents, frequently the child fails to perform, strikes out or drops an easy ball in a Little League game, or becomes emotional, shy, uncomfortable, and withdrawn. In like manner, adults sometimes succumb to stage fright and perform miserably, even after excellent practice sessions. Conversely, it sometimes happens that a student leaves an examination after an exceptionally fine performance and then announces that his or her knowledge was not truly measured. As these examples show, the influence of motivation, incentive, or other factors can cause a great discrepancy between the quality of performance and the amount of learning that has taken place. Consequently, one must be cautious about taking performance to represent how much a performer has learned.

THE MEASUREMENT OF PERFORMANCE

Criteria for Performance Measures

Measurement is one of the foremost problems in the evaluation of the effectiveness of teaching and research procedures. What method or type of measure should be used to evaluate performance? Fitts and Posner (1967) illustrated the dilemma in the case of batting skill. Batting average is the most commonly used index of batting skill, and yet it does not accurately represent all the elements of success. A lead-off batter with a low batting average might be highly successful if he or she receives a great number of walks and is good at stealing second base. A clean-up batter might be selected, not because of a high batting average, but because of his or her ability to hit a long ball or because he or she has few strikeouts. This player might have a low batting average but a high average of total bases per hit and might hit many sacrifice flies. As a clean-up batter, he or she might record as many runs batted in as could a player with a high batting average.

Fitts and Posner indicated that some measures are more revealing than others about important aspects of human performance, and they suggested several criteria for optimal measurement of skills. All performance measures relate events in an individual's environment (input) with his or her observable responses (output). The first criterion is that a measure must be sensitive to input, output, and the relation or balance between them. Evaluation of the performance of sports skills is often based on a single index, which may or may not truly indicate the quality of the performance. Consider such indices as tackles per game in football, points per game in basketball, and batting average or a pitcher's won-lost record in baseball. The number of tackles (output) depends on which position one plays and on the relative strength of the opposition (input). A high points-per-game average (output) could be achieved by a player who scores many points against weak teams but few against strong opposition (input). A good won-lost record or a high batting average would be meaningless if the players had never faced strong opponents. Thus, performance must be viewed in relation to environmental input. Descriptions of skill improvement and comparisons of performances should take into account the degree to which output reflects stimulus input.

The second criterion suggested by Fitts and Posner is that a measure should be appropriate to the type of task, either discrete, continuous, or serial, to which it is applied. A system of measurement must also allow for meaningful comparisons between performances of different types of tasks.

A performance measure must be sensitive to the accuracy of a performer's responses. For example, a high points-per-game average in basketball could be achieved by a player who takes few shots with great accuracy, one who takes many shots with poor accuracy, or one who makes few field goals but is fouled frequently. The batting average is not sensitive enough to distinguish between strikeouts and well-hit balls that are caught by a fielder. A measure must be sensitive to many aspects of performance, even those that do not appear to contribute directly to success. Without this sensitivity, improvement in performance cannot be accurately determined and comparisons of players at different levels of skill cannot be clearly drawn.

Because many motor skills depend at least partly on timing, a measurement system must take into account the length of time taken for a performance as well as the accuracy with which the skill is performed. Sensitivity to time is important because accuracy is often related to the speed with which a task is performed.

Finally, Fitts and Posner suggested that a measure must be general, so that it can be applied to gross motor skills, fine motor skills, perceptual skills, and other skills used in performance. Generality of measures allows for the broadest investigation of human skills. In some cases, however, the most effective means of evaluation is not the most general.

Further difficulties in obtaining an adequate performance measure lie in reliability theory (Kroll, 1967), reliability of scoring methods (Malina, 1968), and types of scoring (McCraw, 1955) used in evaluation.

Performance Measures

The measures most commonly used to assess performance and motor learning are the following:

1. amount of response
2. latency of response
3. rate of response
4. number, kind, and location of errors
5. reminiscence
6. number and time of trials
7. retention (or extinction) of response

Examples are given in Table 3.1. In considering them, keep in mind the criteria suggested by Fitts and Posner. It is often the case that no one measure accurately displays the changes in performance that are used to infer the occurrence of learning. For example, in an analysis of mirror-tracing performance measures, Drowatzky (1969) found that no single measure fully meets all requirements for optimal measurement. Consequently, mirror-tracing performance must be evaluated on the basis of more than one measure. Performance curves plotting mean score values obtained in that study are shown in Figure 3.1. The different performance measures yield curves of different shapes.

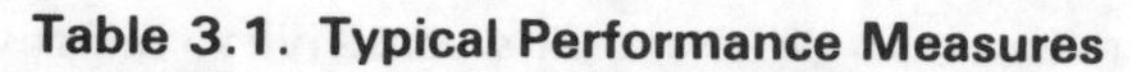

Table 3.1. Typical Performance Measures

MEASURE	EXAMPLES
Amount of response	Number of repetitions, endurance, galvanic skin response
Latency of response	Reaction time
Rate of response	Speed of movement, tapping speed, motor speed
Error	Kind of error, number of errors, location of errors
Reminiscence	Pursuit rotor, kinesthetic tests, gross motor skills
Trials	Time per trial, number of trials
Retention (extinction)	Kinesthetic tests, gross motor skills, fine motor skills

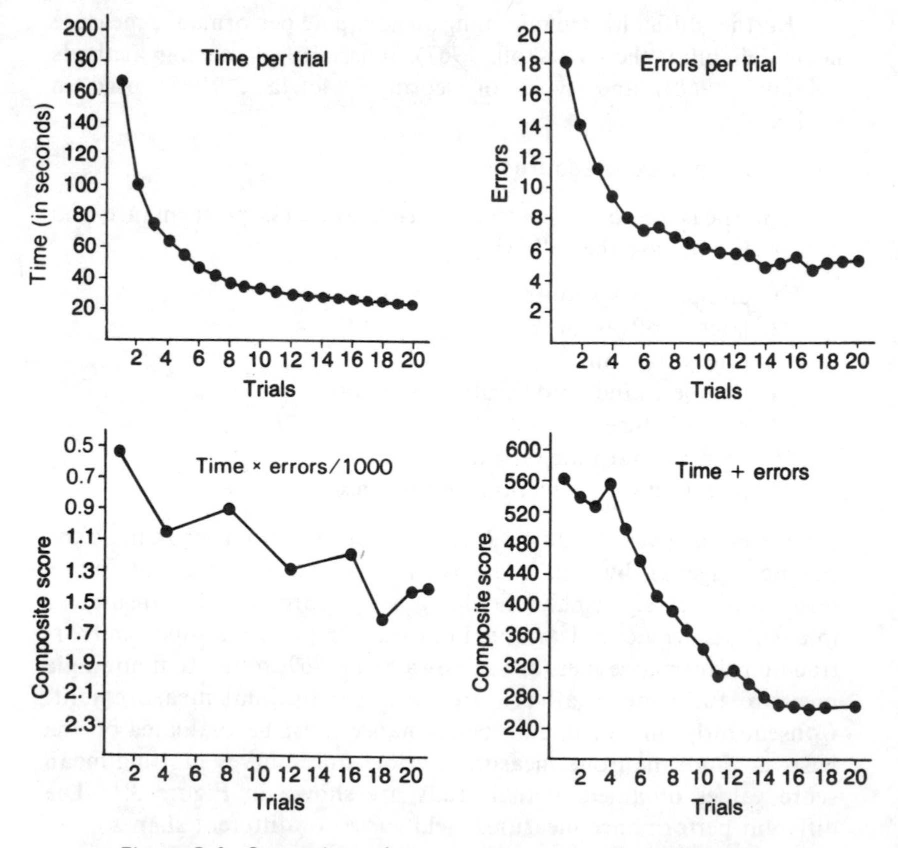

Figure 3.1. Comparison of mirror-tracing performance measures.

The following paragraphs describe performance measures that are frequently used in motor learning studies and give examples of the kinds of studies in which they have been used. Different measures can be combined to provide more comprehensive information than can be obtained with only one.

Amount of Response. In many cases, improvement in learning or performance is accompanied by a decrease in the amount of response. For example, beginning handball players typically make extraneous movements and uneconomical responses, but with the acquisition of skill, a player's movements become more appropriate and efficient. Improvement is accompanied by the elimination of movements that do not contribute to success in handball, and the performance therefore shows a decrease in the amount of response.

There are conditions, however, under which improved performance is accompanied by an increase in the amount or amplitude of response. Laycoe and Marteniuk (1971) used increases in the amount of response as a measure of performance improvement in their analysis of increases in strength. They found that both physiological changes induced by training and neuromotor coordination patterns developed through learning contribute to increased maximal strength. In like manner, Nelson (Clarke, 1966) observed the amount of response on an elbow flexion ergograph test to evaluate the effect of motivation on performance. This technique differentiated between subjects with low, moderate, and high levels of motivation.

A decrease in the amount of response indicates improvement in performance as extraneous movements are eliminated. An increase indicates improvement as the activity is sustained for more repetitions or longer periods of time. Caution must be used in determining whether changes in the amount of response are caused by learning or by some other factor, such as motivation.

Latency of Response. The latent period in learning is the time that elapses between the presentation of a stimulus and the initiation of a response. Latency of response is commonly called reaction time. It has been observed to change under the influence of such factors as task complexity (Blair, 1970; Henry and Rogers, 1960), type of set (Henry, 1960), and type of stimulus (Slater-Hammel, 1955; Wilson, 1959). Although reaction time is an important indicator of performance and learning, it does not indicate the strength of learning but only the rapidity of response.

Rate of Response. Rate of response is frequently used to evaluate performance of tasks that have already been mastered by a subject, so that it is virtually impossible for the subject to make an error. Change in performance is then assessed in terms of speed or movement time, which is the period of time that starts when the movement is initiated and ends when it is completed. Rate appears to be more valuable as a measure of the effects of factors such as movement complexity (Henry, 1961) and motivation (Howell, 1953) than as an indicator of acquisition or learning.

Error. Investigators have also looked at kinds of error, number of errors, and location of errors in performance. These have been used to evaluate performance in such diverse tasks as mirror tracing (Drowatzky, 1969), timing (Ellis, 1970), balancing (Richardson and Pew, 1970), and the fencing lunge (Ehrlich, 1943). Errors have been found to decrease with increased practice and to be influenced by variations in the rate of practice. One way to evaluate performance errors is to analyze the number of correct responses in each trial. Errors provide important information about performance, but they are often used along with some other measure, such as rate, for purposes of evaluation.

Reminiscence. Some people apparently do much better on tests of recently learned skills if they are given a rest between the practice session and the testing period. This phenomenon is known as reminiscence. Abbey (1962) observed that the amount of reminiscence decreases as skill improves. Studies of softball (Fox and Lamb, 1962) and the wall volley in badminton (Fox and Young, 1962) indicate that reminiscence effects occur with these motor skills. Studies of the short serve in badminton (Fox and Young, 1962) and balance skills (Ryan, 1962; Meyers, 1967), however, have not shown any reminiscence effect. It is believed that factors other than learning, such as reactive inhibition (due to fatigue) and the type of skill, can also produce effects that resemble those of reminiscence.

Trials. Some of the commonest indicators of performance are the amount of time required by a subject to complete a trial, the number of trials that must be completed to reach a performance criterion, and the level of performance attained after a prescribed number of trials. These measures vary greatly with individual subjects and can obscure the effects of other variables or conditions.

The amount of time required by subjects to complete a trial was one of the performance measures used by Vincent (1968) to discover that performance can be improved through transfer between similar perceptual components of motor tasks. To investigate the effect of intelligence in motor learning, Ellis et al. (1960) calculated the mean number of trials required by subjects of varying intellectual abilities to reach a criterion performance on a shielded maze task. Their results dramatically illustrate the influence of intelligence on the rate of acquisition for that motor task. Students' performance on badminton skill tests were used by Gray and Brumbach (1967) to determine that the supplemental use of loop films showing the basic strokes hastened the learning process. Other analyses of performance in terms of trial variables can be found throughout the motor learning literature.

Retention. Measures of retention—how long learned information is retained, how fast forgetting or extinction occurs, and the amount of savings in time or number of trials needed for relearning a task—can be used to infer that learning has taken place. Recall and recognition, evidenced in written examinations and frequently involving written or oral information, are also sometimes used in motor skill studies. The concept of savings applies transfer principles to the study of retention. A savings score is computed as follows: the difference in the number of trials (or the amount of time) needed for learning and for relearning a task is divided by the number of trials (or the amount of time) needed for learning the task the first time. This quotient is usually multiplied by 100 and expressed as a percentage:

$$\frac{\text{original trials (or time)} - \text{relearning trials (or time)}}{\text{original trials (or time)}} \times 100$$

Amount of skill retention, amount of forgetting, and savings scores have all been used as performance measures in motor learning studies. Wilberg (1969) asked subjects to reposition the handle of an apparatus to an initially known position; his data show that short-term memory is better if subjects receive visual input than if they are restricted to kinesthetic information. In an investigation conducted by Chasey (1971), overlearning was found to be a factor in reducing the amount of forgetting among mentally retarded persons. A savings score and the amount of recall were two of the measures employed by Melnick (1971) to evaluate the effects of overlearning on the acquisition of a balance skill; his data indicate that overlearning increases the amount of retention for periods of 1 week and 1 month. Factors that contribute to both short-term and long-term memory have come under increasing scrutiny by researchers in motor learning and performance. The information gained through these studies should help teachers facilitate the retention of new skills by students.

LEARNING CURVES

It is impossible to learn new motor skills without some type of practice. Although simple associations and recombinations of learned skills can be accomplished in one trial, progress in acquiring a new motor skill is gradual. The plotting of learners' scores in the course of practice produces a *learning curve,* or (more appropriately) a *performance curve.* The abscissa of such a curve usually represents the number of trials or the length of the training period. The ordinate generally represents scores such as the time needed to complete a task or the number of errors. Such curves typically show trial-by-trial improvement, which tapers off as the limits of achievement are approached. This tapering off can be rapid, as it is in most laboratory studies, or it can cover a long period of time, as it usually does in industrial settings. Differences in the length of time required for performance to approach the limits of achievement and differences in the shapes of performance curves have been shown to result from task complexity (Norrie, 1967; Krueger, 1947; Schmidt et al., 1971).

The four common types of motor performance curves in Figure 3.2 illustrate different kinds of information. Curve *A* represents cases in which improvement is evidenced by longer periods of activity. It is constructed from data obtained in regularly spaced practice trials. Curve *B* shows improvement in the form of higher scores. It displays data from practice bouts, or circuits (a bout is a series of practice trials with little time for rest between trials; a longer rest period is allowed between bouts). Curve *C* represents cases in which improvement is accompanied by a decrease in performance time. This curve illustrates an experiment in which improvement occurred after only a few trials. In contrast, curve *D* (which is plotted on logarithmic paper) displays data collected over many years. It represents improvement in the form of increased efficiency of workers operating a machine at different rates.

Most learning curves are used to compare performances of groups of subjects, but they can also be used to examine the performances of an individual. An individual's performances, however, usually show erratic and irregular variation.

Most performance curves show a negative acceleration. That is, the amount of improvement from one trial to the next decreases as the number of trials performed increases. Negative acceleration is especially characteristic of improvement in most perceptual-motor skills. Other curves are characterized by an increasing rate of improvement per trial (positive acceleration) or show intermediate degrees of change for a given trial.

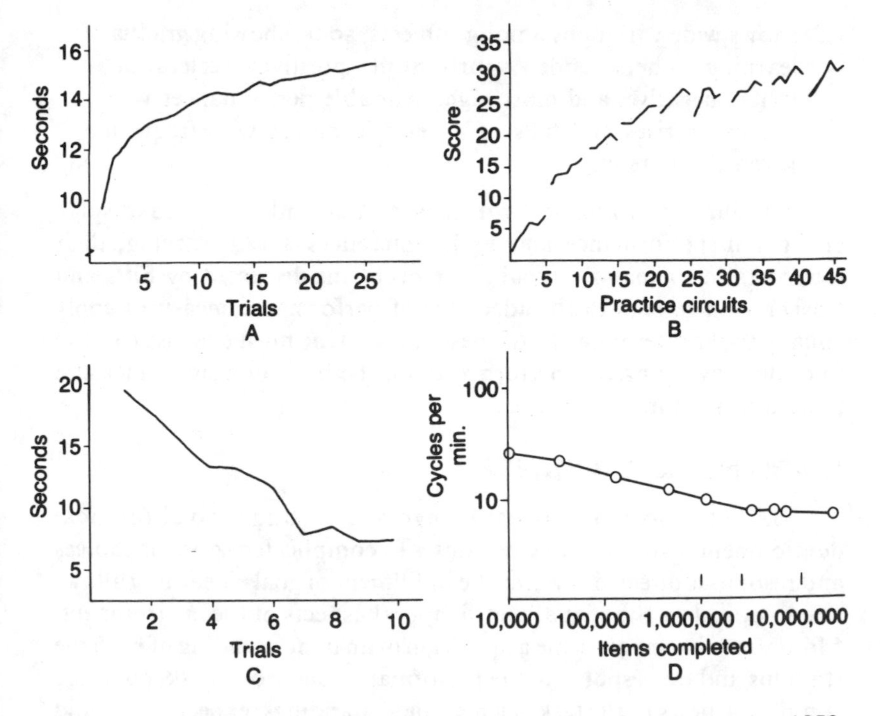

Figure 3.2. Typical motor performance curves. (Data from Crossman, 1959; Whitley, 1970; Singer, 1965; and Oxendine, 1965.)

Bryan and Harter (1897) observed a temporary cessation of progress, or a plateau in the curve, in their work with subjects learning to receive Morse code. It was suggested that such plateaus represent phases of consolidation in learning. Further reports indicate that plateaus are not a general, frequently occurring characteristic of performance curves (Taylor, 1943; Bahrick, Fitts, and Briggs, 1957; Keller, 1958). Progress seems to be erratic rather than characterized by plateaus, particularly in cases of complex skills measured in an indirect manner, using a single performance measure. Chance, rather than a consolidation in learning, is probably responsible for a succession of several scores showing no improvement. According to Bugelski (1956, p. 194),

> The difficulty with interpreting any curve of learning that allegedly reflects the learning of a group of subjects is that examination of the curves of individual subjects frequently

shows wide variations among subjects, some showing gradual learning, others sudden spurts, some positive acceleration, others negative, and most highly variable performances with numerous rises and falls of an erratic nature with frequent reversals of trends.

Although performance curves are frequently used to display changes in performance and make inferences about learning, their interpretation remains difficult. The problems discussed by Fitts and Posner with respect to the adequacy of performance measures apply equally to the interpretation of these curves. One must exercise caution in evaluating changes in performance on the basis of a single measure plotted in the form of a curve.

LEARNING AS A PROCESS

Skilled motor performance evolves through psychological development, from reflexive responses to complicated series of choices and responses directed towards the fulfillment of goals. Learning allows one to adjust to the spatial and temporal aspects of the environment. Motor learning involves the acquisition of an understanding of both the stimulus and the response in the performance of a motor task, but more complex aspects of the task, such as understandings, expectancies, and overall strategies, also play a role in learning.

Closed Skills and Open Skills

The acquisition of skilled motor performance involves the learning of two components, muscular response and perceptual cues. Perceptual cues, which result from the processing of information, relate information from the outside world. Muscular response, the motor element of the task, indicates what one does with the information that is received. All motor tasks require both components, but their relative importance varies widely from situation to situation.

The performance of some tasks depends more on incoming perceptual information, while the performance of others depends more on the motor aspect of the task. Knapp (1961) and Holding (1965) have classified motor tasks as either *closed skills* or *open skills*, in attempts to differentiate between those that are largely motor oriented and those that are largely dependent on perceptual information. Closed skills place less reliance upon information received from the environment and depend more on a consistently replicable, apparently habitual movement. Examples include putting the shot, hitting a golf ball, and weight lifting. Open skills, in contrast, are characterized by continued modification of the movement on the basis of environmental input received by the performer. Examples of open skills are tennis, football, and fencing.

Classification of movements into closed skills and open skills can aid in the development of a teaching strategy. If a closed skill is being taught, consistency of movement must be emphasized. Perceptual cues and their meanings must be emphasized in the teaching of open skills. Because no skill is purely open or purely closed, the best approach is to teach the more important component first, then to teach the other component, and finally to combine the two into the unified task. Following this approach, a golf instructor might emphasize consistency of the swing, and a basketball coach working with advanced performers might emphasize how to make decisions about the proper response.

Phases of Learning

Regardless of whether the skills it involves are open or closed, performance is an information-processing task. In the case of a closed skill, the information originates largely from within, as proprioceptive and kinesthetic perception. Open skills emphasize the processing of external information received through the senses. All persons, except for very young infants, acquire new skills against a background of highly developed skills, either general or specific, which have already been mastered. Learning generally consists of setting up a general execution program and then developing appropriate subroutines to develop previously acquired experience into the skills needed for performance. A person's background is not always helpful, as new challenges might not fit any of his or her past experiences. Nonetheless, people still try responses that have been successful in the past, even in totally new situations.

According to Fitts (1964), skill learning has an early, cognitive phase; an intermediate, associative phase; and a late, autonomous phase. The cognitive phase is the short time that is required to understand instructions, complete a few preliminary details, and establish the proper cognitive set for the task. The associative phase involves two kinds of mediation processes: first, the formation of specific associations and learning to respond to specific cues and, second, cognitive set learning, which enables one to deal successfully with related skill situations. (Chapter 7 deals with this stage.) The autonomous phase is characterized by continued improvement in performance as acquisition of the skill is completed. Performance of sports skills continues to improve and rarely reaches a peak after daily practice for many years. Decrements in performance appear to be caused by physiological aging and loss of motivation rather than by a limit to the capacity for improvement.

In spite of the distinction of three separate phases in acquisition, learning is a continuous process, even in the acquisition of a smooth movement that consists of a series of discrete skills. It is somewhat misleading to separate the process into distinct stages with easily identifiable beginnings and ends. The separation into phases is necessary for an understanding of the learning process, however. For practical purposes, teachers must recognize that different abilities and techniques contribute to success at different stages of the process. Teachers must therefore be aware of gradual shifts in the factor structure of skills and in the procedures, strategies, and tactics to be used as learning progresses. They can then adjust their teaching techniques appropriately for different students and different situations.

For a learner to pass successfully from the early phase to the late phase, requirements must be met in sequence. First, the learner must comprehend the task. Teachers must organize their instructions to develop a thorough understanding of what needs to be learned. Next, the material must be placed in some type of short-term storage until it can be placed in long-term memory. This process can be facilitated through physical practice. It can also be hindered by subsequent activities that are similar enough to cause interference. Finally, the learner must be able to retrieve the material for later use. Retrieval is easier if few possibilities exist, if the response is probable, and if associations or verbal mediations have been formed (Welford, 1976). Teachers must plan instructional units to facilitate this sequence of events.

VARIABILITY

Perhaps one of the most striking characteristics of a class in physical education is the many different levels of ability exhibited by the students. Providing for this range of abilities is one of the most challenging tasks to confront teachers, because they must take into consideration both the general level of skill in the class as a whole and the extent to which individual students' levels of skill differ from the average.

On the one hand, teachers must take into account the *central tendency*, or the average level of performance, of the group. Three measures—the mean, the median, and the mode—are used to identify the central tendency. The mean score is the arithmetic average. The median is the point at which 50 percent of the scores fall above and 50 percent fall below. The modal score is the score that occurs most frequently. Each of these can help teachers to determine the general level of performance. In a perfectly normal distribution, all three measures coincide, but in most actual situations they are different.

On the other hand, teaching must accommodate *variability*, or dispersion, which refers to the manner in which scores fall around the mean. With reference to groups, such as a class of students, variability reflects differences in abilities of the group's members. If all performances are nearly alike, so that scores cluster closely around the mean, the class is said to be *homogeneous*. *Heterogeneous* classes, in contrast, record scores that are widely separated, and the performances of class members are noticeably different. With reference to a single individual, variability indicates the degree of consistency in that individual's performance. Both the variability of group scores and the variability of an individual's scores are important in the determination of instructional strategy.

It is possible for two groups to show the same variability and yet to have different central tendencies (see Figure 3.3). Conversely, two groups could have the same value for the central tendency and yet differ in variability (see Figure 3.4). Two groups can also differ in both central tendency and variability (see Figure 3.5). An understanding of these indices of performance is valuable in planning for instruction and in evaluation.

Changes in Variability

The nature and implications of changes in variability are also important to teachers. Improvement in performance is usually accompanied by improvement in mean scores. Most novice teachers, however, mistakenly assume that improvement in mean performance also produces a reduction in variability and individual differences. Although the effect of practice on variability has not been exhaustively studied, research has indicated some general trends. As a rule, improvement in the average or typical performance also increases variability in the class. That is, a rise in the central tendency accentuates individual differences among students.

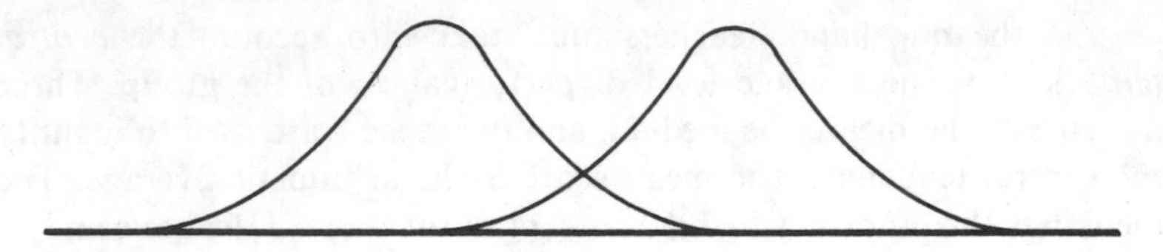

Figure 3.3 Distributions with the same variability but different values of central tendency.

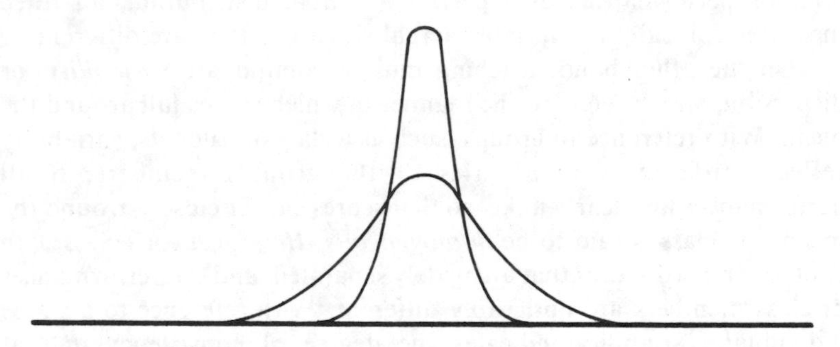

Figure 3.4. Distributions with the same value of central tendency but different variability.

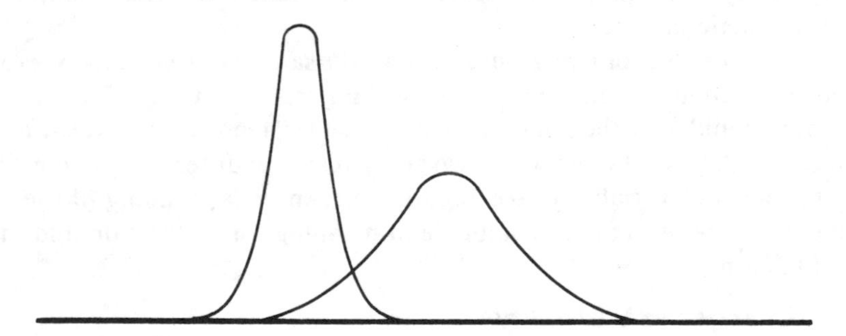

Figure 3.5. Distributions with different variability and different values of central tendency.

For example, Lersten (1968) used a pursuit rotor to evaluate the effects of practice on individual differences. He observed that the differences among subjects increased rapidly with practice until the variability was eight times greater than it was at the start. At that point, the variability stabilized, and little or no more increase was observed in the degree of individual differences. Lersten further observed that the passage of time between practice days increases variability among members of a group. This increase was also noted by Carron and Marteniuk (1970). Individual differences in retention and memory further contribute to variability among students. Retention appears to be affected differently in high-ability and low-ability groups; high-ability groups appear to retain more.

Alderman (1968) and Noble (1970) observed an increase in variability with practice on a pursuit rotor. Their studies suggest that sex also determines differences in variability. Individual differences were greater among men than among women at the beginning of practice but greater among women at the end. Women's variability increased more than men's and declined only slightly after peaking, while men's variability (in Noble's study) declined more sharply in the course of an extended series of practice sessions. The final individual differences, however, were still more pronounced than those observed at the beginning of practice. A graphic representation of the results of Noble's study is given in Figure 3.6.

Other investigations have shown that individual differences on gross motor tasks are also accentuated by practice. Meyers (1968) found that variability among subjects increases as a result of practice on the Bachman ladder-climb task. Analysis of data obtained by Lowe (1971),

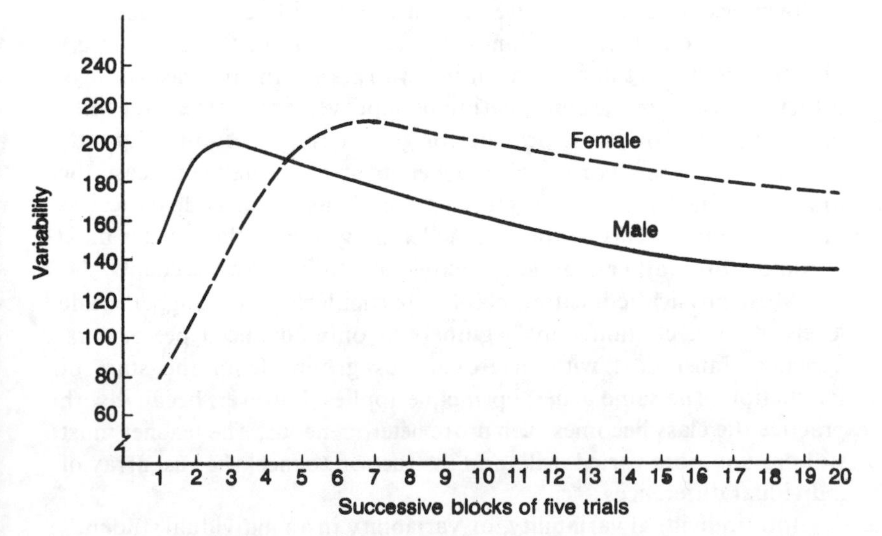

Figure 3.6. Variability indicated through targeting variance as a function of successive practice blocks for men and women. (Modified from Noble, 1970.)

in a study of performance on a footprint pathway task, indicated an increase in variability, for performance on both simple and complex pathways. Thus, practice appears to increase the differences among individuals' performances in a wide variety of situations.

An exception to this general rule occurs in cases of simple discrete skills, such as lifting one's hand off a telegraph key in response to a stimulus. Meyers et al (1969), in their study of the effect of strenuous activity on reaction time, reported data suggesting that individual differences in simple reaction time tasks decrease with experience. Therefore, practice affects variability differently according to whether the task is simple or complex or whether the skill is discrete or continuous.

Implications of Variability for Teachers

Group variability must be taken into consideration in student placement and instructional planning. Teachers first need to understand what the differences are, and then they must determine what factors influence them and in what manner they can be changed. Such information can be used to enhance the teaching and learning situation as drill progressions and individualized instruction based on students' needs and abilities are employed.

The two effects of practice, a rise in the general level of group performance and an increase in individual differences, place two requirements on a teacher's plans for instruction. First, the teacher must plan for progressive improvement in performance and increase the task difficulty to ensure the continuation of improvement. At the same time, however, the plans must provide for greater ranges of ability among students. In other words, the teacher must continually increase the difficulty of task requirements for some students but provide basic, less difficult requirements for others. As learning occurs, the teacher must become more, rather than less, flexible in dealings with students.

Most physical education classes, particularly at the higher grade levels, do not contain only beginners or only advanced performers. Teachers must deal with heterogeneous groups from the start of instruction. The same general principle applies, however, because with practice the class becomes even more heterogeneous. The teacher must still present more varied drills and instruction to meet the vast array of individual differences.

Intraindividual variability, or variability in an individual student's performance, changes with practice in another manner. It is an index of the consistency of performance. In most activities, performance becomes more consistent through practice under standardized conditions. Objective and subjective observations of an individual student generally show increased consistency, both in skill and in endurance tasks, after practice.

Thus, teachers must consider more than the average level of a group's performance in planning for instruction. Both group variability and intraindividual variability must be considered in the development of class organization and teaching materials. With practice and learning, individual differences become more apparent so that teachers must provide not only for improved abilities but also for more widely divergent abilities. The range of instructional tasks must become greater and more varied. Superimposed on the increase in individual differences is the change in each student's consistency. Students not only become more different in ability, but they also become consistently more different.

ERRORS

Another dimension of motor learning, which also changes with practice, is the nature and location of errors in performance. Errors can occur in a performer's perception of the stimulus situation, in the translation of perception into action, or in the control of the response (Welford, 1976; Rabbitt, 1967; Rabbitt and Vyas, 1970). Errors are important in learning, and probably we would not learn without them. The problem for teachers lies in preventing the development of learned errors in a skill pattern.

According to Lawther (1968), the nature of errors changes as a person's skill develops, and the teaching emphasis should change accordingly. Beginning performers often make errors at random. That is, different errors are made from trial to trial. Consequently, in working with beginners, a teacher should emphasize correct form rather than errors, although major deviations from proper form and errors that persist after several trials should be corrected. In contrast, advanced performers generally repeat the same errors, which they have learned and incorporated into the performance. They are usually unaware of their errors so that a teacher must direct their attention to flaws before the skill pattern can be corrected. Teachers must recognize that under stress the old, incorrect pattern tends to reappear until the correct pattern has been acquired to such an extent that it becomes dominant.

Von Wright (1957*a*, 1957*b*) indicated that learning must be structured so that the learner makes a decision about the response and is not merely a passive observer. Similar results were reported by Holding and Macrae (1964). Learners must be provided with some opportunity to make decisions about the required performance. Teaching should not be conducted in a completely error-free environment, in which no demands are placed on learners to make decisions.

THE PREDICTION OF ABILITIES

Teachers and coaches are generally interested in the prediction of students' or ahtletes' performances on the basis of current observations. In the case of coaching, the problem relates to the selection of team members who have the greatest potential in the near future. Coaches are likely to select athletes who have had the most experience and whose skills are more fully developed than others', but a coach with ample time and facilities for the development of talent (such as several years and many assistants) might be more willing to consider potential performance. In the case of teaching, the potential performance level of students is an important factor in curriculum development. Predictions of future abilities have been used to determine the offering of advanced courses and to estimate the number of students who would enroll.

To enhance the benefits of physical activity programs, attempts have been made to form homogeneous groups on the basis of predicted abilities, so that each class would be composed of students with equal levels of skill. According to Clarke (1967), two major procedures have been followed in attempts to produce homogeneous groups: students are classified according to their performance of specific activities or according to their general abilities. The first procedure requires an evaluation of each student's performance in each activity in the program. Depending on which activity is being taught at a particular time, the composition of groups can be changed to preserve homogeneity. To group students by general abilities, measures of all-around athletic or motor ability are employed. These typically include an integrated composite of individual traits such as strength, endurance, coordination, reaction time, speed, power, agility, and balance. These measures do not indicate skill in any particular activities; rather, they indicate potential for good performance in a number of activities. The composition of groups formed according to general abilities remains the same, regardless of which activity is being taught.

A number of early motor ability and capacity tests have been used in attempts to predict potentials for good performance. These include such indices as the Strength Index, McCloy's Strength Index, McCloy's General Motor Ability Test, the McCloy Motor Capacity Test, the Larson Tests, the Newton Motor Ability Test, Cozen's Athletic Ability Test, the Barrow Motor Ability Test, the Iowa-Brace Test, and the Metheny-Johnson Test. Typically, as reported by the developers of these instruments, correlations between performance on these tests and performance of selected sports skills range from .51 to .97. These results were obtained under various conditions and using subjects of various ages (Clarke, 1967).

Because students with varying degrees of experience, ability, and interest were used as subjects, these test results do not answer the question of whether success in a motor skill can be predicted from one's initial performance of the skill. Few studies have looked at this question, but those that have are remarkably consistent in their findings that initial performances alone are not reliable predictors. For example, Trussell (1965) taught 40 college women a ball-juggling task over a 9-week period. She found no relationship between students' initial scores and final performance levels. Predictions could be made, however, on the basis of initial scores plus learning scores accumulated over several days. Observation of students can be as efficient and accurate for predicting future performance as statistical techniques such as the use of regression equations. Both direct observation and statistical analysis, however, are open to considerable error.

Similarly, Welch (1963) found no relationship between initial performance on a ladder-climbing task and performances conducted after the first 3 days of practice. She did find, however, that reasonable prediction could be achieved if the initial estimates were combined with results from at least the first half of the 3-day period. Scores from the final stages of training were found by Adams (1953) to be a reasonable predictor of final performance on a complex psychomotor task, but he concluded that printed tests, simple psychomotor tasks, and measures obtained from the initial stages of training are all poor predictors of final performance. Consequently, in evaluating students, teachers must remember that present levels of performance have little or no relationship to the levels of performance that students can achieve after instruction and practice.

Many factors determine students' ability levels. These factors include growth and development, amount and quality of past experiences, each student's potentials, and personality factors such as interest, persistence, and motivation. Tests to predict future performance are successful only to the degree that they account for these factors. Initial scores are not adequate predictors of a student's final level. Tests can be an aid in the grouping of students according to their abilities if instructors realize that such classification must undergo continuous revision as learning occurs. Prediction remains more an art than a science.

EFFECTS OF PRACTICE

Practice brings about several types of change. Not only do motor abilities change in the course of practice, but the relative importance of different abilities shifts as well. Perceptual skills also change, as individuals attend to different forms of information and process it differently after practice. Skilled teachers recognize that these changes occur and make provisions for them in instruction. A teacher-student relationship is characterized by a series of complex interactions of abilities, task requirements, and understandings.

Changes in Abilities

Not only do particular abilities and characteristics contribute to success in performance, but clusters of abilities or relationships between abilities also determine performance level. Physical fitness components, such as endurance and strength, affect the quantity of output (for example, how long one can sustain an activity). Motor ability factors, such as balance, agility, and coordination, influence the quality of performance. Underlying each of these general abilities are groups of more specific factors. General balance ability appears to be determined by several unrelated types of specific balance skills, each of which contributes to performance in specific motor skills (Drowatzky and Zuccato, 1967).

Motor ability factors affect the quality of performance. They determine how skillfully one can perform an activity, as opposed to how long one can perform the activity. Guilford (1958) reviewed numerous studies of psychomotor abilities and developed a matrix of factors believed to be influential in performance. This matrix, presented in Table 3.2, classifies psychomotor factors according to parts of the body and kinds of motor abilities:

1. strength—the amount of force that one can exert at a given time

Table 3.2. Matrix of Psychomotor Factors

	STRENGTH	IMPULSION	SPEED	STATIC PRECISION	DYNAMIC PRECISION	COORDINATION	FLEXIBILITY
Gross body	General strength	General reaction time		Static balance	Dynamic precision	Gross body coordination	Flexibility
Trunk	Trunk strength						Trunk flexibility
Limbs	Limb strength	Limb thrust	Arm speed	Steadiness	Aiming		Leg flexibility
Hand-finger		Finger-tapping speed		Hand aiming	Finger and hand dexterity		

From J. P. Guilford, A system of psychomotor abilities, *American Journal of Psychology* 71 (1958) 165. Reprinted by permission.

2. impulsion—the rate at which a person can initiate movement from a stationary position
3. speed—the rate of movement after movement has been started
4. precision—the accuracy with which one can hold body positions and the accuracy of directed movements
5. coordination—the effective integration of different body parts in skilled tasks
6. flexibility the freedom of movement in the joints of the body

Guilford did not believe that this system includes all possible psychomotor factors. Vacant cells in the matrix suggest others. The important concept is that skilled performance is determined by a variety of influences in combination, including anatomy and psychomotor factors and also perception and personality.

Factor-analytic studies have been conducted in attempts to isolate abilities or clusters of abilities that contribute to success in complex psychomotor skills. Safrit (1969) studied object projection skills in two sets of subjects, a highly skilled group and a heterogeneous group, to determine whether successful performers in both groups would show the same factor patterns of abilities. She isolated several factor patterns, including overarm skills, kicking, pushing skills, striking skills, power, and the ability to perform repeated wall volleys. The factor pattern obtained for subjects in the highly skilled group was generally the same as the pattern obtained for subjects in the heterogeneous group. The primary difference was that the cluster of overarm skills appeared only in the highly skilled sample. These findings suggest that the same types of abilities contribute to successful performance at all levels of skill.

Fleishman and Hempel (1956) extracted nine factors that affect the complex psychomotor performance and related skills required of pilots: (1) the coordination of large muscles in the body; (2) the coordination of more than one body part during gross adjustments; (3) the interpretation of spatial characteristics of the stimulus and response; (4) the ability to rapidly discriminate directions of movement; (5) proper coordination of both hands or of hands and feet; (6) pursuit, or the ability to make anticipatory adjustments in relation to changes in speed and direction of a continuously moving object; (7) facility in making rapid comparisons of visual forms with accurate descriptions of similarities and differences; (8) the ability to make precise manipulations under speed conditions; and (9) the ability to perform mental manipulations of visual images. They concluded that, "contrary to the previous belief that motor skills are narrow in scope and highly specific to the task, the present results confirm that there are certain broad group factors of psychomotor skill which may account for performance on a wide variety of different psychomotor tasks" (p. 104).

Different abilities influence performance at different stages of learning. That is, not only do different abilities produce variations in performance, but their relative contributions to performance change with practice. For example, Fleishman and Rich (1963) tested subjects' spatial abilities and then gave them extended practice on a two-hand coordination task involving both spatial-visual and proprioceptive cues. Their results indicate that sensitivity to spatial-visual cues is critical in the early stages of learning, while sensitivity to proprioceptive cues contributes more in later stages. West (1967) reported that typists perform better in early practice sessions if they are allowed to see what they type. Later, however, they rely less on vision and make greater use of tactile and kinesthetic cues.

Other studies confirm that different abilities contribute to successful performance at different stages of practice. Fleishman and Hempel (1955) investigated several abilities that affect the acquisition of discrimination reaction time. Performance curves from their study, presented in Figure 3.7, show that word knowledge and instrument comprehension are more important at the beginning than at the end of practice, while jump visual reaction time and rotary aiming are more important at the end than at the beginning.

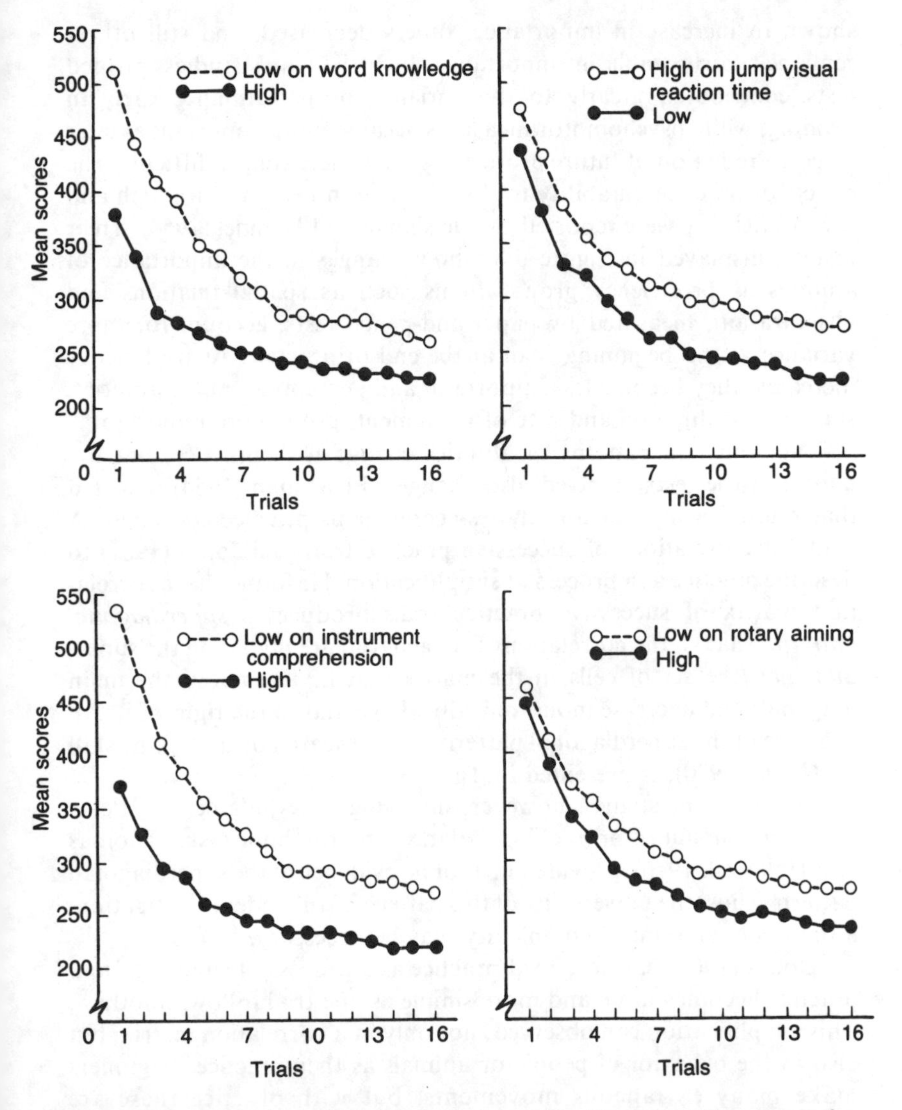

Figure 3.7. Comparison of discrimination reaction time acquisition curves for groups stratified on different predictor variables. (Modified from Fleishman and Hempel, 1955.)

Factor-analytic studies of clusters of related abilities have reported similar results. Fleishman (1957, 1970) observed considerable and systematic changes in patterns of abilities that affect performance on complex tasks as subjects' proficiency increases. Some abilities were shown to increase in importance, others decreased, and still others remained fairly stable in importance. In Fleishman's studies, printed tests contributed greatly to the variance of performance early in training, while psychomotor measures became more important at later stages. Prediction of future proficiency grew increasingly difficult. The effects of practice on ability to discriminate in persons with high and low proficiency were reported by Fleishman and Hempel (1954). Their results, displayed in Figure 3.8, show changes in the importance of abilities as proficiency grows. Items such as spatial relations and visualization, measured by paper-and-pencil tests, account for more variance at the beginning than at the end of practice. As proficiency increases, they become less important, and perceptual-motor abilities, such as coordination and rate of movement, grow more important.

Not only do patterns of abilities change with practice, but the nature of the tests involved also changes. Fleishman (1954) reported that a test becomes factorially less complex as practice continues. A study of correlations of successive practice trials led Jones (1962) to describe practice as a process of simplification. He found that a correlation matrix of successive practice trials produces a *superdiagonal pattern.* That is, the correlations for each trial are highest in the superdiagonal (the set of cells in the matrix that lie just above the main diagonal) and decrease monotonically above and to the right of it. An example of the superdiagonal pattern, from research on a tracking skill by Noble (1970), is presented in Table 3.3.

More recent studies, however, involving time judgments (Hicks, 1976) and pursuit rotor tracking, balance, and rhythmic tasks (Thomas and Halliwell, 1976), provided little or no evidence of the superdiagonal pattern. Thus, the universality of this pattern is still under investigation; a minimum amount of complexity may be necessary.

Jones (1962) has described practice as a process of simplification; practice becomes more and more simple as one trial follows another. This simplification can observed, not only in a correlation matrix, but also in the behavior of people or animals as they practice. Beginners make many extraneous movements, but with practice these are eliminated until the performer becomes highly skilled and is a model of movement efficiency. By Jones's definition, practice is the portion of the learning sequence that follows the formation of a correct hypothesis. In this sense, practice coincides with the intermediate phase and the final phase of learning in Fitts's (1964) model.

The elimination of extraneous movement was observed by Humphrey (1963), who studied movements made at the beginning and

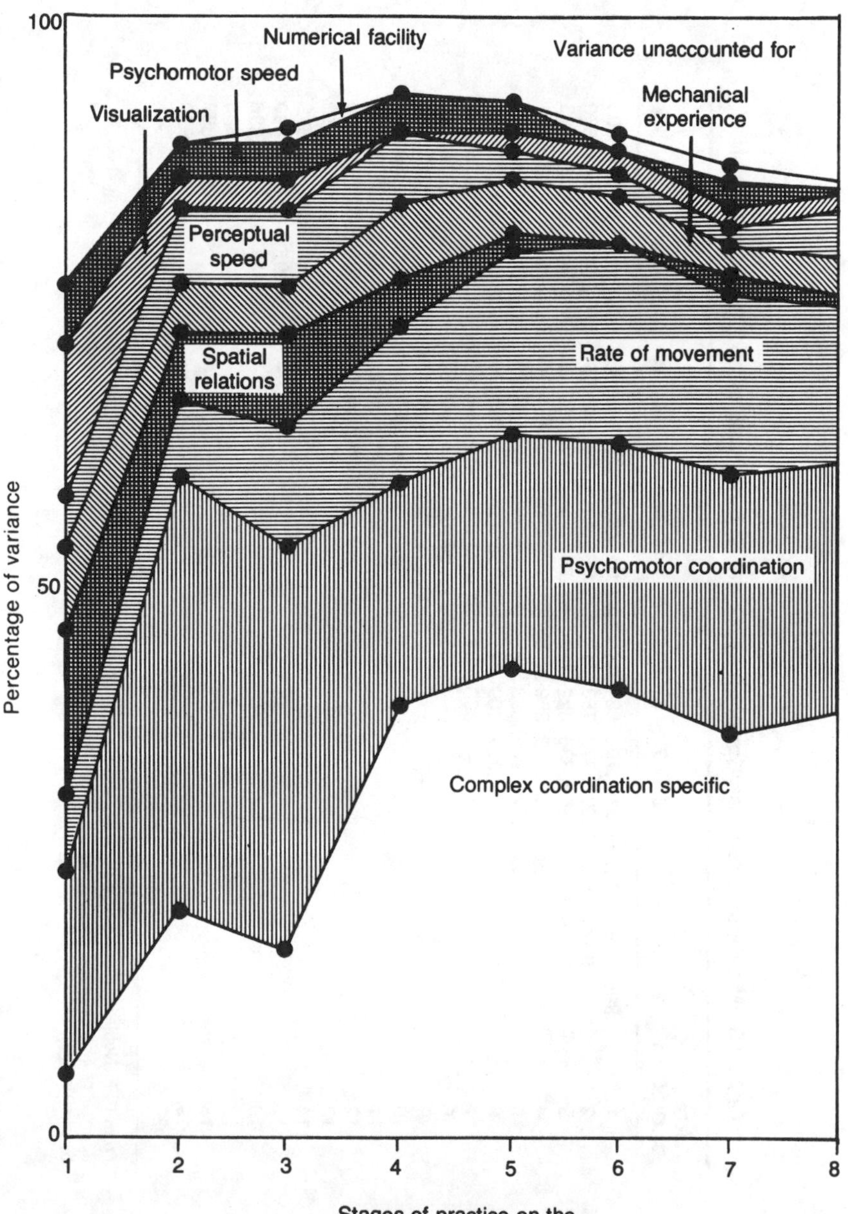

Figure 3.8. Percentage of variance (shaded area) represented by each factor at different stages of practice on the Complex Coordination Test. (Modified from Fleishman and Hempel, 1954.)

Table 3.3. Matrix of Interblock Correlations for the Rotary Pursuit Task During 100 Trials

TRIAL BLOCK	1	2	3	4	5	6	7	8	9	10	11	12	13	14	15	16	17	18	19	20
1	–	.890	.819	.784	.749	.710	.705	.684	.635	.630	.625	.605	.598	.579	.563	.558	.568	.535	.534	.503
2		–	.902	.866	.839	.802	.779	.753	.717	.705	.688	.670	.660	.648	.619	.615	.625	.580	.587	.560
3			–	.911	.893	.861	.836	.822	.780	.767	.742	.724	.712	.684	.667	.649	.661	.626	.634	.593
4				–	.925	.886	.868	.859	.815	.801	.778	.761	.736	.724	.704	.688	.686	.659	.657	.621
5					–	.926	.902	.893	.858	.841	.826	.795	.782	.758	.731	.715	.711	.689	.693	.658
6						–	.927	.909	.871	.865	.853	.824	.813	.793	.766	.758	.750	.734	.723	.697
7							–	.930	.894	.891	.883	.865	.842	.816	.802	.793	.789	.778	.773	.732
8								–	.923	.907	.896	.881	.870	.837	.829	.814	.802	.790	.793	.756
9									–	.919	.910	.892	.884	.874	.861	.841	.835	.830	.832	.805
10										–	.928	.903	.896	.885	.871	.861	.851	.855	.839	.814
11											–	.918	.907	.896	.881	.869	.862	.851	.838	.826
12												–	.928	.916	.902	.891	.885	.878	.872	.860
13													–	.922	.906	.904	.892	.886	.882	.859
14														–	.923	.919	.888	.894	.888	.878
15															–	.919	.895	.902	.902	.890
16																–	.919	.914	.903	.896
17																	–	.910	.899	.895
18																		–	.921	.897
19																			–	.920
20																				–

From C. E. Noble, Acquisition of pursuit tracking skill under extended training as a joint function of sex and initial ability, *Journal of Experimental Psychology* 86 (1970):368. Copyright 1970 by the American Psychological Association. Reprinted by permission.

end of a training period in which subjects tracked a moving target with the hand. More movement was recorded at the beginning of practice. By the end of the training period, muscular activity had been narrowed down so that only the muscles that are actually required for performance of the task were being used.

Studies by Fleishman and coworkers (1954, 1955, 1956, 1957, 1963, 1970) show that performers rely on general abilities early in the learning of a task and on more specific abilities later. Similarly, Jones (1966) described the factors that drop out during training as more general than those that remain. In a later work, Jones (1972) postulated three superdiagonal forms: increasing, level, and decreasing (see Table 3.4). The increasing form is a pattern in which correlations between successive trials grow stronger with practice. In the level form, correlations in the superdiagonal remain the same throughout the training period. The decreasing form is characterized by correlations that weaken with practice and finally vanish. Jones believes that the superdiagonal pattern is universal, so that one or another of these forms is always recognizable and present in practice.

Both Jones and Fleishman with his coworkers have described an important change that occurs with practice: a process of simplification. Movements become simplified as extraneous activity is eliminated and general abilities are replaced by increasingly task-specific abilities.

This change in abilities at different levels of performance has also been reported in other studies. For example, Graybiel, Jokl, and Trapp (1955) reported a summary of Russian research on vision in champion athletes. All types of athletes studied—javelin throwers, discus throwers, hammer throwers, skiers, figure skaters, and gymnasts—gave greatly diminished performances if their peripheral vision was eliminated. They had less difficulty if their central vision was occluded and, in some cases, if all vision was blocked. These findings contrast with the tendency of beginners to use central vision and ignore peripheral information (just recall what you watched when you were learning to drive). Central visual cues become integrated, reduced in number, and consequently simplified. Therefore, as skill improves through practice and cues become increasingly familiar, performers apparently tend to place less emphasis on central vision and use peripheral vision more, to the extent of learning to rely on it for large amounts of information.

Table 3.4. Hypothetical Increasing, Level, and Decreasing Superdiagonal Forms

TRIAL	1	2	3	4	5	6
1	—	.70	.66	.60	.60	.60
2		—	.80	.73	.73	.73
3			—	.82	.82	.82
4	Increasing			—	.92	.92
5					—	.92
6						—
1	—	.81	.72	.69	.63	.60
2		—	.80	.77	.70	.67
3			—	.82	.75	.72
4	Level			—	.79	.76
5					—	.81
6						—
1	—	.70	.41	.19	.07	.02
2		—	.47	.22	.08	.01
3			—	.29	.11	.00
4	Decreasing			—	.14	.03
5					—	.04
6						—

From M. B. Jones, Individual differences, in *The psychomotor domain,* ed. R. N. Singer. Philadelphia: Lea & Febiger, 1972, p. 110. Reprinted by permission.

Changes in Perception and Information Processing

Changes also occur in speed and timing during the course of practice. Not only are movements performed faster, but less time is taken between movements that form a series. This decrease in time between movements is believed to result from improvement in central decision processes (Wehrkamp and Smith, 1952; Seymour, 1959). That is, a learner acquires greater efficiency in dealing with incoming information, in forming responses, and in initiating action.

The progression-regression hypothesis was proposed by Fuchs (1962) as an explanation for changes in central processing during practice. The progression hypothesis states that, in perceptual-motor skill development, an individual learns to respond to higher derivatives[1] of the error signal's amplitude and weighs these selectively to minimize errors and enhance performance. For example, a beginner attends to position and then to speed, while an advanced performer merges the

[1]A *derivative* is defined as a ratio of the change in a function to the corresponding change in its independent variable as the latter change approaches zero.

two into a single, more complex cue, either acceleration or velocity. A beginning tennis player deliberately positions his or her body with respect to the direction of the ball's flight and then swings either too early or too late and misses it. As position cues and speed cues merge, an advanced performer can predict the flight and bounce of the ball and then plots a course to intercept it at the optimal time. The player checks the original hypothesis as he or she progresses to the intercept point. By merging several lower-order cues into a single, more complex, higher-order cue, the performer responds to that one cue instead of several. Consequently, cues as well as movements are reduced in number during practice.

The regression hypothesis further emphasizes this change. It states that perceptual-motor skill development consists of a reduction in the weight assigned to the position of a stimulus and a corresponding increase in the weights assigned to velocity and acceleration. Direct and accurate perception of velocity and acceleration incorporates both concrete and abstract characteristics of the motion viewed by the performer. Rosenbaum (1975) proposed that the motion perception system is tuned to accelerated motion rather than to motion at a constant velocity. Three elements are necessary for accurate responses to such movement: (1) a determination of the rate and direction of the object's motion, (2) an extrapolation of the object's path, and (3) the initiation of a response, which must take into account the spatial and temporal requirements of the performer's own movements as well as the spatial and temporal characteristics of the moving object.

According to Kinchla (1977), a performer decides whether a particular stimulus target is present by integrating various environmental cues in some weighted manner. The weighting is usually hierarchical with higher-order and lower-order forms. For example, a person's body might be analyzed into higher-order parts such as the head, arms, and legs, which in turn might be analyzed into lower-order parts such as the nose, mouth, and eyes. After repeated practice with fixed stimulus situations, the grouping can become automatic, as in the case of speed and direction combined into velocity, so that perceptual processing requires little time and attention in an advanced performer.

Improvement in perceptual-motor performance therefore depends on a performer's ability to perceive and weigh subtle stimulus cues. This ability develops gradually through practice. The performer then becomes involved in a complicated sequence of information processing, in which input is received, responses are developed, and performance is continually modified on the basis of feedback that is received. The Russian studies of vision cited previously (Graybiel, Jokl, and Trapp, 1955) give some indirect support to this proposal; they indicate that central visual cues become integrated and that peripheral cues accordingly acquire greater weight in the perceptual hierarchy.

The progression-regression hypothesis has also been indirectly supported by data collected by Williams (1968). Significant differences were found in the abilities of skilled and unskilled males to make visual-perceptual judgments about objects traveling in three-dimensional space. The ages of the subjects (junior high school, high school, and college students) had little effect on the speed and accuracy of their judgments. Accuracy depended on the speed and the horizontal and vertical direction of the motion. The flight of objects projected at a high angle was judged more accurately at lower speeds. For objects projected at a low angle, judgments were more accurate at higher speeds. The flight of objects projected at high angles was judged best if they were directed toward the observer, but the horizontal direction of low-angle projectiles made little difference in accuracy.

In today's environment, we are constantly bombarded with high-speed, horizontally moving objects, whose motion we must judge accurately. We need this ability when we are confronted with crossing a street or learning to catch a ball. Our exposure to high-speed objects moving at high angles is not as prevalent and must be developed. It appears that experience does indeed reduce the importance of the position component and increase the weight given to velocity and acceleration components so as to permit other types of coding. We judge best with movements that we have experienced. A highly skilled player has less to do than does a beginner to achieve the same result. There is a great deal of truth in the impression that a skilled performer has plenty of time in which to perform.

Coding procedures are also used for other types of motor responses. Diewert and Roy (1978) found that, in reproducing movement extent responses, subjects use information about where a movement should end (location cues) rather than information about how far to move (extent cues). If location cues are unavailable, however, the subjects counted during the movement, which appeared to enable them to code movement extent in terms of movement time. Diewert and Roy reported that both strategies are effective but that memory based on location strategy requires processing capacity, while memory based on the counting strategy does not.

The pace at which one performs can vary considerably. Kreifeldt (1972) noted the great importance of the complete spatial-temporal trajectory in continuous tasks, such as the tracking task described above. In such tasks, performers must pace themselves according to the demands of the task. Self-pacing, in which a performer sets his or her own rate of activity to maximize accuracy, is the most common and realistic mode of pacing in many activities. The pace in skills such as walking, jumping, and throwing is usually left to the individual. In situations in which a performer can freely choose a rate of work, he or she tends to pick a rate at which the physiological cost is lowest, errors are minimized, and efficiency is highest (Salvendy, 1972). Individual differences are also minimal during self-paced activity. If temporal requirements are set by external conditions, however, so that an individual must consider the duration of an operation or related temporal factors, self-pacing becomes less strict and one must predict movements in advance. Running the 100-yard dash or swimming in a race could be self-paced activities, but usually an element of forced pacing enters, dictated by the performance of one's competitors or by other external conditions. The ability to integrate information gained from such external conditions therefore becomes important in performance.

Many changes in abilities, perceptual skills, forms of information used, and pacing occur during the course of practice. Skilled teachers recognize that these changes occur and make provisions for them in instruction.

DEVELOPMENTAL ASPECTS

Two types of skills that are greatly influenced by developmental factors are continuous skills, such as tracking a moving object (e.g., hitting a pitched baseball), and serial skills (e.g., playing basketball or driving a car). These place severe demands on an individual's ability to process information and make appropriate responses.

Developmental aspects of the capacity to judge the flight of a moving object have been studied by Williams (1967). Elementary school children observed the flight of a tennis ball projected by a machine into the air and then intercepted by the roof of a pavilion. They were instructed to pick out the spot where the ball would have landed if it had continued its flight to the ground. The experiment therefore involved children's predictions of a trajectory on the basis of an observed portion of the flight. All children, regardless of age or sex, responded to the ball equally quickly; all subjects started to move soon after the ball was projected into the air. Significant differences were found in the accuracy of judgments made by children of various ages. Students in the fourth, fifth, and sixth grades were significantly more accurate than first-, second-, and third-graders. The younger children moved, on the average, 22 feet beyond the point where the ball would have fallen, but the older children's mean error was 2.5 feet.

Williams noted that 6-, 7-, and 8-year-old children responded quickly to the moving objects but were not able to use the visual information and accurately direct their motor behavior. Nine-year-old children could make very precise perceptual judgments but took a great deal of time to make them. In 10-year-olds, the rate of sensory processing increased, but the accuracy of judgments decreased slightly. By 11 years of age, the children made decisions about the flight of the ball both quickly and accurately. Williams concluded that the abilities needed to judge the flight of a moving object in space are functionally mature by the age of 11 years.

The development of tracking abilities can be an important deteminant of program content and instructional strategies. It would be unrealistic to expect children with inadequate levels of development to be successful in activities such as baseball. Tracking activities within their capacities, however, must be provided to facilitate development of their abilities.

The ability to combine a variety of discrete movements or skills into a coordinated serial skill also determines success or failure in many sports activities. Serial learning has long been of interest to psychologists; it was the subject of some of the first studies of learning (Ebbinghaus, 1913). There is a paucity of studies investigating the acquisition of serial motor skills, however.

Perhaps the most striking and consistent characteristic of serial learning is the serial position effect, which is especially pronounced in verbal learning studies, such as the one conducted by Hovland (1938). For example, the serial position effect appears in experiments in which subjects are asked to recall words in a series: recall is best for words at the beginning of the list, second best for words at the end of the list, and poorest for words in the middle of the list. The learning of the initial stimuli in a series is called the primacy effect, because of the primary (first) position of these stimuli in the series. The learning of the last stimuli in a series is called the recency effect, because these stimuli were presented more recently than the rest.

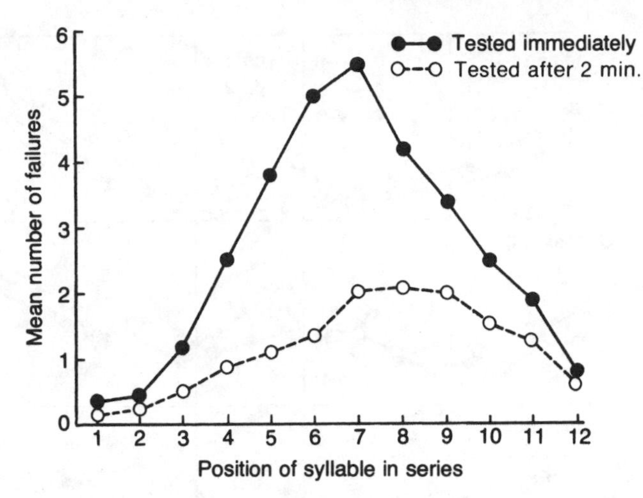

Figure 3.9. Typical bow-shaped curves showing mean number of failures of recall of syllables in a series. (Redrawn from C. I. Hovland, Experimental studies in rote-learning theory: II. Reminiscence with varying speeds of syllable presentation, *Journal of Experimental Psychology* 22 [1938]: 347. Copyright 1938 by the American Psychological Association.)

Deese and Hulse (1967) reviewed a number of theoretical explanations of this phenomenon and suggested three reasons for it. First, the beginning and end of a series are highly discriminable and isolated positions, which thus become "perceptual anchors." Second, the primacy of the beginning position results in less uncertainty about its uniqueness, and therefore stimuli in that position are recalled best. Third, an interference effect exists in the middle of the series because of intraseries confusion.

Explanations of the serial position effect have become more difficult since recent studies have demonstrated that the grouping of input by the experimenter produces a multibowed curve rather than the usual bow-shaped curve (Harris and Lown, 1968; Harris and Burke, 1972). It is believed that the grouping of items within a series produces a greater number of anchor points and facilitates recall at more positions in the series. An example of a multibowed curve is shown in Figure 3.10.

Early studies generally involved adult subjects, but children have been shown to be rapid and efficient processors of information that is presented for short periods of time. In a study of visual short-term memory, Haith (1971) found that preschool children, presented with tachistoscopic information in a range from 50 to 100 milliseconds,

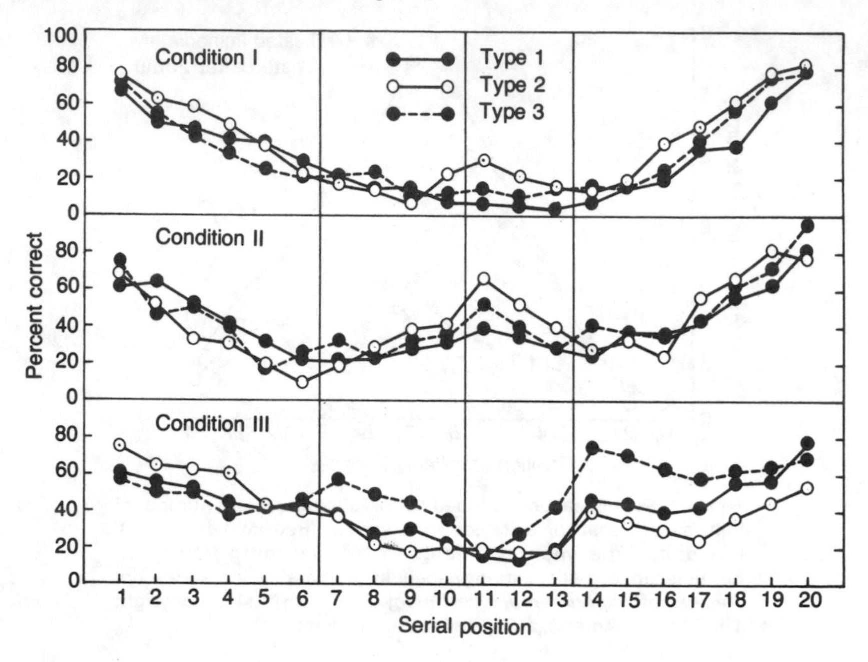

Figure 3.10. A multibowed curve is produced if the serial stimuli are progressively grouped. Condition I: 20 digits are presented separately. Condition II: 20 digits are presented in two groups of 10 each. Condition III: 20 digits are presented in three groups of 6, 7, and 8 digits. (Redrawn from G. Harris and B. Lown, Interitem time distribution and response compatibility in the short-term serial retention of digits, *Psychonomic Science* 10 [1968]: 296.)

performed as well as adults. They were also able to deal adequately with multiple stimuli if strategies were imposed on the data for them. They lacked the ability to develop their own strategies for handling the information, however. Adults' superiority in multiple-stimulus memory tasks was interpreted as being related to their greater verbal labeling skill and stronger rehearsal abilities, which serve as mediators for memory.

This finding was supported in part by Hagan, Meacham, and Meisber (1970), who found that verbal labeling imposed by the experimenter on older subjects did not affect overall memory except for subjects of college age, among whom it produced a memory decrement. These results support the belief that older children and adults engage in active rehearsal strategies, which facilitate their performance; the imposed labeling hindered the use of these strategies.

A study of the development of perceptual-motor sequencing ability in 5-, 7-, and 9-year-old children was conducted by Zaichkowsky (1973). These children learned a random pattern and an organized pattern of stimulus-response activities on a Serial Perceptual-Motor Discriminator requiring hand and foot responses to appropriate stimulus lights. Zaichkowsky observed that many of the principles of serial verbal learning apply to this perceptual-motor task. Significant differences were noted in the children's abilities to complete the random pattern and the organized pattern; the random pattern produced significantly more errors. Although age had little effect on errors in the organized pattern (except for a slightly higher number of errors among 5-year-olds), errors in the random pattern decreased with age. A primacy effect was also observed on the random task, although the recency effect was absent. It therefore appears that only the first movements in the series have perceptual anchoring capacities. From this data, Zaichkowsky concluded that sequencing ability improves with age. Performance of young children on serial tasks with low information loads is similar to that of older children, but their performance on tasks with high information loads is markedly poorer than older children's. This difference is probably due to the ability of older children to use mediators, such as verbal labeling and rehearsal abilities, more effectively. Zaichkowsky believes that a child's ability to serially order perceptual-motor tasks begins at about 5 years of age.

Marsh, Chang, and Rose (1972) indicated that children between 8 and 12 years old perform tracking tasks more poorly and with greater variability than adults do. Their study also indicated that the tracking ability of children improves with age. The difference between younger and older children appears to lie in the fact that younger children are less able to adjust their performances with training. These authors suggested that the lag in adjustment is related to the slower reaction time reported in younger children, which in turn is believed to represent a longer time needed for central processing.

A part of this delay in processing, both for tracking skills and for serial skills, appears to be related to an individual's ability to code and organize the material. According to Marmurek and Johnson (1978), organizational learning requires more than an awareness of spatial-temporal relationships among items. In addition, a person must experience the material in unique subgroups. These subgroups have been described by Restle (1976) as a somewhat complex sequence within a larger pattern, which sets apart the important components of the pattern. A subgroup may be unique in the interrelations of its components or in the manner in which it is distinguished from the larger pattern. Even young (4-year-old) children appear to master sensorimotor patterns through the use of verbal skills (Livesey and Little, 1971). According to Hogan and Yanowitz (1978), verbal labeling might be an ancillary process during early skill learning when some knowledge of results is present, but, later, verbal evaluations of movement are used to solve movement problems.

Studies in both verbal learning (Moscovitch and Craik, 1976) and motor learning (Ho and Shea, 1978) indicate that uniqueness of material alone is insufficient for learning to occur. An instructor must ensure that the material is distinctive enough that a student can discriminate between it and extraneous material and that the response and the cue form an integrated unit. Further, learning is superior if students are able to provide their own verbal labels to facilitate recall, rather than use labels provided by the teacher. Increased memory span appears to develop from the greater ease with which children can identify the individual items in a series and their ability to encode information about the items' order. Memory representations apparently change less than the identity and encoding abilities (Huttenlocher and Burke, 1976). Thus, an instructor must change the nature and amount of verbal information provided to a child as the child's capabilities change. Older children who can encode information must be encouraged and provided with opportunities to make use of this ability.

In summary, several characteristics of serial learning should be noted by physical education teachers and coaches. First, the ability to learn serial tasks develops with age, as verbal abilities and other forms of abstract reasoning are acquired. This improvement appears to continue until adult modes of functioning are attained. A teacher must make sure that the serial requirements of a task do not exceed the ability of the students. A teacher can improve serial learning in young children by organizing the task for them (through drills and the like) and thereby providing perceptual anchor points. Without anchor points, a primacy effect is usually noted: the first part of the task can be learned easily, but the remainder is learned with considerable difficulty because of interference. Detailed organization of the task by the instructor does not appear to benefit older children and adults in the same manner. By knowing what to expect from students in serial tasks, an instructor can provide encouragement and develop drills and instructional techniques to aid the acquisition of skills. The encouragement of verbal mediation and other learning strategies on the part of the student is an important aspect of assisting in the acquisition of serial skills.

GUIDING PRINCIPLES FOR THE TEACHER

1. Learning cannot be observed directly. Consequently, the occurrence of learning is inferred from changes in performance. Teachers observe changes in performance, not learning. These changes can result from learning or from other factors, such as motivation.

2. Measures used to assess performance and to infer that learning has occurred include amount of response, latency of response, rate of response, errors, reminiscence, trials, and retention (or extinction). No one of these can measure performance fully and accurately.

3. Changes in variability occur with practice. Groups of students become more variable, and individuals become more consistent in their performances. The increased variability in a class is due to individual differences in such factors as learning rates, forgetting rates, and motor ability. As practice continues, students become consistently more different.

4. Learning is a process of simplification having three phases—early (cognitive), intermediate (associative), and late (autonomous). After one gains an understanding of the task, it becomes simpler as extraneous movements are dropped and new kinds of cues are used. Visual-perceptual cues are more important early in the learning process. Specific neuromuscular coordination becomes predominant later.

5. Spatial and other visual abilities are more important during early stages of learning. Tactile and proprioceptive cues are used more during performance after the skill has been acquired.

6. The nature of the stimulus information used by a performer also changes with experience. In the early stages of learning, emphasis is placed on the position of a stimulus (such as a moving ball). An advanced performer relies less on position cues and uses velocity and acceleration cues instead.

7. Self-pacing, in which an individual chooses his or her own rate of performance, is the most common and realistic mode of pacing in many activities. A performer adopts a rate at which physiological cost is lowest, errors in performance are minimal, and efficiency is highest.

8. Verbal labeling enables a performer to code and organize the material, that is to be learned. Verbal labeling might be an ancillary process during early learning when some knowledge of results is present, but, later, verbal evaluations of movement are used to solve

movement problems. Even young children can master sensorimotor patterns through the use of verbal skills.

SUMMARY

Learning is a process that influences every aspect of our lives. It is defined as a relatively permanent change in behavior as a result of experience. Although learning and performance are not the same, the effects of learning are commonly inferred from performance. Consequently, the measurement of learning remains one of the most frustrating problems faced by teachers and coaches. Criteria for adequate measures of performance have been proposed, but it has often proved impossible to find a single measure that fulfills these criteria. The most common performance measures include amount of response, latency of response, rate of response, errors, reminiscence, trials, and retention (or extinction).

Scores obtained during practice are often plotted in learning curves, or (more appropriately) performance curves. These curves can be developed either for individuals or for groups. They show great variety, depending the type of skill and the performance measures that are involved. Such curves are often used to display changes in performance after practice, but caution must be exercised in using them to make inferences about learning. As graphic displays of performance, they reflect all the factors that influence performance: learning, type of task, motivation, and other factors.

Learning can also be described as a process through which one acquires the ability to adjust to the spatial and temporal requirements of the environment. Three phases of learning have been distinguished: the initial or cognitive phase, the intermediate or associative phase, and the late or autonomous phase, in which the skill becomes perfected.

Closed skills rely greatly on internally derived information. Open skills modify movement on the basis of information derived from the environment. Instructional technique should be adapted to accommodate the type of skill being taught.

The range of individual differences among students is perhaps the most striking characteristic of a class. Variability among students increases with practice. An instructor is continually faced with the problem of providing more individualized drills and techniques as instruction progresses. Variability is due to all the factors associated with learning and performance, including innate abilities, past experiences, and differences in memory. As an extension of the problem of class organization, little or no relationship has been found between one's initial performance on a skill and his or her final ability. Thus, if students are grouped into classes on the basis of initial performance, the composition of the groups must be adjusted as practice and instruction progress.

Clusters of abilities, or relationships between various abilities, have been found to relate to success in skilled performance. Several different factor patterns of abilities have been proposed. The importance of these patterns changes with practice. More general abilities become less important, and abilities specifically related to the task become more important. Therefore, practice has been described as a process of simplification.

Continuous skills and serial skills have important developmental aspects. The organization of material by an instructor can aid the acquisition of serial skills in young children. This technique does not appear to be helpful with older children.

REFERENCES

Abbey, D. S. 1962. Age, proficiency, and reminiscence in a complex perceptual-motor task. *Perception and Motor Skills* 14:51-57.

Adams, J. A. 1953. The prediction of performance at advanced stages of training on a complex psychomotor task. United States Air Force Human Resource Research Center, Research Bulletin, 4 (no. 53–49).

Alderman, R. B. 1968. Reminiscence effects on inter- and intra-individual differences in pursuit rotor performances. *Research Quarterly* 39:423–427.

Bahrick, H. P., Fitts, P. M., and Briggs, G. E. 1957. Learning curves—facts or artifacts? *Psychological Bulletin* 54:256–268.

Blair, S. N. 1970. The effect of stimulus and movement complexity upon reaction time and movement time. In *Contemporary psychology of sport: Proceedings of the Second International Congress of Sport Psychology*, ed. G. S. Kenyon. Chicago: Athletic Institute.

Bryan, W. L., and Harter, N. 1897. Studies in the physiology and psychology of telegraphic language. *Psychological Review* 4:27–53.

Bugelski, B. R. 1956. *The psychology of learning*. New York: Holt, Rinehart and Winston.

Carron, A. V., and Marteniuk, R. G. 1970. Retention of a balance skill as a function of initial ability level. *Research Quarterly* 41:478–483.

Cattell, R. B., and Eber, H. W. 1970. *Handbook for the Sixteen Personality Factor Questionnaire*. Champaign, Ill.: Institute for Personality and Ability Testing.

Chasey, W. C. 1971. Overlearning as a variable in the retention of gross motor skills by the mentally retarded. *Research Quarterly* 42:145–149.

Clarke, H. H. 1966. *Muscular strength and endurance in man*. Englewood Cliffs, N.J.: Prentice-Hall.

———. 1967. *Application of measurement to health and physical education*. 4th ed. Englewood Cliffs, N.J.: Prentice-Hall.

Crossman, E. R. F. 1959. A theory of the acquisition of speed-skill. *Ergonomics* 2:153–166.

Deese, J., and Hulse, S. 1967. *The psychology of learning.* New York: McGraw-Hill.

Diewert, G. L., and Roy, E. A. 1978. Coding strategy for memory of movement extent information. *Journal of Experimental Psychology: Human Learning and Memory* 4:666–675.

Drowatzky, J. N. 1969. Evaluation of mirror tracing performance measures as indicators of learning. *Research Quarterly* 40:228–230.

Drowatzky, J. N., and Zuccato, F. C. 1967. Interrelationships between selected measures of static and dynamic balance. *Research Quarterly* 38:509–510.

Ebbinghaus, H. 1913. *Memory: A contribution to experimental psychology.* Translated by H. A. Ruger and C. E. Bussenius. New York: Teachers College, Columbia University Press.

Ehrlich, G. 1943. A method of constructing learning curves for a motor skill involving total body speed and accuracy. *Journal of Applied Psychology* 27:494–503.

Ellis, M. J. 1970. Proprioceptive factors in operative timing. In *Contemporary psychology of sport: Proceedings of the Second International Congress of Sport Psychology,* ed. G. S. Kenyon. Chicago: Athletic Institute.

Ellis, M. R., Pryer, M. W., Distefano, M. K., Jr., and Pryer, R. S. 1960. Learning in mentally defective, normal, and superior subjects. *American Journal of Mental Deficiency* 64:725–734.

Fitts, P. M. 1964. Perceptual-motor skill learning. In *Categories of human learning,* ed. A. W. Melton. New York: Academic Press.

Fitts, P. M., and Posner, M. I. 1967. *Human performance.* Monterey, Calif.: Brooks/Cole.

Fleishman, E. A. 1954. Dimensidnal analysis of pyschomotor abilities. *Journal of Experimental Psychology* 48:437–454.

———. 1957. A comparative study of aptitude patterns in unskilled and skilled psychomotor performances. *Journal of Applied Psychology* 41:263-272.

———. 1970. Perceptual-motor abilities and learning. In *Contemporary psychology of sport: Proceedings of the Second International Congress of Sport Psychology,* ed. G. S. Kenyon. Chicago: Athletic Institute.

Fleishman, E. A., and Hempel, W. E., Jr. 1954. Changes in the factor structure of a complex psychomotor test as a function of practice. *Psychometrika* 18:239–252.

———. 1955. The relation between abilities and improvement with practice in a visual discrimination reaction task. *Journal of Experimental Psychology* 49:301–312.

———. 1956. Factorial analysis of complex psychomotor performance and related skills. *Journal of Applied Psychology* 40:96–104.

Fleishman, E. A., and Rich, S. 1963. Role of kinesthetic and spatial visual abilities in perceptual motor learning. *Journal of Experimental Psychology* 66:6–11.

Fox, M. G., and Lamb, E. 1962. Improvement during nonpractice period in a selected physical education activity. *Research Quarterly* 33:381–385.

Fox, M. G., and Young, V. P. 1962. Effect of reminiscence on learning selected badminton skills. *Research Quarterly* 33:386–394.

Fuchs, A. H. 1962. The progression-regression hypothesis in perceptual-motor skill learning. *Journal of Experimental Psychology* 63:177–182.

Gray, C. A., and Brumbach, W. B. 1967. Effect of daylight projection of film loops on learning badminton. *Research Quarterly* 38:562–569.

Graybiel, A., Jokl, E., and Trapp, C. 1955. Russian studies of vision in relation to physical activity and sports. *Research Quarter'* 26:480–485.

Guilford, J. P. 1958. A system of psychomotor abilities. *American Journal of Psychology* 71:164–174.

Hagan, J., Meacham, J., and Meisber, G. 1970. Verbal labeling, rehearsal, and short-term memory. *Cognitive Psychology* 1:47–58.

Haith, M. 1971. Developmental changes in visual information processing and short-term visual memory. *Human Development* 14:249–261.

Harris, G., and Burke, D. 1972. The effects of grouping on short-term serial recall of digits by children: Developmental trends. *Child Development* 43:710-716.

Harris, G., and Lown, B. 1968. Interitem time distribution and response compatibility in the short-term serial retention of digits. *Psychonomic Science* 10:295-296.

Henry, F. M. 1960. Influence of motor and sensory sets on reaction latency and speed of discrete movements. *Research Quarterly* 31:459-468.

———. 1961. Stimulus complexity, movement complexity, age, and sex in relation to reaction latency and speed in limb movements. *Research Quarterly* 32:353-366.

Henry, F. M., and Rogers, D. C. 1960. Increased response latency for complicated movements and a "memory drum" theory of neuromotor reaction. *Research Quarterly* 31:448-458.

Hicks, R. E. 1976. Effect of information feedback upon intertrial consistency of time judgment. *Acta Psychologica* 40:265-270.

Ho, L., and Shea, J. B. 1978. Levels of processing and the coding of position cues in motor short-term memory. *Journal of Motor Behavior* 10:113-121.

Hogan, J. C., and Yanowitz, B. A. 1978. The role of verbal estimates of movement error in ballistic skill acquisition. *Journal of Motor Behavior* 10:133-138.

Holding, D. H. 1965. *Principles of training*. London: Pergamon Press.

Holding, D. H., and Macrae, A. W. 1964. Guidance, restriction, and knowledge of results. *Ergonomics* 7:289-295.

Hovland, C. I. 1938. Experimental studies in rote-learning theory: II. Reminiscence with varying speeds of syllable presentation. *Journal of Experimental Psychology* 22:338-353.

Howell, M. L. 1953. Influence of emotional tension on speed of reaction and movement. *Research Quarterly* 24:22-32.

Humphrey, G. 1963. *Thinking: An introduction to its experimental psychology*. New York: John Wiley and Sons.

Huttenlocher, J., and Burke, D. 1976. Why does memory span increase with age? *Cognitive Psychology* 8:1-31.

Jones, M. B. 1962. Practice as a process of simplification. *Psychological Review* 69:274-294.

———. 1966. Individual differences. *Acquisition of skill*. ed. E. A. Bilodeau. New York: Academic Press.

———. 1972. Individual differences. In *The psychomotor domain: Movement behavior*, ed. R. N. Singer, Philadelphia: Lea & Febiger.

Keller, F. S. 1958. The phantom plateau. *Journal of the Experimental Analysis of Analytic Behavior* 1:1-13.

Kinchla, R. A. 1977. The role of structural redundancy in the perception of visual targets. *Perception and Psychophysics* 22:19-30.

Knapp, B. N. 1961. A note on skill. *Occupational Psychology* 35:76-78.

Kreifeldt, J. G. 1972. A dynamic model of behavior in a discrete open-loop self-paced motor skill. *Systems, Man and Cybernetics* 2:262-273.

Kroll, W. 1967. Reliability theory and research decision in selection of a criterion score. *Research Quarterly* 38:412-419.

Krueger, W. C. F. 1947. Influence of difficulty of perceptual-motor task upon acceleration of learning curves. *Journal of Educational Psychology* 38:51-53.

Lawther, J. D. 1968. *The learning of physical skills*. Englewood Cliffs, N.J.: Prentice-Hall.

Laycoe, R. R., and Marteniuk, R. G. 1971. Learning and tension as factors in static strength gains produced by static and eccentric training. *Research Quarterly* 42:299-306.

Lersten, K. C. 1968. Inter- and intra-individual variations during the progress of motor learning. *Research Quarterly* 39:1913-1924.

Livesey, P. J., and Little, A. 1971. Sequential learning by children. *Journal of Genetic Psychology* 188:33-38.

Lowe, J. M., Jr. 1971. Motivation, task complexity, and utilization in performance of a motor skill. Ed.D. dissertation. University of Toledo.

McCraw, L. W. 1955. Comparative analysis of methods of scoring tests of motor learning. *Research Quarterly* 26:440-453.

Malina, R. M. 1968. Reliability of different methods of scoring throwing accuracy. *Research Quarterly* 39:149-160.

Marmurek, H. H. C., and Johnson, N. F. 1978. Hierarchical organization as a determinant of sequential learning. *Memory and Cognition* 6:240-245.

Marsh, N. W. A., Chang, J. W. K., and Rose, E. 1972. Compensatory tracking performance of children in terms of linear operator theory. *Acta Psychologica* 36:388-407.

Melnick, M. J. 1971. Effects of overlearning on the retention of a gross motor skill. *Research Quarterly* 42:60-69.

Messick, S. 1961. Personality structure. In *Annual review of psychology*. Vol. 12, ed. P. R. Farnsworth. Palo Alto, Calif.: Annual Reviews.

Meyers, C. R., Zimmerli, W., Farr, S. D., and Baschnagel, N. A. 1969. Effect of strenuous physical activity upon reaction time. *Research Quarterly* 40:332-337.

Meyers, J. L. 1967. Retention of balance coordination learning as influenced by extended lay-offs. *Research Quarterly* 38:72-78.

———. 1968. Motor learning and retention: Influence of practice and remoteness on individual differences. *Research Quarterly* 39:314-320.

Moscovitch, M., and Craik, F. I. M. 1976. Depth of processing, retrieval cues and uniqueness of encoding as factors in recall. *Journal of Verbal Learning and Verbal Behavior* 15:447-458.

Noble, C. E. 1970. Acquisition of pursuit tracking skill under extended training as a joint function of sex and initial ability. *Journal of Experimental Psychology* 86:360-373.

Norrie, M. L. 1967. Practice effects on reaction latency for simple and complex movements. *Research Quarterly* 38:79-85.

Oxendine, J. B. 1965. Effect of progressively changing schedules on the learning of a motor skill. *Research Quarterly* 36:307-315.

Rabbitt, P. M. A. 1967. Time to detect errors as a function of factors affecting choice-response time. *Acta Psychologica* 27:131-142.

Rabbitt, P. M. A., and Vyas, S. M. 1970. An elementary preliminary taxonomy for some errors in laboratory choice RT tasks. *Acta Psychologica* 33:56-76.

Restle, F. 1976. Structural ambiguity in serial pattern learning. *Cognitive Psychology* 8:357-381.

Richardson, J. R., and Pew, R. W. 1970. Stabliometer motor performance. In *Contemporary psychology of sport: Proceedings of the Second International Congress of Sport Psychology*, ed. G. S. Kenyon. Chicago: Athletic Institute.

Rosenbaum, D. A. 1975. Perception and extrapolation of velocity and acceleration. *Journal of Experimental Psychology* 104:395-403.

Ryan, E. D. 1962. Retention of stabliometer and pursuit rotor skills. *Research Quarterly* 33:593-598.

Safrit, M. J. 1969. A study of selected object-projection skills performed by subjects above average in skill. *Research Quarterly* 40:788-798.

Salvendy, G. 1972. Physiological and psychological aspects of paced and unpaced performance. *Acta Physiologica Academiae Scientiarum Hungaricae* 42:267-275.

Schmidt, R. A., Zuckerman, J., Martin, H. A., and Wolfe, K. F., Jr. 1971. A novel discrete gross motor learning task: Modifications of the Bachman ladder. *Research Quarterly* 42:78-82.

Seymour, W. D. 1959. Experiments on the acquisition of industrial skills. *Occupational Psychology* 33:18-35.

Singer, R. N. 1965. Effect of spectators on athletes and nonathletes performing a gross motor task. *Research Quarterly* 36:473-482.

Slater-Hammel, A. T. 1955. Comparisons of reaction time measures to a visual stimulus and arm movement. *Research Quarterly* 26:470-479.

Taylor, D. W. 1943. Learning telegraphic code. *Psychology Bulletin* 40:461-487.

Thomas, J. R., and Halliwell, W. 1976. Individual differences in motor skill acquisition. *Journal of Motor Behavior* 8:89-99.

Trussell, E. 1965. Prediction of success in a motor skill on the basis of early learning achievement. *Research Quarterly* 36:342-347.

Vincent, W. J. 1968. Transfer effects between motor skills judged similar in perceptual components. *Research Quarterly*. 39:380-388.

Von Wright, J. M. 1957*a*. An experimental study of human serial learning. *Societas Scientarium Fennica. Commentationes Humanarum Litterarum*, vol. 23, no. 1.

———. 1957*b*. A note on the role of guidance in learning. *British Journal of Psychology* 48:133-137.

Wehrkamp, R., and Smith, K. U. 1952. Dimensional analysis of motion: 2. Travel-distance effects. *Journal of Applied Psychology* 36:201-206.

Welch, M. 1963. Prediction of motor skill attainment from early learning. *Perceptual and Motor Skills* 17:263-266.

Welford, A. T. 1968. *Fundamentals of skill.* London: Methuen.

———. 1976. *Skilled performance: Perceptual and motor skills*. Glenview, Ill.: Scott, Foresman.

West, L. J. 1967. Vision and kinesthesis in the acquisition of typewriting skill. *Journal of Applied Psychology* 51:161-166.

Whitley, J. D. 1970. Effects of practice distribution on learning a fine motor skill. *Research Quarterly* 41:576-583.

Wilberg, R. B. 1969. Response accuracy based upon recall from visual and kinesthetic short-term memory. *Research Quarterly* 40:407-414.

Williams, H. G. 1967. The perception of moving objects by children. Unpublished manuscript, University of Toledo.

———. 1968. The effects of systematic variation of speed and direction of object flight and of skill and age classification upon visual-perceptual judgments of moving objects in three-dimensional space. Doctoral dissertation, University of Wisconsin, Madison.

Wilson, D. J. 1959. Quickness of reaction and movement related to rhythmicity or non-rhythmicity of signal presentation. *Research Quarterly* 30:101-109.

Zaichkowsky, L. D. 1973. The development of perceptual-motor sequencing ability. Doctoral dissertation, University of Toledo.

4 Feedback

In the preceding chapters, learning has been described as an adaptive process. This adaptation involves receiving input about a particular situation, processing the information and its meaning, forming a response, and finally evaluating the effects of the response. After the evaluation is completed, judgments are made about how good or how correct the response is and about the need for modifications in future responses. Several types of information are used to assess the effects of one's response and to judge the need for modification: the "kinesiological feel," the immediate effect of the response, the long-range consequences of the response, and other ramifications of the performance. This evaluative process requires information in the form of feedback. *Feedback* can be described as a part of the output, or response, that is returned to the performer as input. It can lead either to a revision of the response just made or to a confirmation of the correctness of the response.

The concept of feedback has been developed in the theory of *cybernetics,* a term coined by Wiener (1961) from the Greek word *kubernetes* ("steersman"). His approach to behavior takes the human organism to be no different in operation than a machine, seen from the point of view of communications. That is, successful action depends not only on good effectors (muscular systems) but also on the proper monitoring of output by the performer. The monitored output, or feedback, allows the performer to determine the extent to which his or her responses are adequate to accomplish a particular task. If a response is inadequate, feedback indicates how future responses should be modified to achieve success. Movement therefore becomes regulated in some degree by the extent to which the task has not yet been accomplished. Feedback reduces the disparity between the performer's present status and the anticipated outcome.

The cybernetic model for human operation is the servomechanism (see Figure 4.1), a continuous closed-loop, electromechanical control system. Such a system receives an input and consequently produces output, some of which is sent to an effector and some of which is sent back into the servomechanism in the form of feedback. This feedback enables the system to continuously adjust its output. The servomechanism uses both feedback and new input to produce smooth performance based on a forecast of the future. Servomechanisms have been used with radar in fire control apparatus to track and destroy enemy aircraft.

Human feedback takes a number of forms, for example, social interactions, kinesiological sensations accompanying motor performance, verbal praise, sounds accompanying performance, or the sight of a basketball going into a basket. Some feedback affects only a single individual, but in other cases it affects interaction among members of a social group. Different situations are likely to produce different types of feedback; also, different degrees and types of feedback can result from similar situations.

To further explain the concept of feedback, consider the schematic diagrams of three different types of classroom control sequences, shown

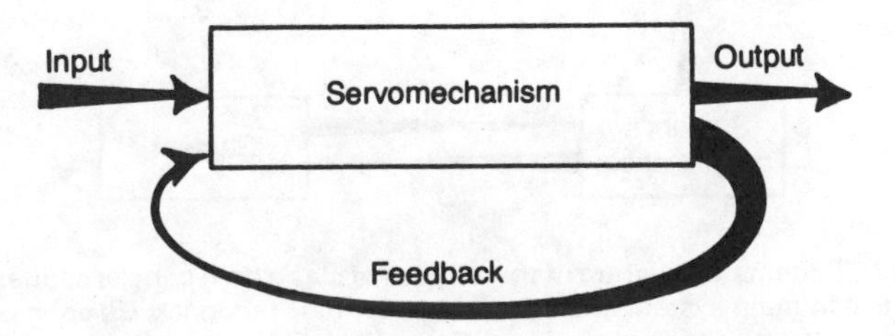

Figure 4.1. Schematic drawing of a servomechanism.

in Figure 4.2. In an open control system (diagrammed in part *A* of the figure), the teacher does not use any feedback to control his or her performance. Rather, teaching style is characterized by a rigid adherence to plans, with little or no modification of the plans during teaching. In this scheme, the subject matter dictates the pace of instruction. The ability or inability of the students to grasp the material has no effect on the teacher's presentation. Similarly, the student's progress is determined by the subject matter, as their performances are not modified by their own feedback. In part *B* of the figure, the teacher's performance is modified during the teaching process by feedback he or she receives. The students' performances, however, still have little or no influence on the teacher.

The feedback loop displayed in part *C* of Figure 4.2 represents the ideal teaching situation. Both the teacher's and the students' performances affect the teaching strategy. The teacher continually monitors the students' performance. If they experience difficulty with the material, the teacher slows the pace of instruction. If no difficulty is experienced, the rate is accelerated. Such a teacher recognizes and uses

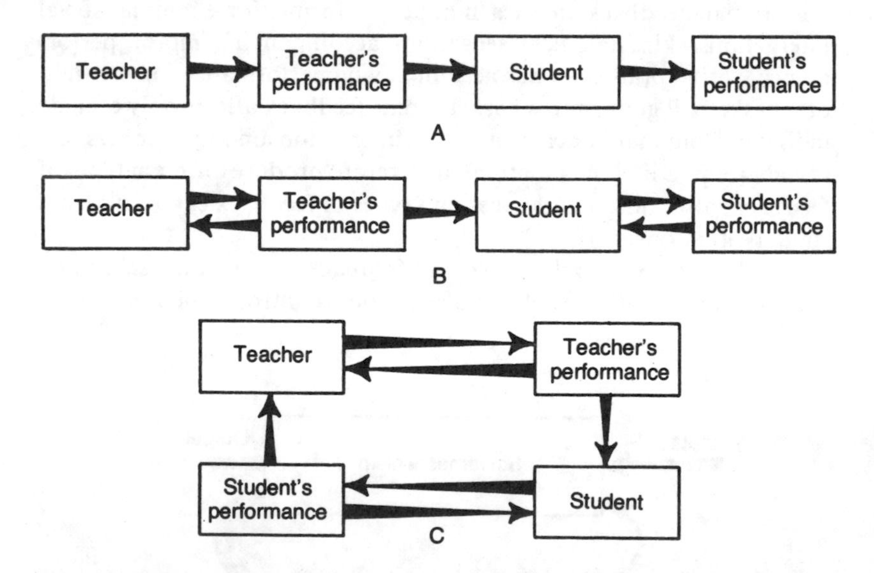

Figure 4.2. Schematic diagram of three types of classroom control sequences: (*A*) open control in main system and subsystems with no feedback; (*B*) open control in main system and feedback control in subsystems; (*C*) feedback loops in both main system and subsystems.

teacher-learner interactions to determine teaching strategy. The important guiding principle is not how much material can be covered in a set time but whether the students are ready to progress to the next stage of instruction. Such a teacher is student-oriented. He or she teaches students, not a required amount of instructional material.

The third model in Figure 4.2 indicates that information feedback is an important controlling factor at all levels of performance. Individual students, as well as teachers, use feedback to modify responses, because it can provide information about performance, act as a reinforcer (that is, give satisfaction or dissatisfaction), and raise motivation through an energizing function.

TYPES OF FEEDBACK

Feedback has been classified according to distinctions between the various types of information that it provides (Holding, 1965; Bilodeau, 1969). Holding originally devised a classification in the form of a tree with 18 branches representing the differing types. A more inclusive view of feedback is represented by a tree with 22 branches. One side of such a tree is in Figure 4.3.

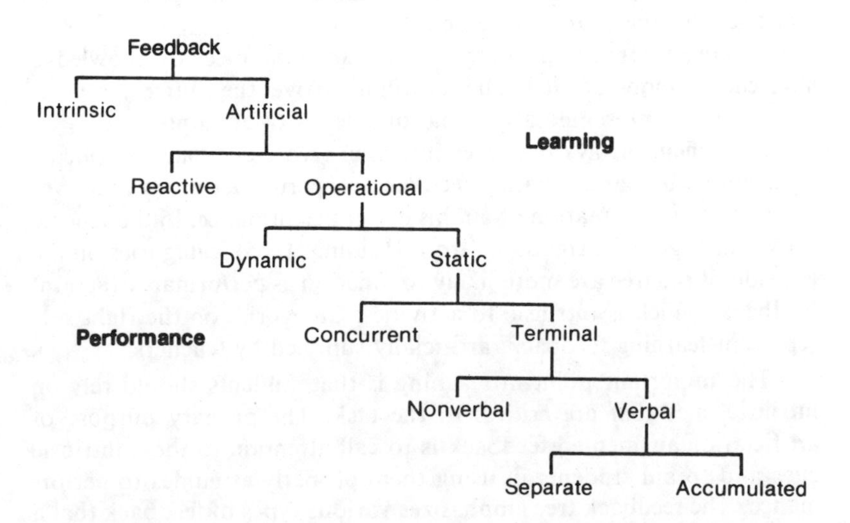

Figure 4.3. Varieties of feedback involved in motor performance.

Feedback is first classified on the basis of its integration into a task. *Intrinsic* feedback is naturally present in the performance of a task. *Artificial* feedback is information that is added by a teacher or an experimenter. It is often called augmented feedback, because it is added to supplement or augment the intrinsic feedback. For example, artificial feedback can take the form of encouragement given by a teammate or a coach for an outstanding performance.

Information produced directly by movement itself is *reactive* feedback. *Operational* feedback is concerned with the effects of movement on the environment.

Dynamic feedback relates to changes in the effects of movement. *Static* feedback refers to effects that do not change.

Concurrent and terminal feedback are distinguished by their temporal relation to the task. *Concurrent* feedback is present during the entire time the performer is responding. *Terminal* feedback is produced after the response is completed. For example, a wrestler deals primarily with concurrent feedback, but a bowler receives mostly terminal feedback. Similarly, feedback is classified according to whether it is presented immediately, as the skill is performed, or delayed until the performance has been completed.

Feedback can also be presented either verbally or nonverbally. *Verbal* feedback takes the form of words or scores. *Nonverbal* feedback is characterized by physical measures, such as nearness, correct kinesthetic feel, or the sound of buzzers.

Finally, feedback can be given as a *separate* piece of knowledge after each response, or it can be *accumulated* over the course of several responses and presented at the end of a series of attempts.

Movement always produces intrinsic, reactive, dynamic, concurrent, nonverbal, and separate feedback. A performer always receives some kind of information about his or her performance. In the scheme shown in Figure 4.3 (modified from Holding, 1965), categories on the left side of the tree are more likely to function as performance (action) feedback, which is intrinsic to activities. Categories on the right side represent learning feedback, artificially supplied by teachers.

The important point in teaching is that students should rely on intrinsic cues that are critical to the task. The primary purpose of artificial or augmented feedback is to call attention to these intrinsic cues and to aid students in using them properly as guides to performance. The feedback tree emphasizes various types of feedback that a teacher can use to draw attention to intrinsic cues. A further role of artificial feedback is that it provides standards against which performance can be assessed. In any event, students must be directed toward and come to rely on intrinsic feedback and intrinsic measures of performance.

FEEDBACK IN MOTOR LEARNING

Feedback, in one form or another, is a vital factor in the acquisition of motor skills from birth through adulthood. An infant learns to grasp an object through the integration of many forms of sensory feedback. Only after a prolonged apprenticeship can an infant use kinesthetic and visual cues to form an image and plan future movements. The development of a smooth, efficient reach and grasp from a coarse, jerky attempt requires still further experience with feedback. Once a child has learned isolated movements, the same process must be followed to combine these into fundamental motor patterns.

Feedback associated with knowledge of results apparently brings about improved performance in two stages. First, an approximate performance is learned, and then fine adjustments are made (Baker and Young, 1960). Learning that occurs in the first stage remains if knowledge of results is withheld, but the fine adjustments do not remain without this feedback (Welford, 1976). Disruption can also occur if a performer is required to attend to some activity during the time interval between the response and the receipt of feedback.

In a learning situation, feedback is always present, and improvement occurs as individuals learn what information to use as feedback and how to use it. Many cues can be used to provide feedback. Payne and Artley (1972, p. 47), reported that "otherwise ineffective supplementary cues can be transformed into highly effective regulators of psychomotor performance by differential conditioning procedures." Bowden (1976) observed that light and click cues, after conditioning, provided the necessary feedback for children to learn a tennis stroke. If such a variety of cues can be effective as feedback, instructors must ensure that students focus attention on relevant aspects of the situation and learn what cues should be used as feedback.

The dependence on feedback for successful performance in fundamental motor patterns is illustrated by Barsch's (1968) description of rolling. He proposed that rolling, a movement pattern about the vertical axis of the body, establishes the foundation for vertical alignment of the body segments. The vertical axis is usually considered to be an ordinate of erect posture, but since a performer's own body serves as his or her basis for all references, the vertical axis is just as important in other postures. Therefore, coordinates within and without the performer serve to define his or her space of movement.

Barsch identified four types of rolling patterns and analyzed them to develop scoring techniques (see Figure 4.4). Few, if any, persons can roll along a true course without errors from start to finish, but a small percentage can manage to roll along a path with minimal errors. People in this group, given a score of 1, continually use subtle and rapid correcting actions to maintain their course. Their accurate rolling patterns are accomplished by the rapid use of visual information and the

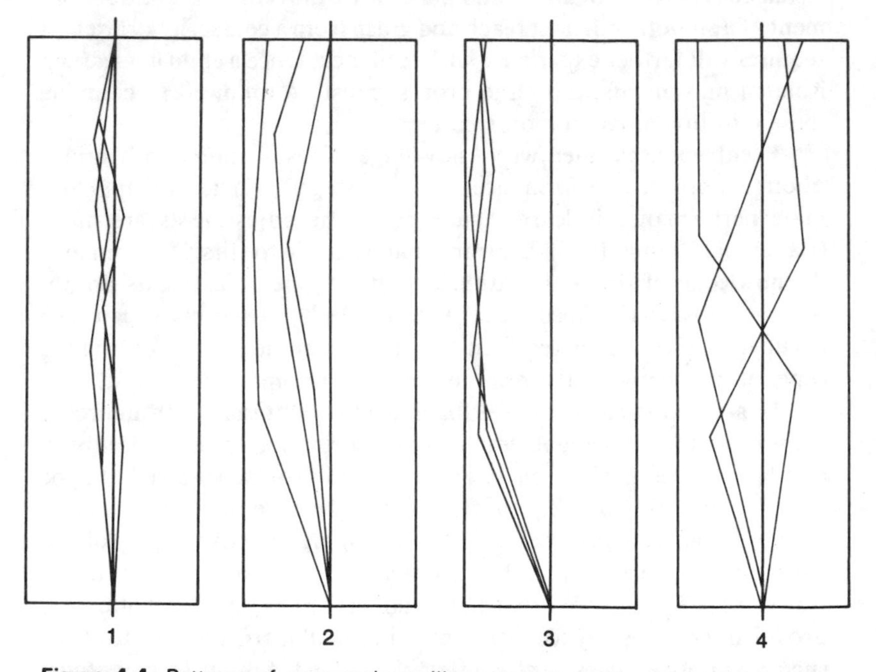

Figure 4.4. Patterns of consecutive rolling attempts, with a four-point scoring system to analyze rolling performance. Score 1: The roller demonstrates minimal deviation from the true midline and corrects alignment as he or she proceeds according to visual targeting. Score 2: From an initial trial that manifests a significant deviation from the midline, the subsequent t ials indicate an effort to improve alignment and hold course. Score 3: The same pattern of deviation is present in all three trials, and the roller seems unable to modify the pattern. Score 4: Each trial deviates significantly from the midline in an erratic and confused set of rolling patterns. (Redrawn from R. H. Barsch. *Enriching perception and cognition: Techniques for teachers.* Vol. 2. Seattle: Special Child Publications, 1968, p. 123.

introduction of kinesthetic corrections. They are able to use proprioceptive feedback to advantage.

Persons receiving a score of 2 show marked improvement in their second and third trials. They benefit from feedback in their attempts to regulate movement in response to their own observations of deviation from a true path. People with a score of 3 roll with a consistent pattern of deviation, which they are unable to correct. They do not benefit from feedback and repeat the same mistakes time and time again. People with a score of 4 are highly erratic and unpredictable. They lack the ability to produce consecutive patterns that are similar in any way. Each roll deviates extensively from a true line, and the types of errors differ from trial to trial. These subjects are unable to sustain visual fixation on a target and seem to be unable to use proprioceptive processes. They have little awareness of their position in space or where they are going. These directionally disorganized individuals do not use feedback.

Barsch's study indicates in behavioral terms how feedback can be used in motor performance analysis. His work provides a useful model for behavioral analysis of many gross motor skills. Most research, however, has not been conducted according to this type of analysis. Typically, feedback research has looked at how internal and external cues can be used but has not involved an evaluation of the consistency of consecutive trials.

Closed Skills

Closed skills place heavy demands on a person's ability to use internal cues, since visual cues and other external stimuli are not an integral part of these tasks. Consequently, closed skills require the replication of movements on the basis of proprioceptive feedback, so that sensitivity to kinesthetic information is a prerequisite for success. Studies conducted to investigate internal feedback have traditionally involved replicating movements of body parts, positioning a lever or some similar apparatus to predetermined positions, or tossing objects such as balls or darts at unseen targets. The principle behind these studies is that a more accurate response indicates the ability to use feedback and less accurate responses show a reduced ability to use feedback. Most research confirms the finding that immediate, accurate feedback improves performance in closed skills.

For example, Lorge and Thorndike (1935) tested adults who tossed balls over their heads at unseen targets and then received information about their performance, either after a delay ranging from 0 to 6 seconds or after the completion of an intervening throw. These investigators concluded that some feedback must follow the performance if learning is to occur. The presence of an intervening response, however, eliminates the value of feedback so that learning does not occur.

A similar study, in which college students threw darts at an unseen target, was conducted by Alexander (1951). Information about performance was provided by lights, after a delay ranging from 0 to 16 seconds. This study indicated that the length of delay has little or no effect on learning (determined by the number of hits or the score obtained on each trial). The ability of the subjects to predict the results of their toss was affected by the length of delay, however. The poorest predictions came with either very short or very long delays. A study by Weinberg, Guy, and Tupper (1964), investigating the effect of feedback delayed from 1 to 20 seconds, also indicated that moderate delays are superior to very short and very long ones. They concluded that a 5-second delay is optimal in the facilitation of performance.

Many questions still remain about the exact value of delayed knowledge of results. McGuigan (1959) asserted that the improved performance observed with moderate delays might be due to the amount of rest between trials or the amount of time allowed between the knowledge of results and the next trial. In any event, moderate delay periods still produce optimal performances.

Bilodeau (1956) found that if additional trials intervene before knowledge of results is given, the value of the feedback decreases and performance errors increase. These findings point to the importance of an intervening response in determining the effectiveness of delayed knowledge of results. A similar study by Lavery and Suddon (1962) also indicated that intervening trials detract from learning. These investigators, however, provided far more practice trials than other studies did, and they found that people eventually can learn tasks even though intervening trials are present. Further, subjects who learned a task with intervening trials retained the skill better than persons who learned it with no intervening trial. These findings suggest that artificial knowledge of results that enhances intrinsic cues produces better retention of the skill. The artificial feedback enables subjects to ignore intervening events and use intrinsic information.

Open Skills

Open skills involve the integration of information received as feedback from several sources, such as vision, proprioception, and hearing.

We all experience performances that "feel" good, "look" good, and provide positive results in closely successive time intervals. Vision, however, appears to be the most important sense in open motor skills, and consequently it has been studied the most.

The great importance of vision in movement has been described by Smith and Smith (1962) in their neurogeometric theory of perceptual-motor organization. They proposed three movement systems, which depend on reactions to gravity, kinesthetic sensation, and vision (see Figure 4.5). Postural movements are general, gross movements that regulate the body's position with respect to gravity. The body is moved through space by means of transport (locomotor) movements, which depend on gravity, kinesthesis, and vision. Transport movements are integrated with postural movements. The third system is composed of fine manipulations, which depend on kinesthetic and visual information received by the sense organs. Regardless of which category of movement is involved, a person reacts through feedback to the detection of spatial and temporal differences in patterns of stimulation. Some of these differences are produced by internal stimulation, others by external stimulation. A person's movements never produce homeostasis, or equilibrium, but rather they create additional stimulus patterns, which constitute feedback, to produce further behaviors.

A later application of cybernetic principles (Smith and Smith, 1966) views the different types of learning as reflections of differences in patterns of feedback control. According to this view, feedback is different from reinforcement. Responses to the spatial characteristics of the environment are seen as being guided within a framework provided by the movement systems of the body. The spatial organization of movement is always subject to control by visual and kinesthetic feedback, which is produced by movements and always relates to the individual's position in and movement through space. Movements that individuals acquire are learned primarily in terms of their feedback guidance properties (Smith and Smith, 1970).

The next few studies to be considered concern the effect of visual and verbal feedback in learning open skills. It is important to remember, however, that visual and kinesthetic input are interrelated.

Johnson (1961) investigated the rate of acquisition of tennis skills by two groups. One group was instructed in a traditional manner, but members of the other group received the results of their performances each day and also were told the scores of all other subjects in the group. No differences were found in the rate of acquisition for the two groups.

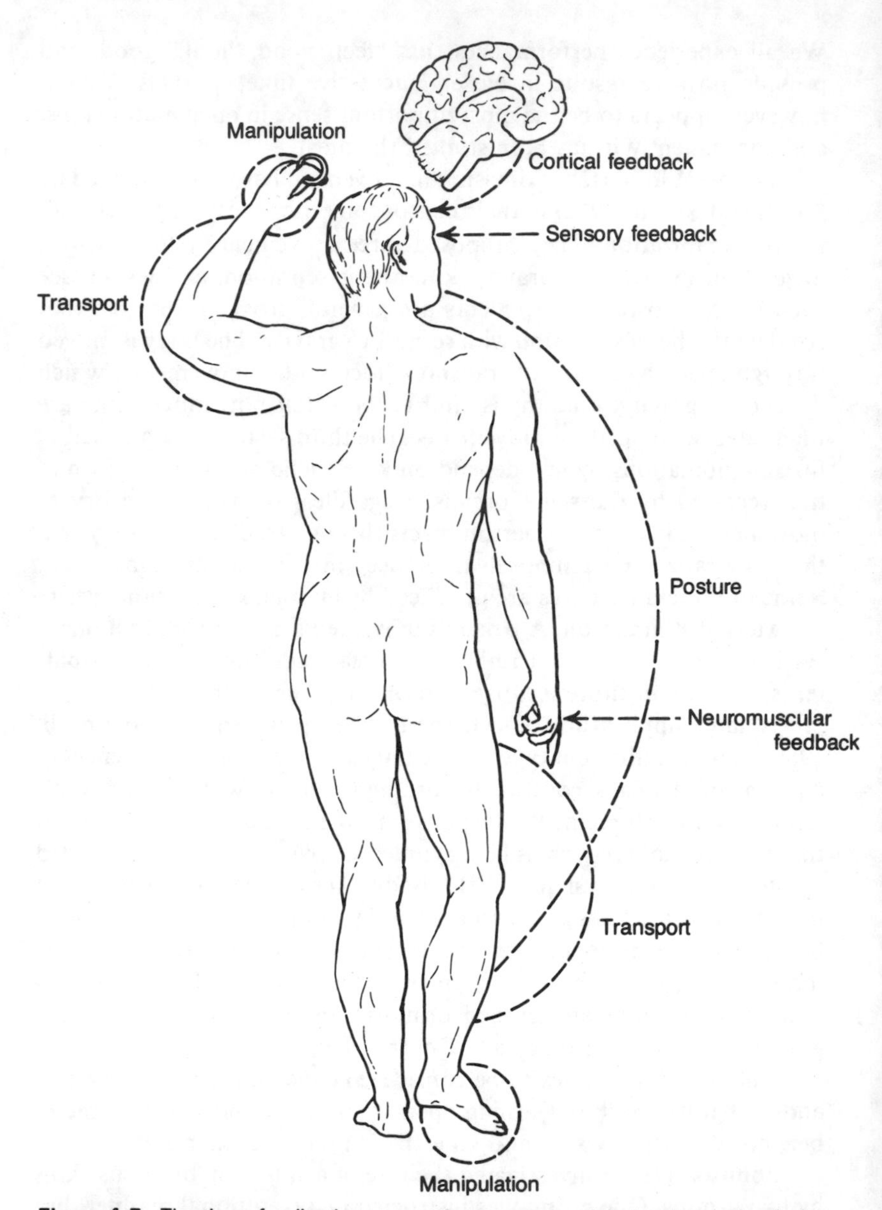

Figure 4.5. The three feedback systems of movement and their related stimulation patterns. Posture is organized with respect to gravity, transport movements are organized with respect to free space, and manipulative movements are organized with respect to contact with objects. Transport movements further interact with both posture and manipulative movements. (Modified from Smith and Smith, 1962.)

Johnson suggested that this finding might be due to a high level of motivation in both groups. An equally feasible explanation, however, is that beginning performers are unable to use such information to modify their performances. Such feedback does not supply information about the intrinsic requirements of the task.

One method of providing artificial visual feedback during the acquisition of a motor skill is to show motion pictures so that subjects can observe their own performances. This type of feedback is delayed, accumulated, and terminal. Watkins (1963) used this technique with highly skilled varsity college baseball players in an attempt to improve their batting performances. He found that players who observed themselves on film decreased their mistakes more than players who did not view their batting.

Other studies, however, have not shown improvement to result from the viewing of motion pictures. It appears that several conditions must be met for such a technique to be effective. First, the performers must be highly skilled. Beginning performers make errors at random, as opposed to the consistent, learned errors of advanced performers. Errors that can be effectively corrected through this technique must be present consistently. Next, the delay between the filming and the viewing must be reasonably short. This prerequisite was emphasized in the discussion of feedback for closed skills. Finally, the filming must highlight the intrinsic components of the task. The films must be shot from the proper angle, must emphasize relevant parts of the body, and must be taken at the proper speed. A clutter of movement and body parts is of little value if it provides so much interference (noise) that it obscures the feedback.

A variation of the filming technique was used in a study of beginning learning of badminton skills by Gray and Brumbach (1967). They showed preconstructed film loops of a skilled tournament player executing basic strokes, both at normal speed and in slow motion. Students who had access to the film loops acquired a higher level of badminton skills during the first 5 weeks of instruction than did a control class taught without such aids. However, at the end of 10 weeks, no differences were observed between the performances of the two groups. These findings support the view that skill acquisition is a three-phase process. The first phase, which involves cognitive understanding of the task, can be facilitated by the availability of a visual model. The second and third phases, however—fixation of correct movement patterns and development of autonomous skills—require repetitive physical practice. As a consequence, this technique can help students to develop an understanding of a skill in less time, but it does not reduce the time required for refinement of the skill through extended practice.

Another photographic technique, employing a Polaroid graph check sequence camera, was used by Thompson (1969) to provide immediate visual feedback for the drive and the five-iron approach shot of beginning golfers. She concluded that this immediate artificial feedback facilitated the initial acquisition of golf skills. Once again, the feedback aided beginners if it contributed to an understanding of the skill requirements to be mastered.

A modern technique that provides terminal visual feedback after a short delay is the videotape replay. Eckert (1970) contrasted the effectiveness of a videotape replay of a maze-tracing performance with that of viewing the completed tracing only. She found no differences between these two types of terminal feedback. Delays of as much as 30 seconds had no effect on performance. The effectiveness of the videotape replay was probably reduced by the simplicity of the skill.

A television monitor display can provide artificial concurrent visual feedback. Drowatzky (1971) used this technique to augment inherent feedback with concurrent dynamic feedback in a study of the acquisition of a stabliometer balance skill by college men and women. Two camera setups were used: one provided a frontal picture in mirror image, the other a back view with no reversal of right and left. The results of this study, displayed in Figure 4.6, show that such feedback can improve, disrupt, or have no effect on balancing performance, depending on the sex of the subjects and the location of the camera. The artificial feedback had no effect on the performances of males. Females viewing their performances on the monitor from the back were aided, however, and those viewing the frontal, mirror image were disrupted. Therefore, one must carefully consider technical aspects such as camera placement before audiovisual aids are used in instruction.

A survey of the literature by Oxendine (1973) indicated that both open- and closed-circuit television systems are used in physical education. Most research on the use of television in physical education has been concerned with instant replay as feedback, the effectiveness of television feedback as a teaching aid, and evaluative processes related to microteaching. Oxendine cited several studies showing that augmented feedback via instant replay facilitates the learning of skills by beginners. He emphasized, however, that the effective use of this medium requires adequate technical skills (filming and editing), editing to provide information about the inherent components of the task (and to eliminate

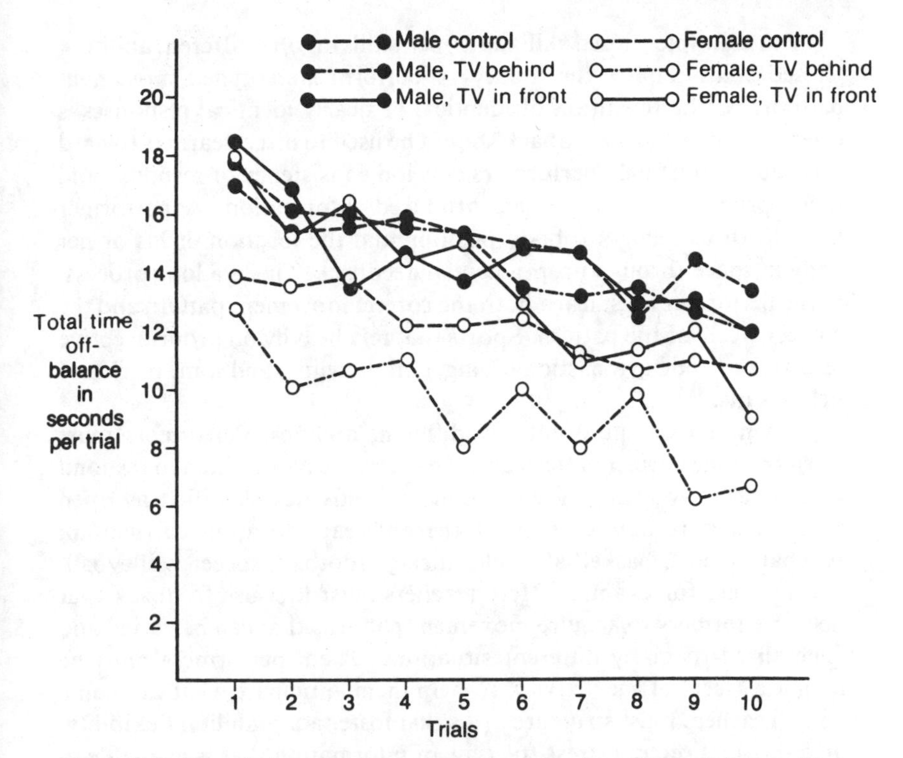

Figure 4.6. Mean balance performances of groups given feedback by television monitor. (Redrawn from J. N. Drowatzky, Television augmented feedback in learning a balance skill, *International Journal of Sport Psychology* 2 [1971]: 121.)

ineffective, confusing material), and teaching learners how to observe the videotape replay. Careful planning is required if the use of television feedback is to be an effective teaching aid.

FEEDBACK AND INSTRUCTION

Feedback is an important aspect of learning. Without it, any change in performance and subsequent improvement would be impossible. In fact, it is impossible to prevent human performers from receiving intrinsic feedback unless they are placed in artificial learning situations. Successful use of feedback, however, depends on the individual, the type of skill, the type of feedback, and technical aspects of feedback production. Effective feedback must relate to inherent aspects of the task.

For example, closed skills and open skills involve different abilities. Closed skills require the ability to perform stereotyped movement patterns, as the repetition of identical or nearly identical responses is essential for success. Feedback should be used to direct learners toward this end. It must help performers develop consistency of response and focus primarily on movement-produced information. A performer must learn to recognize body position and the location of his or her body in space through proprioceptive feedback. This is a long process, as the performer must learn both the correct movement pattern and the correct "feel" of the pattern. Sports that rely heavily on proprioceptive feedback include gymnastics, diving, golf, bowling, and some track and field events.

Open skills require entirely different abilities. Performers must learn both the correct pattern and the correct ways in which to respond to a constantly changing environment. Activities classified as open skills constitute a large part of the physical education curriculum: baseball, tennis, basketball, field hockey, football, soccer, volleyball, and fencing, for example. Here teachers must first use feedback that helps performers to acquire movement patterns that can be varied and generalized to many different situations. Then, performers must be taught a "feel" of the activity, to help them anticipate what can come next. Teachers must structure drills that foster adaptability, flexibility, and anticipation and stress the type of information that is available to students during a performance. Consequently, a performer learns to use such cues as the trajectory patterns of balls, his or her court position, the opponent's court position, and the playing styles of others, to develop successful strategies of placement.

Thus, performers must be aware of the relevant dimensions of a task: the important stimuli and the corresponding responses. Not only must they be able to determine what movements produce the correct performance, but also they must recognize the connection between their movements and the resulting feedback. Furthermore, they must be able to recognize similarities between sets of stimuli, to modify their responses, and to resist the desire to produce the same response over and over. They must also recognize what constitutes an error and what are the significant aspects that they must evaluate during performance.

Ability levels should be considered when one is providing feedback. Beginners appear to benefit more from feedback that directs them toward the correct performance pattern than from feedback that points out their errors. Emphasis on errors is less effective because of the continual change in the nature of errors committed by beginners. Advanced performers receive more benefit from feedback that points out their errors. They are concerned with errors that have been learned and incorporated into their performance, and such errors must be recognized before they can be eliminated.

The time frame in which artificial feedback is provided is another important consideration. A brief delay between the performance and the presentation of feedback appears to enhance its value. The feedback should be provided before an intervening response is made.

Smoll (1972) indicated that there is an optimal level of exactness of feedback. That is, if either too little or too much is provided, the feedback can be disruptive rather than helpful. The nature of the optimal level has not been adequately investigated, however. Likewise, Malina (1969) reported that performance levels (in the acquisition of speed and accuracy of throwing) are related to both the type and the completeness of the feedback that is either present or withheld during practice. Chansky (1960) found that the most economical type of feedback is intermittent information by which the teacher notifies students of their errors and directs them toward the correct response. The need for detailed, sophisticated feedback that changes as students change their performances was emphasized by McNeil (1962).

Feedback is available from several sources during skilled performance. Klein and Posner (1974) indicated that performers selectively choose between visual and kinesthetic feedback. They reported that vision dominates kinesthesis. Kinesthetic cues are apparently ignored if visual cues are present. This is the case even though the initiation of simple responses is delayed as a result. Reliance on kinesthetic cues apparently changes with practice, however, as the performer learns the correct kinesthetic feel associated with the skill. According to Fleishman and Rich (1963), as the performance of complex movement skills improves, the importance of kinesthesis increases. Better performance in tracking tasks also results if a variety of kinesthetic cues are available (Notterman and Page, 1962).

According to Howell (1956), a graphic analysis of complex motor patterns can aid learning if it is made available immediately after a performance, so that mistakes can be identified and corrected and the relevant physical principles can be understood. In a similar manner, Bilodeau and Bilodeau (1961) stressed the need for feedback to regulate functions of errors before it contributes to improved performance.

Teachers can use the following guidelines as they develop ways to provide effective feedback to students (Ammons, 1956):

1. A performer usually has one or more hypotheses about the skill to be performed and how to perform it. These hypotheses affect and are affected by his or her knowledge of performance.
2. Some knowledge of performance is always available to performers. This knowledge affects rates of learning, levels of performance reached, and motivation.
3. Specific feedback leads to more rapid improvement and higher levels of performance than general feedback does. If feedback is reduced, performance decreases.
4. The removal of augmented, or supplementary, feedback can cause a decrease in performance or systematic "undershooting" or "overshooting" unless the performer is able to substitute intrinsic cues for the artificial information that was removed.

Teachers must integrate supplementary information with inherent characteristics of a task. Although the general nature of the response might remain if feedback is removed, the fine adjustments in performance are quickly lost. Students also quickly learn that seemingly unimportant cues can provide feedback once they are taught to attend to those cues. Teachers must recognize that students already have some idea about what must be done and how to do it, on the basis of their past experiences. Teaching strategies cannot ignore student expectancies. Many factors that have not been extensively investigated influence the effectiveness of artificial feedback on learning and performance.

Perhaps the best summary of the complex, dynamic feedback loops involved in competitive, skilled motor performance is contained in Figure 4.7. Half of the figure, showing the first competitor and the interacting environment, displays feedback loops for closed skills. The whole figure represents feedback loops for open skills. Relations between internal and external information loops are shown. Internal loops represent interactions of sensory, central nervous, and response systems. External loops involve the observation of one's responses, the effects of the environment, and the opponent's responses. All of these dynamic forces must be considered by a performer and integrated before the next series of movements is made.

GUIDING PRINCIPLES FOR THE TEACHER

1. Feedback is the part of a subject's output that returns to the subject in the form of input for monitoring. By means of feedback,

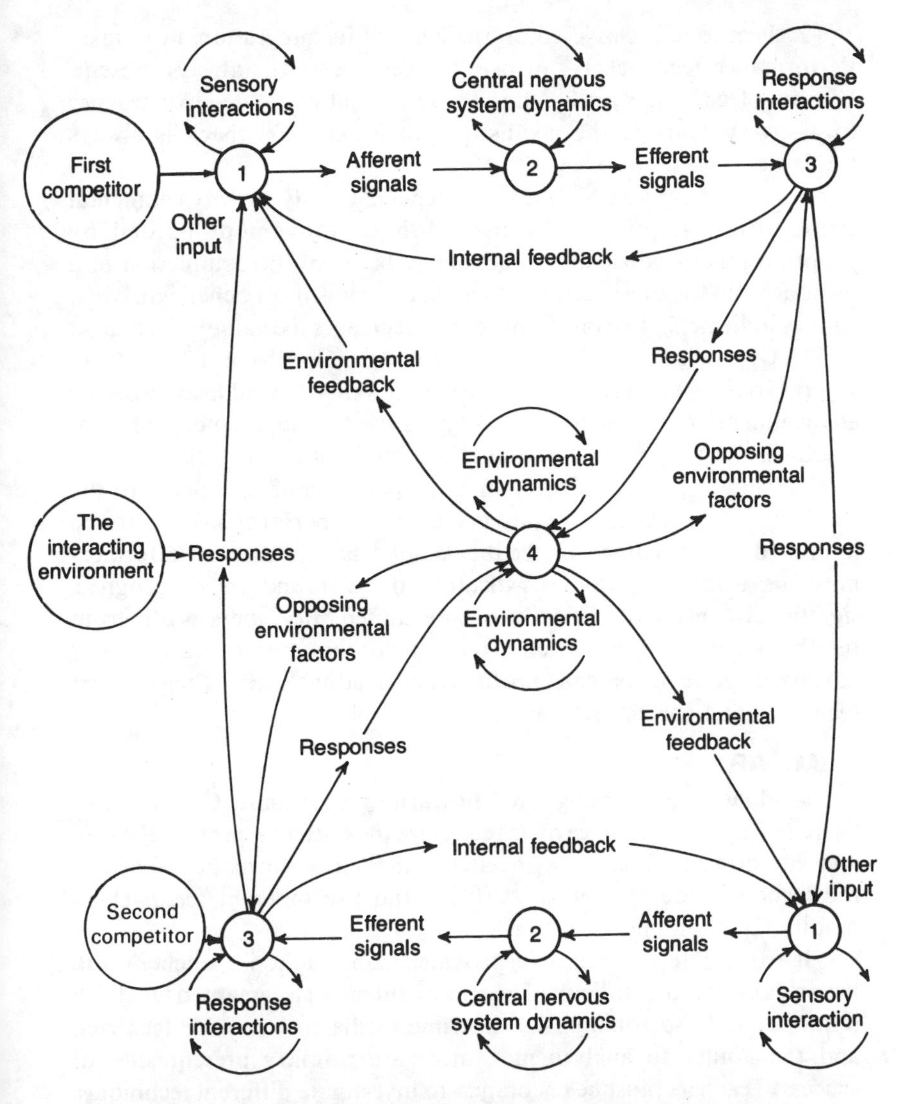

Figure 4.7. Schematic diagram of the dynamic feedback loops involved in competitive skilled performance. (Modified from Fitts, 1962.)

movement becomes regulated by the extent to which a task has not yet been accomplished. Teachers should monitor their students' progress and adjust their teaching style according to their own performance and their students' performance.

2. Feedback is classified on the basis of its integration into a task. Performance feedback is intrinsic to the task and is always present. Learning feedback is artificial, in the sense that it is added by a teacher to assist students in the acquisition of a skill. Feedback is always available in some form.

3. Closed skills, which do not depend greatly on environmental stimulation, require the replication of movement guided by proprioceptive feedback. A slight delay between the completion of a response and the presentation of feedback seems most beneficial. Most studies indicate that an intervening trial decreases the value of feedback.

4. Open skills require the integration of feedback arising from several sources of sensation, because these skills depend heavily on the environment. Artificial feedback that is used to supplement inherent feedback must emphasize cues that are inherent in the task.

5. The degree of accuracy in one's performance is related to the accuracy of feedback. If the accuracy of performance is to be improved, the accuracy of feedback must be increased. Performers must be aware of what constitutes an error and must recognize significant aspects of the task to be evaluted. Beginners profit from feedback that directs them toward correct performance, and advanced performers can profit from feedback that helps them recognize and correct their errors.

SUMMARY

Feedback cannot be ignored in learning situations. Care must be exercised to ensure that learners recognize the critical aspects of the skill and the nature of feedback associated with their performance. Teachers must show students how to evaluate and use inherent feedback to modify their responses.

If artificial feedback is to be provided in instruction, a teacher's task becomes even more difficult. The successful use of augmented feedback requires careful planning. Skill in using media that provide feedback and the ability to analyze movement are primary prerequisites of success. Teachers must be encoraged to investigate different techniques that are available.

REFERENCES

Alexander, L. T. 1951. Knowledge of results and the temporal gradient of reinforcement. *American Psychologist* 6:292 293.

Ammons, R. B. 1956. Effects of knowledge of performance: A survey and tentative theoretical formulation. *Journal of General Psychology* 54:279 299.

Baker, C. H., and Young, P. 1960. Feedback during training and retention of motor skills. *Canadian Journal of Psychology* 14:257–264.

Barsch, R. H. 1968. *Enriching perception and cognition: Techniques for teachers*. Vol. 2. Seattle: Special Child Publications.

Bilodeau, E. A., and Bilodeau, I. McD. 1961. Motor-skills learning. In *Annual review of psychology*. Vol. 12, ed. P. R. Farnsworth. Palo Alto, Calif.: Annual Reviews.

Bilodeau, I. McD. 1956. Accuracy of a simple positioning response with variation in the number of trials by which knowledge of results is delayed. *American Journal of Psychology* 69:434–437.

———. 1969. Information feedback. In *Principles of skill acquisition*, ed. E. A. Bilodeau and I. McD. Bilodeau. New York: Academic Press.

Bowden, M. E. 1976. Preconditioned cues of performance: Effects on acquisition of a serial motor task. Ph.D. dissertation, University of Toledo.

Chansky, N. M. 1960. Learning: A function of schedule and type of feedback. *Psychological Reports* 7:362.

Drowatzky, J. N. 1971. Television augmented feedback in learning a balance skill. *International Journal of Sport Psychology* 2:118–124.

Eckert, H. M. 1970. A comparison of delayed static and dynamic visual feedback. *Research Quarterly* 41:39–43.

Fitts, P. M. 1962. Factors in complex skill training. In *Training research and education*, ed. R. Glaser. Pittsburgh: University of Pittsburgh Press.

Fleishman, E. A., and Rich, S. 1963. Role of kinesthetic and spatial-visual abilities in perceptual-motor learning. *Journal of Experimental Psychology* 66:6–11.

Gray, C. A., and Brumbach, W. B. 1967. Effect of daylight projection of film loops on learning badminton. *Research Quarterly* 38:562–569.

Holding, D. H. 1965. *Principles of training*. London: Pergamon Press.

Howell, M. L. 1956. Use of force-time graphs for performance analysis in facilitating motor learning. *Research Quarterly* 27:12–22.

Johnson, J. 1961. The effect of knowledge of results on the learning of tennis, Unpublished research project, University of Southern California. Cited by V. L. Bell, *Sensorimotor learning: From research to teaching*. Pacific Palisades, Calif.: Goodyear Publishing, 1970.

Klein, R. M., and Posner, M. I. 1974. Attention to visual and kinesthetic components of skills. *Brain Research* 71:401–411.

Lavery, J. J., and Suddon, F. H. 1962. Retention of simple motor skills as a function of the number of trials by which KR is delayed. *Perception and Motor Skills* 15:231–237.

Lorge, I., and Thorndike, E. L. 1935. The influence of delay in the after-effect of a connection. *Journal of Experimental Psychology* 18:186–194.

McGuigan, F. J. 1959. Delay of knowledge of results: A problem in design. *Psychological Reports* 5:241–243.

McNeil, J. 1962. An experimental effort to improve instruction through visual feedback. *Journal of Educational Research* 55:283–285.

Malina, R. M. 1969. Effects of varied information feedback practice conditions on throwing speed and accuracy. *Research Quarterly* 40:134–145.

Notterman, J. M., and Page, D. E. 1962. Evaluation of mathematically equivalent tracking systems. *Perceptual and Motor Skills* 15:683–716.

Oxendine, J. B. 1973. The use of television in physical education. *National College Physical Education Association for Men Proceedings* 76:121–127.

Payne, R. B., and Artley, C. W. 1972. Facilitation of psychomotor learning by classical differentiated supplementary feedback cues. *Journal of Motor Behavior* 4:47–50.

Smith, K. U., and Smith, M. F. 1966. *Cybernetic principles of learning and educational design*. New York: Holt, Rinehart and Winston.

Smith, K. U., and Smith, T. J. 1970. Feedback mechanism of athletic skill and learning. In *Psychology of motor learning*, ed. L. E. Smith. Chicago: Athletic Institute.

Smith, K. U., and Smith, W. M. 1962. *Perception and motion: An analysis of space-structured behavior*. Philadelphia: W. B. Saunders.

Smoll, F. L. 1972. Effects of precision of information feedback upon acquisition of a motor skill. *Research Quarterly* 43:489–493.

Thompson, D. H. 1969. Immediate external feedback in the learning of golf skills. *Research Quarterly* 40:589–594.

Watkins, D. L. 1963. Motion pictures as an aid in correcting baseball batting faults. *Research Quarterly* 34:228–233.

Weinberg, D. R., Guy, D. E., and Tupper, R. U. 1964. Variation of postfeedback interval in simple motor learning. *Journal of Experimental Psychology* 67:98–99.

Welford, A. T. 1976. *Skilled performance: Perceptual and motor skills*. Glenview, Ill.: Scott, Foresman.

Wiener, N. 1961. *Cybernetics or control and communication in the animal and the machine*. 2d ed. Cambridge, Mass.: MIT Press.

5 Timing

Successful performance of movement and sports skills requires participants to consider spatial and temporal characteristics of both the environment and their own responses. An awareness of spatial relationships is developed as one moves through space and encounters objects in it. The temporal aspect of movement, or *timing*, is developed as one learns how movements relate to each other in time. Timing contributes to success or failure in sports performance in many ways. One must be able to initiate a proper sequence of movements, each beginning and ending at the appropriate time, to produce a well-coordinated performance. A successful batter can accurately predict the optimal moment to begin a swing to make contact with a pitched baseball. A runner who has good reaction time leaves the starting block sooner than others. Once all the runners have left the starting blocks, speed becomes the critical factor in the race. These examples illustrate the importance of the temporal dimension in motor performance.

Kephart (1964, p. 205) proposed that a developing child must learn and generalize three types of temporal relations—synchrony, rhythm, and sequencing:

> As with the relationships in space, relationships in time also developed first in the motor activities of the child. Synchrony is

> observed when the muscles move in concert. Rhythm is developed when muscles move alternately or recurrently. Sequence is observed when movements occur in coordinated patterns. From the generalization of many such observations, a temporal system evolves and a temporal dimension develops.

Just as our spatial reference system has a point of origin (usually the vertical axis of the body), so does our temporal reference system. Synchrony provides a point of origin in time; that is, it marks the start of a particular response or movement. An understanding of synchrony must be developed before a child can make judgments about serial movements and potentially conflicting events. Synchrony provides a point of origin for a temporal scale characterized by equal, stable units. Rhythm provides this scale; it enables one to estimate and evaluate temporal intervals in performance. Finally, motor events are ordered in time through sequencing. Sequencing, in concert with synchrony and rhythm, enables a performer to impose order on the temporal scale and organize events on the basis of their temporal relationships. The performer therefore is not overwhelmed by a series of stimulus events or responses having different points of origin and termination.

The temporal and spatial components of movement follow their own developmental patterns, but they must also merge. Smooth, efficient performance requires a performer to consider these components together. We move through space with a knowledge of proper spatial relations and correct timing of movements. Any analysis of performance should therefore include both dimensions.

Speed and timing are frequently used as performance measures and as experimental variables in the study of motor learning. The reason for their use is obvious: every response takes time, and time can be measured. Measures of speed and timing can be obtained relatively easily and are applicable to a wide variety of activities. Speed of performance is useful as an index of achievement, on the principle that the more completely a person learns a task, the more rapidly it can be performed. Timing reflects processes in the nervous system. The more complex the neurological processes involved in a response, the longer the processing takes.

Reaction time and movement time are the simplest and most frequently used measures of timing in physical education. They can best be explained through a description of a simple experiment (see Figure 5.1). Assume that a subject stands on a pad and awaits a specified

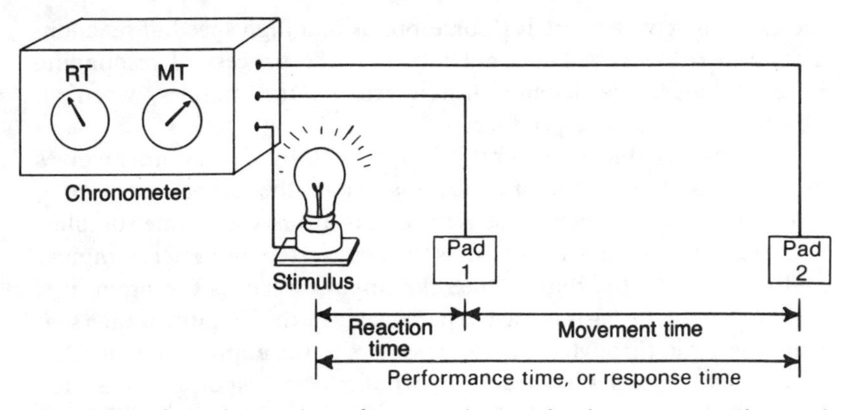

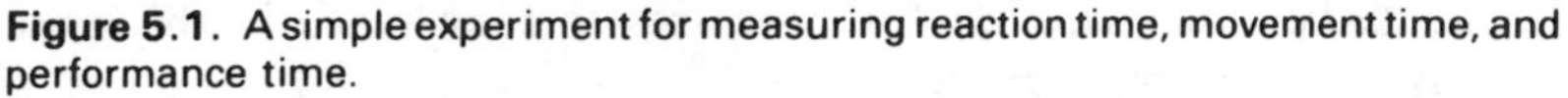

Figure 5.1. A simple experiment for measuring reaction time, movement time, and performance time.

stimulus, such as the flashing of a light. When the light flashes, the subject runs to a second pad, some distance away. Once the stimulus has been presented, some time elapses before the subject begins an overt response. The interval between the presentation of the stimulus and the beginning of the response is called *reaction time* (RT). *Movement time* (MT) begins once the subject has initiated a response and continues until the required response is completed. In this example, reaction time is the interval between the flashing of the light and the subject's leaving the first pad. Movement time is the period that begins when the subject steps off the first pad and ends when he or she steps on the second pad.

The total time required for the subject to respond, from the presentation of the stimulus to the completion of the response, is known as *performance time* (PT), or *response time*. It is the sum of reaction time and movement time. RT, MT, and PT are subject to variation due to several causes and are distinctly response variables. This chapter is concerned with an analysis of these aspects of timing and the factors that produce variation in them.

REACTION TIME

Reaction time is probably the simplest case of timing. It is commonly known as response latency—the time that elapses between the presentation of a stimulus and the appearance of a response to it. In other words, RT is the time that is required for an overt response to get started. It reflects the speed with which one can perceive and respond to the environment; a short RT corresponds to a high speed of reaction. The term *response latency* indicates that the process of responding remains hidden, or latent, until it reaches the muscles, when an observable response is produced.

Latency is due to several factors. RT, by definition, involves processes of the central nervous system in the development of a volitional response. First, a sense organ is aroused by some stimulus. The excitation of the sense organ is then converted into a nerve impulse and carried into the brain. Once the impulse reaches the brain, it is interpreted on the basis of past experience. Another impulse is then sent from the brain through the nervous system to the appropriate muscles. Finally, the muscles contract to produce the response. Thus, RT includes the time required for processes to take place in the sense organs, brain, nerves, and muscles.

Of all the steps involved, the work performed in the brain consumes by far the most time. The complexity of the stimulus and of the response dramatically affects RT. In complex situations, more time is spent by the brain in identifying relevant stimuli, interpreting them, and producing responses. RT is consequently used to evaluate these processes. The term *information processing* is used to describe this neurological activity, by which a horde of incoming information must be quickly assessed to produce a proper course of action. According to Posner (1966), the speed with which one can respond reflects the difficulty encountered during the processing of information, and the rate of performance is thus limited by the central nervous system. The difficulty of processing can be reduced, however, through practice and the use of appropriate stimulus and response codes.

The role of the central nervous system in the production of muscular responses can be best illustrated by the increases in RT for responses of increasing complexity (see Table 5.1). The nervous system is involved the least in movements that are produced by direct stimulation of a muscle with electrical current. A latent period of 0.015 seconds elapses between the application of the current and the beginning of the muscular contraction. More involvement of the nervous system occurs with the eye-blink reflex, for which the latent period is 0.04 seconds. If an impulse is required to travel greater distances, as in the case of the patellar tendon reflex, still more time passes before an overt response is initiated. The central nervous system is not responsible for forming any of these responses, however, and the latent periods of such responses are called reflex times. For the simplest

Table 5.1. Typical Latent Periods in Selected Reflex and Reaction Times

TYPE OF MOVEMENT	TIME (IN SECONDS)
Direct muscular stimulation	0.015
Eye-blink reflex	0.04
Patellar reflex	0.08
Finger reaction time (hand)	0.15
Body reaction time	0.30
Choice reaction time (hand)	0.50

tasks that involve the central nervous system, such as lifting a finger off a telegraph key in response to a light, the shortest possible latent period is about 0.15 seconds. Intervals of 0.20 or 0.25 seconds are more typical of simple RT experiments. Movement of larger body parts or of the entire body requires still more time for its initiation. Responses that involve choices between several stimuli or complicated movements are typically characterized by latent periods of 0.50 seconds or more.

The central nervous system limits the rate at which people can respond (Posner, 1966). RT increases in proportion to the extent of cortical involvement. The longer time, for the most part, reflects increased information processing in the brain, rather than processes carried out in the peripheral nervous system and muscles.

Experimenters have generally classified reaction time in one of two categories. The first type, *simple RT,* is measured in situations in which a subject makes a single, predetermined response to a single, predesignated stimulus. The response can vary from lifting a finger off a telegraph key to running several feet after leaving a pad. Simple movements made in response to simple stimuli are produced fastest, as choices are minimal. *Choice RT* is measured in situations in which a subject is required to discriminate among stimuli and respond to one of them or respond differently to several of them. Logarithmic increases in reaction time have been reported with increases in the number of stimuli or the number of responses or both (Fitts and Posner, 1967). Simon and Slaviero (1975) have proposed that choice RT involves a perceptual phase, a central processing phase, and a motor phase, while simple RT involves only the perceptual and motor phases.

A sequence of tasks, each of which is characterized by simple RT or choice RT, is used to measure *serial RT.* The same factors that affect response latency in simple and choice tasks also affect serial RT.

Factors Influencing Reaction Time

Factors that influence response latency fall into two broad categories. First, RT is determined by characteristics of individual subjects, such as age, sex, learning, motivation, and physical and mental abilities. The second category contains factors associated with characteristics of the task. Task variables include the nature and complexity of the stimulus and the complexity of the task. Some of these factors fall under the control of teachers. Others are relatively uncontrollable, but their influence must still be recognized.

Age. A subject's age indicates his or her level of maturation and is thus related to his or her levels of experience and learning. (Because of the close interaction of maturation and learning, no attempt will be made here to distinguish between the influences of these two factors.) Learning reduces the amount of time required for decision making and consequently decreases reaction time. There is no doubt that RT can be improved through practice. Gibson, Karpovich, and Gollnick (1961), for example, reported reductions in both reaction time and performance time through training. Generally, RT can be decreased by approximately 10 percent after training. Effects of long-term experience are more difficult to isolate. Henry and Rogers (1960), studying subjects aged 8, 12, and 24 years, found that reaction time decreases as age increases, for both simple and complex movements. They also found less variability of reaction times among older subjects than among younger ones (see Figure 5.2). These results were interpreted as reflecting the influence of experience.

Mendryk (1960) reported lower RTs among 22-year-old men than among 12-year-old boys and 48-year-old men. A later study by Norrie (1967) supports these findings. Norrie's research implies that, in the learning of simple movements, the simplification process is limited in duration and occurs early in practice, but in the learning of complex movements, a longer time is required for simplification and thus more practice is required. Hodgkins (1963), studying male and female subjects from 6 to 84 years old, found that RT decreases until early adulthood and then increases (see Figure 5.3).

These findings are representative of the results of studies of age (and experience) in relation to response latency. The early, rapid decrease in RT is due to the simplification process associated with practice. The increase in RT during adulthood is probably due to lowered physiological function and interference of other acquired knowledge or skills.

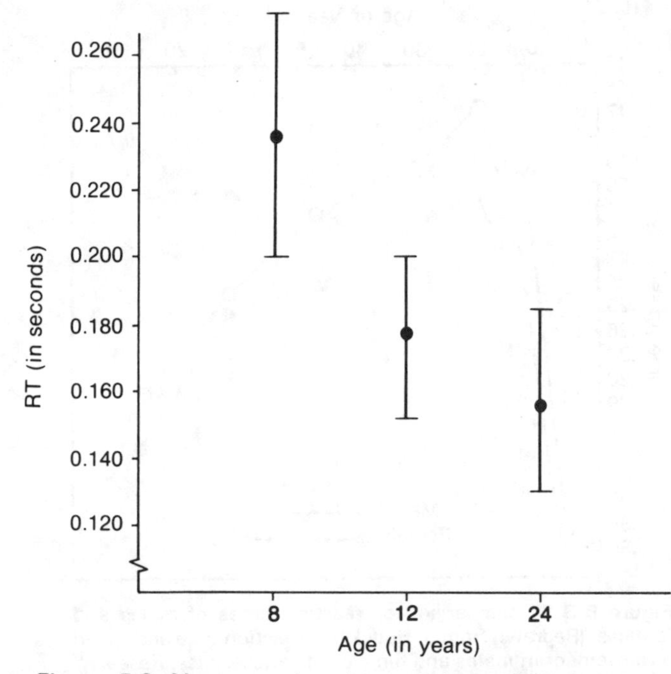

Figure 5.2. Mean reaction times and standard deviations, showing decreases in reaction time and variability with increasing age. (Data from Henry and Rogers, 1960.)

This decline in speeds of reaction in adults, however, is generally believed to be one aspect of a speed-accuracy trade-off. Older people become slower but more efficient and tend to make fewer performance errors than younger individuals do. Thus, if accuracy rather than speed of response is the criterion, older subjects are clearly superior (Welford, 1958). Clarkson and Kroll (1978) reported that life-style can also influence RT in adults. Their study indicates that regular physical activity can reduce the increase in latency associated with aging.

Sex. Most studies investigating sex as a variable have reported lower RT values for male subjects than for female subjects. Henry and Rogers (1960) found this to be true under all their experimental conditions. Hodgkins (1963) observed not only that men have shorter RTs than women but also that the increase in RT during adulthood occurs faster among men than among women. Both sexes reach their peak speed of reaction about the age of 19 years, but the subsequent decline is more gradual for women than for men. The reasons for this

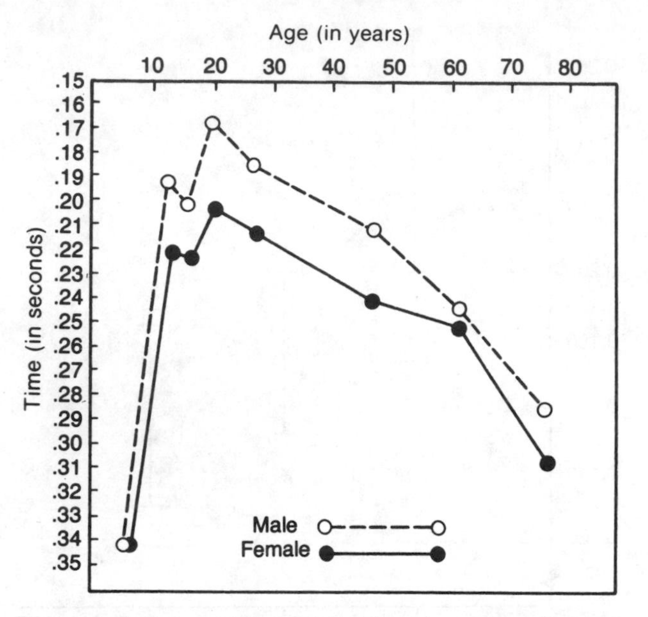

Figure 5.3. A comparison of reaction times of males and females. (Redrawn from J. Hodgkins, Reaction time and speed of movement in males and females of various ages, *Research Quarterly* 34 [1963]: 336.)

difference have not been isolated. It might be caused either by innate factors or by sociological factors.

Reaction Time and Athletics. It is difficult to make general statements about the effect of athletic participation on motor ability factors. It is not clear whether athletic participation improves reaction time or whether athletic activities merely attract individuals who already have short reaction times. As Clarke (1971, p. 255) stated, "Although successful athletes generally have common characteristics, the pattern of these characteristics varies from athlete to athlete; where a successful athlete is low in such a trait, he compensates by strength in another."

Characteristics of athletes differ from sport to sport and from position to position on a team. Most studies indicate that certain types of athletes have shorter RTs than nonparticipants. For example, Keller (1940) found that participants in team sports have shorter RTs than participants in individual sports and nonparticipants do (see Table 5.2). Clarke (1971) also reported differences between the RTs of athletes and nonparticipants.

Table 5.2. Reaction Times of Athletes and Nonparticipants

ATHLETIC GROUP	ARM RT (IN SECONDS)	TOTAL BODY RT (IN SECONDS)
Basketball players	0.250	0.318
Baseball players	0.257	0.303
Football players	0.267	0.309
Swimmers	0.291	0.339
Nonathletes, gymnasts, wrestlers, trackmen	0.283	0.334

Data from Keller, 1940.

The degree of difference depends on the requirements of the sport and the ability of the individual. Outstanding athletes were found to be superior to regular athletes in most cases. Knapp (1961) found that top-class racket games players have shorter RTs to a visual stimulus and less variation in RTs than research students have. Athletes also possess shorter RTs to stimuli in their peripheral field of vision (Young and Skemp, 1959).

The general consensus of research findings is that RTs of athletes in different categories are generally superior to those of nonparticipants. The superiority depends on ability and the requirements of the sport. Performers in sports that do not require fast reactions are not much different from nonparticipants.

Set. A subject's expectations, anxiety level, and the like also influence response latency. Henry (1960) instructed one group of subjects to assume a motor set (in which they would concentrate on a movement they were about to perform in response to a stimulus) and instructed another group to assume a sensory set (in which they would concentrate on being ready for the stimulus). He observed that both men and women react more slowly under the motor set than under the sensory set. Henry's data indicate that most subjects normally use a sensory set, although a few naturally adopt a motor set. The importance of expectancy was also detailed by Mowrer (1941). Whitley (1966) observed that circumstances that increase a subject's conscious and willful intent to respond result in shorter RTs.

Knowledge of one's reaction time for a given task also produces a decrease in RT (McCormack, Binding, and McElhearn, 1963). Intermittent knowledge of results was found to maintain performance as effectively as knowledge provided after every trial.

Anxiety in the form of stress was observed by Nash et al. (1966) to produce longer reaction times.

Therefore, RT decreases under conditions that enhance a performer's understanding of the task and aid in clarifying his or her expectancies, but it increases in stressful situations.

Foreperiod. In some activities, a ready signal warns participants to prepare for the stimulus to which they will respond. The period of time between the presentation of the ready signal and the appearance of the RT stimulus is called the *foreperiod.* Its duration is commonly varied, or false ready signals (not followed by the designated stimulus) are given, to prevent a subject from responding to the foreperiod through anticipation rather than responding to the RT stimulus. Variable foreperiods are employed to start track and swimming events.

Reaction time is greatly influenced by the foreperiods of previous trials, and the foreperiod of the immediately preceding trial has the greatest impact (Underwood, 1966). Karlin (1969) and Wilson (1959) found that average RT increases with increases in the length of the foreperiod. Results of a study by Raab, Fehrer, and Hershenson (1961), however, contradict that finding. Lueft (1970) observed that RTs are shorter if the duration of previous foreperiods has been constant, rather than varied, and that responses are produced fastest after the shortest constant foreperiods. He attributed this effect to expectancies that subjects form on the basis of the method of presentation of foreperiods. Zahn, Rosenthal, and Shakow (1963) found that RT increases after a short foreperiod if previous trials have had longer foreperiods. Subjects are "caught napping" by the short warning period. Conflicting reports about the effects of foreperiods on RT indicate a need for considerably more investigation. These effects might depend on the type of warning that is employed.

Mental Ability. Significant correlations between reaction time and mental ability of normal subjects have not been reported in the literature. Most studies show that reaction time and intelligence are positively related at low levels of ability. For example, Scott (1940) reported that normal children have shorter and less variable reaction times than retarded children of comparable chronological ages. Berkson (1963) also reported that mentally retarded children have consistently longer RTs than normal children and that latency is related to intelligence among defectives.

Among the mentally retarded, mental ability and reaction time are significantly related (Pascal, 1953; Ellis and Sloan, 1957). Bensberg and

Cantor (1957) suggested that this relationship might hold only for familial retardates. This is a logical finding, as brain-damaged retardates also have motor or sensory disabilities to one degree or another, which can mask the differences that result from intelligence. This finding has been supported by Dingman and Silverstein (1964), who reported that motor disability, rather than intelligence level, accounts for differences in RT in brain-damaged retardates.

Retardates appear to exhibit shorter reaction times if the stimulus is presented simultaneously in three different modalities, such as sound, vision, and touch (Holden, 1965). Further, the foreperiod appears to have some influence on retardates' ability to respond. Hermelin (1964) observed that it is difficult for retardates to maintain the set necessary for response after long foreperiods, but Terrell and Ellis (1964) reported that the differences between retardates and normals are diminished if the interval is lengthened. This view is supported by the results reported by Kellas (1967) and Baumeister and Hawkins (1966). The latter study further indicated that regular preparatory periods produce shorter RTs in retardates than irregular intervals. The effects of variations in preparatory periods were explained by the tendency of longer, irregular periods to distract the subjects. Berkson (1963) suggested that the longer RTs observed in retardates might be related to difficulty in the initiation or performance of a response rather than to slowness of sensory and central nervous system function. This hypothesis bears inquiry through research.

Perhaps the most significant difference is the greater variability of reaction times among retarded persons. Both intragroup variability and intraindividual variability have been reported to be greater for retarded subjects than for normal subjects (Berkson and Baumeister, 1967; Baumeister and Kellas, 1968*a*). Baumeister and Kellas (1968*b*) reported that performances of retardates are considerably more spread and more skewed than those of normal subjects (see Figure 5.4). In fact, the modal performances of the two groups were more nearly the same than their mean performances. The inferiority of retardates is better described by a lack of ability to maintain consistent performance than by a depressed level of performance. Inconsistency is even more pronounced if the warning interval is reduced (Nettelbeck and Lally, 1979).

Cerebral Palsy. Individuals with cerebral palsy react more slowly than normal persons do. Lehman (1971) found that cerebral palsied children are slower to react to visual and auditory stimuli than both educable mentally retarded and normal children.

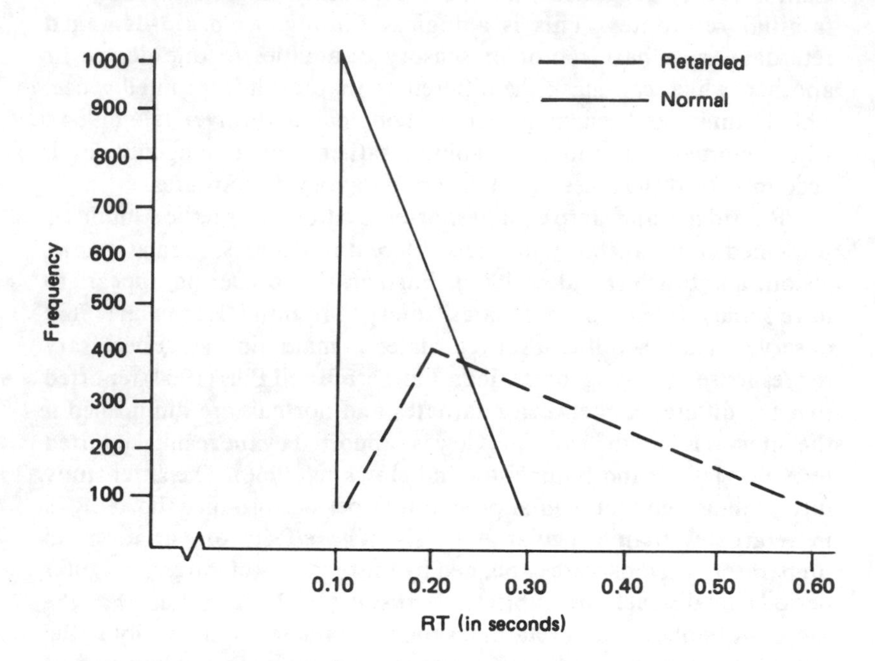

Figure 5.4. Reaction-time distribution of normal and retarded subjects. (Modified from Baumeister and Kellas, 1968*b*.)

Table 5.3. Reaction Times of Cerebral Palsied, Educable Mentally Retarded, and Normal Children (in seconds)

	CEREBRAL PALSIED	EDUCABLE RETARDED	NORMAL
Visual stimulus	0.286	0.230	0.208
Auditory stimulus	0.222	0.189	0.176

Data from Lehman, 1971.

A recent study by McLellan (1978) indicated that the mean reaction time of cerebral palsied persons is greater than that of normal individuals from 5 years to 35 years of age. Simple and choice RTs for tasks requiring accurate movements were measured in this study. At all age levels, increases in task complexity were found to lengthen RT in the same proportion for both groups.

In contrast, a study by Czudner and Rourke (1972) indicated that simple reaction time is greater among cerebral palsied children than among young normals but that older groups of cerebral palsied and normal individuals do not differ. The disagreement between these two studies might be accounted for by differences in experimental design or by problems of uniformity with cerebral palsied subjects. In any event, reaction times of cerebral palsied individuals and groups are more variable than those of normal persons.

Mental Illness. Persons who are clinically depressed also exhibit increased response latency. Psychomotor slowing has been observed in both clinical and experimental situations (Byrne, 1975, 1976). This slowing in the responses of depressed persons is believed to result from an impairment of central information processing mechanisms. Depressed patients can substantially improve their responses, however, if they are motivated (Colbert and Harrow, 1967). Martin and Rees (1966) reported a relationship between RT and the severity of the illness.

Stimulus Characteristics. The nature and complexity of the stimulus that elicits the response has a great effect on response latency. Reaction time varies according to which sense organs are stimulated and according to the intensity of the stimuli. Typical values for different senses are as follows. (Woodworth and Schlosberg, 1954):

Stimulus	*RT (in seconds)*
light	0.180
sound	0.140
touch	0.140

Cattell (1947) ranked the senses in the order of increasing RT: responses are produced fastest in reaction to stimuli that involve the sense of sound, followed by sight, pain, taste, smell, and touch. Slater-Hammel (1955) reported that kinesthetic RT (an arm movement) is less than RT to a light stimulus. Woodworth and Schlosberg (1954) and Cattell 1947) reported that RT varies with stimulus intensity: greater intensity produces shorter RT, to a point.

Stimulus complexity increases the length of time required to initiate a movement (Henry, 1961*b*; Crawford, 1962; Blair, 1970). A person can react faster to a series of rhythmical stimulus signals than to a comparable series of nonrhythmical signals (Wilson, 1959). The effects of temporal uncertainty, which is an index of the duration and variability of foreperiods, are shown in Figure 5.5. Situations that

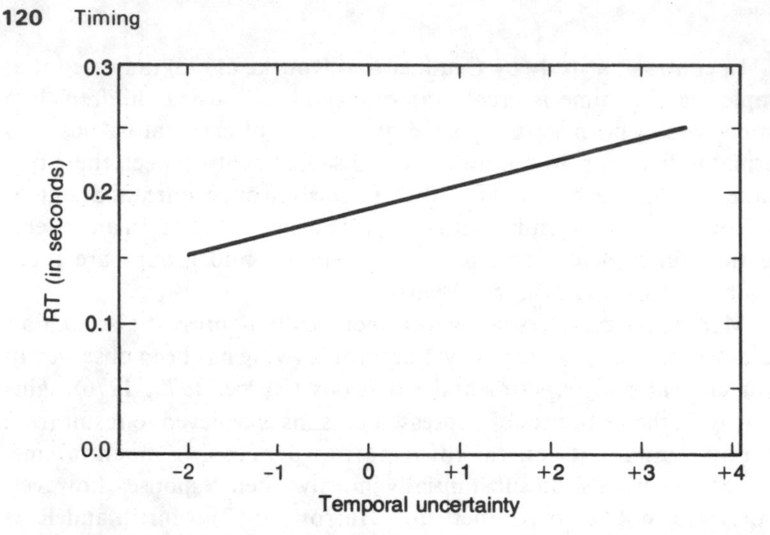

Figure 5.5. The influence of temporal uncertainty on RT. Temporal uncertainty is produced by combining the average length and variability of the warning interval. The reference point (0) represents a 1-second fixed interval; greater values of uncertainty are represented by positive numbers, and lesser values of uncertainty by negative numbers. (Data from Fitts and Posner, 1967.)

involve choice increase the length of the latency period. The amount of information contained in a stimulus is also an important determinant of RT. Hyman (1953) found that RT is related to the number of choices and other stimulus characteristics, so that there is a linear relationship between RT and information in the stimulus situation. Accordingly, if two stimulus-response situations are paired, a delay in the second RT is characteristic (Harrison, 1960; Kroll, 1961). The RT for the first response in the pair is also significantly longer than the simple RT for that task (Slater-Hammel, 1958). Fitts and Posner (1967) describe in detail these and other stimulus factors, such as stimulus-response compatibility (spatial and temporal congruence between stimulus and response) and noise, which affect the speed with which one can respond.

Response Characteristics. Just as characteristics of the stimulus initiating a response has a great effect on RT, so do characteristics of the response. As indicated above, stimulus-response compatibility, situations that involve choice, and the sequencing of RT tasks influence response latency. An increase in the complexity of responses increases RT (Henry, 1960, 1961*b*; Blair, 1970; Mendryk, 1960). The effect of movement complexity must be considered in the evaluation of studies that use RT as an indicator of performance.

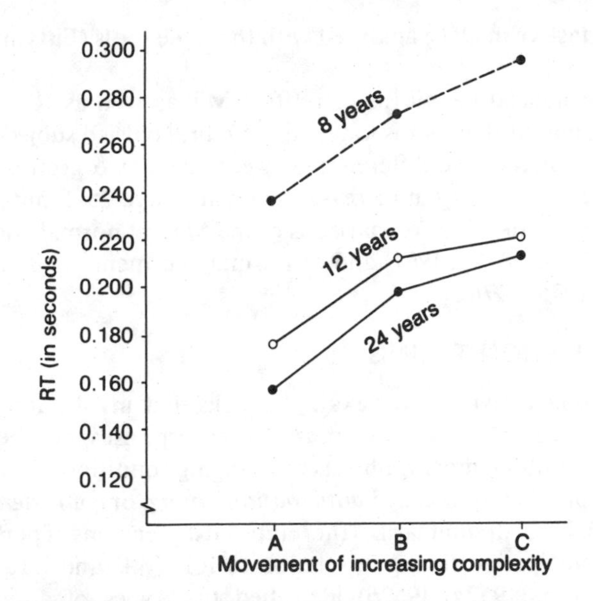

Figure 5.6. Increased reaction time accompanies movements of increased complexity. (Data from Henry, 1960.)

MOVEMENT TIME

Movement time represents the speed of performance. It is the period from the initiation of an overt response to the attainment of a goal or the completion of a required behavior. It is affected by learning, complexity of the experimental situation, and the state of the performer (Blair, 1970; Clarke, 1971; Fitts and Posner, 1967; Henry, 1960, 1961*a*; Mendryk, 1960; Wilson, 1959). Many of the same factors that influence RT also determine MT. Similarities in MT and RT of males and females were noted by Hodgkins (1963); males are faster, having shorter MTs as well as shorter RTs than females. MT decreases until early adulthood and then increases. Peak MT is maintained longer by males than by females, however.

Perhaps the most important determiners of MT are response amplitude, accuracy, and difficulty. The type of task is also significant. Serial and continuous tasks require longer MTs than discrete tasks, but further investigations are required to isolate the critical factors that are responsible for this difference. In any event, serial, continuous, and discrete tasks can all be analyzed with the same tools (Fitts and Posner, 1967).

Neurological handicaps can affect MT as well as RT. McLellan (1978) reported that MT is longer for cerebral palsied subjects than for normal subjects. The difference between these two groups decreases from age 5 to age 25 but increases again after age 25. Similar patterns have been reported in comparisons of the MTs of normal and retarded persons (Drowatzky, 1971) and of normal and mentally ill individuals (Byrne, 1975, 1976).

ANTICIPATION TIMING

In some activities—for example, tasks that involve intercepting a moving target—participants must form responses on the basis of predictions about moving objects or changing conditions. Timing based on such predictions is called *anticipation timing,* or *coincidence timing.* Figure 5.7, which summarizes the temporal dimensions of performance, shows anticipation timing in relation to RT, MT, and PT.

Poulton (1952*a*, 1952*b*) identified two types of anticipation—receptor and perceptual—and their differences were summarized by Adams (1966). Receptor anticipation involves a preview of forthcoming events, so that the performer can prepare for the immediate future. In receptor anticipation tasks, the stimulus events that control future

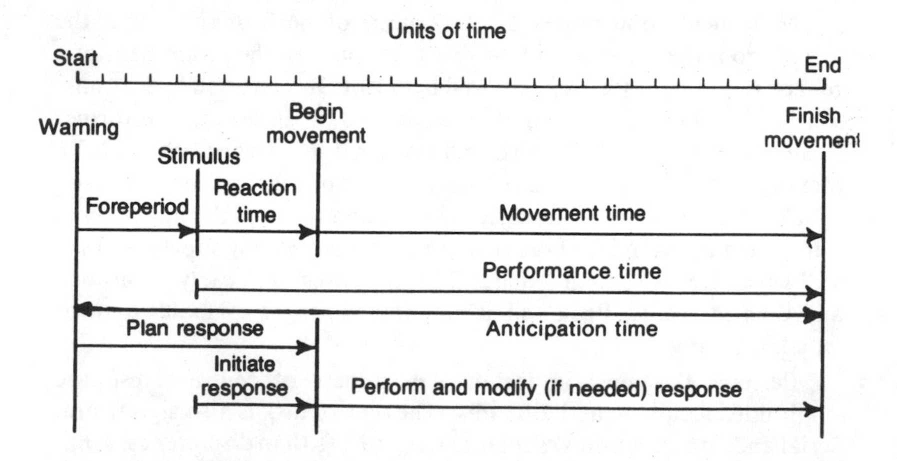

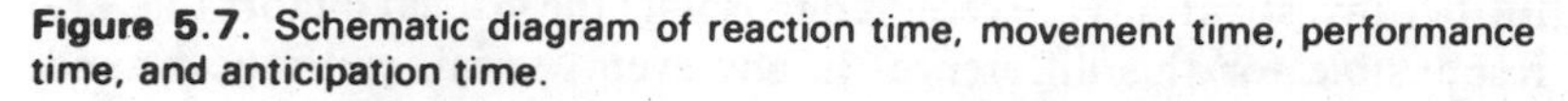
Figure 5.7. Schematic diagram of reaction time, movement time, performance time, and anticipation time.

responses are available for inspection in the present, while the responses are being planned. For example, a motorist who looks down the road and plans for a change in driving conditions uses this type of anticipation. Studies of receptor anticipation have yielded conflicting results. Leonard (1953) reported an improvement in performance after preview, but Guilford (1963) observed a decrement in performance.

Perceptual anticipation depends on learning. It operates in cases in which a performer has no advance information about stimulus conditions. Through experience one learns to recognize regularities in stimuli and can predict their temporal and spatial occurrence. If a performer has full information about the characteristics of the input as well as feedback from his or her responses, performance time shows the effects of anticipation. In tasks that do not facilitate anticipation, any improvement in performance is due to increased response proficiency rather than anticipation (Poulton, 1952*a*, 1952*b*).

Most research on perceptual anticipation timing has involved tracking skills. Adams (1966) concluded that proprioceptive stimuli serve a timing function as well as an internal feedback function in these types of tasks. According to Grose (1967), accuracy in finger and arm coincidence timing tasks failed to improve with practice although whole body movements did improve. The lack of improvement could be a function of greater familiarity with finger and arm movement rather than failure of anticipation or proprioception and the amount of learning in the task. (The tasks may have been too easy!) Knowledge of results has also been found to enhance performance in anticipation tasks (Belisle, 1963).

Performance in sports such as baseball and tennis is more closely related to anticipation timing than to RT. Reaction time might have little or no bearing on performance in these types of sports, in which decisions are made on the basis of some type of predicition or anticipation rather than on simple or choice RT. Success depends on the ability to predict where and when the ball will arrive and to time one's response accordingly. (The acquisition of this learning was discussed in Chapter 3, in connection with the progression-regression hypothesis.)

Whiting (1969, p. 13), disagreeing with the assumption that "keeping the eye on the ball" is essential for successful ball skills, asked,

1. Why do players need to look at the ball?
2. How long does a player need to focus visual attention on the ball in a particular skill?

3. At what stage(s) in the performance does attention need to be on the ball?
4. At what stage(s) in the performance should attention be directed from the ball to the target or other aspects of the display?

Besides questioning the need to keep the eye on the ball until the moment of contact, Whiting noted that it is not always physically possible for performers to do that. Some objects travel too fast to permit constant monitoring. Some are subject to rates of change in velocity (acceleration or deceleration) and therefore require constant adjustment on the part of the performer. In both cases, accurate predictions about flight characteristics are needed for successful performance. The progression-regression hypothesis explains this type of learning (see Fitts et al., 1961; Fuchs, 1962).

Several studies support Whiting's contention that anticipation time, or transit reaction time, is fundamental to the acquisition of ball skills. Taking into account the distance from pitcher to batter, speed of a fast overhand baseball throw, and RT of players, Whiting (1969) found that players with the shortest RTs would have to begin their swing when the ball is 20 feet away. Those with longer RTs would have to allow still more distance. If MT were added to the time involved, the figures would need further adjustment. This conclusion was supported by Miller and Shay (1964). They reported that, on the basis of softball-pitching velocity and mean RT of players, the swing would have to be initiated, on the average, when the ball is 29.33 feet from home plate. Hubbard and Seng (1954) found that it is impossible for professional baseball players to track a pitched ball near the plate. As a consequence, batters are faced with the following problems: (1) prediction of whether or not to swing; (2) decisions about where and when to initiate the swing; and (3) translation from the perceptual monitoring of ball flight into the approximately graded batting response (perceptual anticipation).

The fact that a performer cannot watch the ball to the point of contact with hands, foot, or implement should not be surprising or disturbing. Studies by Williams (1967, 1968) showed that visual-perceptual abilities involved in judging the flight of a ball are functionally mature by the age of 11 years and that children older than 9 years of age can accurately judge a ball's flight on the basis of an early part of the flight. Subjects from elementary school through college can accurately intercept a ball without observing the end of its flight.

Similar findings were reported by Noble (1966), who found that a golf swing could be successfully completed if the subject's view of the ball was limited to a few inches of the backswing. The skill is apparently programmed, and visual information is critical only in the early stages of learning.

If a complete view of the flight and contact of the ball is neither critical nor possible, why do performers maintain that they watch the ball until contact? Moss (1956) suggested that persons who carefully watch the flight of a tennis ball see it with an awareness of the impact between racquet and ball. A similar answer was proposed by Osgood (1964): if a batter can accurately predict a ball's path by seeing a part of its flight, then these visual cues may be merged with the proprioceptive cue from the ball's contact with the bat, to form an illusion of seeing the ball strike the bat and knowing where it will go. Many psychologists have shown that we use perceptions to fill gaps in our sensory information. This filling of gaps provides us with stability in our information.

What must a performer learn to be successful in anticipation timing tasks, such as those encountered in ball skills? The first principle is that one is dealing with an object traveling on a predictable path. A performer learns to judge the trajectory of the ball as he or she experiences the sequential dependencies (what follows what) of cues involving spin, velocity, acceleration, and direction. Secondary cues, such as the pitcher's motions during delivery and the speed at which a racquet is swung, can provide valuable information for the initial prediction. Once a prediction has been made about its course, watching the ball provides confirming information, rather than necessary input. Either it confirms that the ball has not deviated from its predicted path or it determines that a change has occurred. The confirming or disconfirming nature of these observations is exemplified by outstanding performers' complete surprise at missed or muffed shots of balls that follow strange directions with unusual flight characteristics. If such information provided necessary information, rather than confirmation, the performers would be able to adjust missed shots instead of being surprised.

Previews of task requirements can lead to increased timing accuracy and consistency in anticipation tasks (Christina and Buffan, 1976). Such experiences can help a performer acquire knowledge of the sequential dependencies of flight, which is required for success in anticipation tasks.

In a study of coincidence anticipation timing tasks, Dunham (1977) found that 7-year-old children are inferior to older children, that boys are more accurate than girls, and that the performance of all groups improves with practice. Other studies (Halsey and Porter, 1968; Jersild, 1968) suggest that such performance improves with age or maturation. Comparisons of boys and girls have yielded mixed results. Cratty and Martin (1969) reported differences between the sexes in coincidence anticipation tasks, but Bruce (1966), Williams (1968), and Stadulis (1971) did not observe such differences.

CORRELATIONS BETWEEN TIMING MEASURES

Reaction time, movement time, and anticipation time provide information about the temporal aspects of performance. Do they provide the same kinds of information? Are they related? If there were high correlations between timing measures, then a performer with a short RT would be expected to have short MT and anticipation time; that is, the performer would be generally fast. Timing measures have been used extensively in studies of generality versus specificity in motor learning (see Henry, 1958). These studies show, on the whole, that RT, MT, and anticipation timing are highly specific. In other words, timing measures appear to be independent, with little or no relationship among them.

Most of the studies cited in this chapter report intercorrelations of various RT and RT-MT tasks. For example, Grose (1967) found little or no relationship between RT and anticipation timing. Some of the highest intercorrelations were noted by Mendryk (1960), in a study of short-movement and long-movement tasks involving similar arm movements. He reported RT-MT correlations from .02 to .32 for a short movement, correlations between short-movement RT and long-movement RT from .53 to .67, and correlations between short-movement MT and long-movement MT from .41 to .60. Pierson (1959) observed a significant correlation (.56) between the RT and the MT of 400 males ranging in age from 8 to 83 years. He believed that this correlation might represent a function of maturity or employment, as the correlation for subjects older than 21 years (.63) differed from that for subjects younger than 21 years (.50).

The specificity of timing becomes more apparent in comparisons of movements involving different parts of the body. That is, correlations between timing measures are lower for such movements than for movements involving the same body part. For example, an RT-MT correlation of .02 was reported by Henry (1961*a*), and Lotter (1960) found that RT and MT of kicking and throwing movements are not correlated. Slater-Hammel (1952) obtained correlations from .07 to .17 between RT to light and MT of the arm. RT-MT correlations for four large muscles were found by Smith (1961) to range from .06 to .23.

Table 5.4 presents intercorrelations of RT, MT, and PT (performance time) for total body and arm-hand tasks. RT and MT are components of PT, and therefore they correlate more highly with it than with each other.

GUIDING PRINCIPLES FOR THE TEACHER

1. Timing involves temporal aspects of movement. It develops as one learns how movements relate to each other in time. Timing is necessary for a performance to be well coordinated. The performer must initiate a proper sequence of movements, each beginning and ending at the appropriate time.
2. The temporal dimension of movement depends on the development of an understanding of synchrony, rhythm, and sequencing. Synchrony marks the point of origin of a response or movement. Rhythm determines a temporal scale composed of equal, stable units. Movement in coordinated patterns is possible once sequencing has been developed, so that events can be organized on the basis of their temporal relationships.

Table 5.4. Intercorrelations of Reaction Time, Movement Time, and Performance Time for Total Body and Arm-Hand Tasks

	TOTAL BODY TIMES			ARM-HAND TIMES		
	RT	MT	PT	RT	MT	PT
Total body times						
RT		.20	.54	.44	.36	.53
MT			.73	.04	.18	.17
PT				.34	.41	.51
Arm-hand times						
RT					.10	.53
MT						.84
PT						

Modified from Clarke, 1971.

3. Speed and timing are frequently used to measure motor performance. Reaction time is the amount of time that passes between the presentation of a stimulus and the beginning of a response. Movement time is the time that elapses between the start of the response and its completion. The total, RT plus MT, is known as performance time, or response time. Anticipation timing measures an individual's ability to predict the location of a moving target and to respond so as to intercept the target or coincide with its predicted movement.

4. Reaction time, movement time, and anticipation timing are highly specific abilities. There is little or no relationship among these measures of timing.

5. Experimenters classify reaction time as either simple RT or choice RT. Simple RT is measured in situations in which a person makes a single, predetermined response to a single, predesignated stimulus. Choice RT is measured in situations in which an individual must discriminate among several stimuli and choose one or more movements in response. In either case, RT includes the time required for processes to occur in the sense organs, brain, nerves, and muscles. The greatest portion of the latency period occurs in the processing of incoming information in the brain, where responses are formed. The greater the amount of information to be evaluated or the more choices to be made, the longer the response latency.

6. A number of factors influence the amount of the response latency. Some are individual characteristics, such as age, sex, physical and mental characteristics, learning, and motivation. Other influences include task variables, such as the foreperiod, stimulus characteristics, the set of instructions that are given, and response characteristics.

7. Movement time is influenced by the same factors that determine response latency and also by the amount of response that is required and by the accuracy and difficulty of the response.

8. Two types of anticipation timing have been identified: receptor anticipation and perceptual anticipation. In receptor anticipation tasks, stimulus events that determine future responses are available in the present display. Perceptual anticipation tasks supply no advance information about stimulus conditions and depend on a performer's ability to learn where and when the stimulus will occur. This type of timing is required in many sports skills, particularly those involving balls.

9. In anticipation timing skills, such as those in ball games, performers must learn that the moving object follows a predictable path

and must be able to estimate its trajectory. Watching the ball only provides information to confirm or disconfirm the predictions. In addition, performers must learn how to use secondary cues to help predict the ball's flight.

SUMMARY

Knowledge of the temporal characteristics of performance must be combined with knowledge of its spatial characteristics if a successful response is to occur. Since every response requires time, these factors are frequently used by physical educators as measures of performance.

Reaction time is the time that elapses from the presentation of a stimulus to the beginning of an overt response. It is the time required to recognize a stimulus, process the information, and form a response. Simple RT tasks do not involve choices. Choice RT tasks require a subject to choose among stimuli or responses. Serial RT tasks are composed of a sequence of stimulus-response pairs. Reaction time is affected by many factors: age, sex, practice, set, foreperiod, physical and mental abilities, stimulus characteristics, and response characteristics.

Movement time begins with the initiation of an overt response and ends when the response has been completed. A performer can modify his or her responses during movement (except during short, fast, ballistic-type movements). Thus, MT is shorter for well-integrated and learned movements than for new, unfamiliar movements.

Performance time, or response time, is the sum of RT and MT.

Anticipation timing is involved in responses that are based on a performer's predictions about moving objects. It also depends on learning. Many sports skills, such as those that are required in tennis and baseball, involve this aspect of timing. Familiarity with flight characteristics and awareness of secondary cues (such as the pitcher's motion, the speed of the racquet, and the position of one's opponent) affect a performer's anticipation.

Teachers and coaches must be aware of the varying requirements of sports activities and must adjust their instruction or strategy accordingly. This requires careful analysis of characteristics of the stimulus and the response as well as an understanding of what must be learned in each situation—speed of response, speed of decision making, sensory set, or motor set.

REFERENCES

Adams, J. A. 1966. Some mechanisms of motor responding: An examination of attention. In *Acquisition of skill*, ed. E. A. Bilodeau. New York: Academic Press.

Baumeister, A. A., and Hawkins, W. F. 1966. Variations in the preparatory interval in relation to the reaction times of mental defectives. *American Journal of Mental Deficiency* 70:689-694.

Baumeister, A. A., and Kellas, G. 1968*a*. Intrasubject response variability in relation to intelligence. *Journal of Abnormal Psychology* 73:421-423.

———. 1968*b*. Distributions of reaction times of retardates and normals. *American Journal of Mental Deficiency* 72:715-718.

Belisle, J. J. 1963. Accuracy, reliability, and refractoriness in a coincidence-anticipation task. *Research Quarterly* 34:271-281.

Bensberg, G. J., and Cantor, G. N. 1957. Reaction time in mental defectives with organic and familial etiology. *American Journal of Mental Deficiency* 62:534-537.

Berkson, G. 1963. Psychophysiological studies in mental deficiency. In *Handbook of mental deficiency: Psychological theory and research*, ed. N. R. Ellis. New York: McGraw-Hill.

Berkson, G., and Baumeister, A. A. 1967. Reaction time variability of mental defectives and normals. *American Journal of Mental Deficiency* 72:262-266.

Blair, S. N. 1970. The effect of stimulus and movement complexity upon reaction time and movement time. In *Contemporary psychology of sport: Proceedings of the Second International Congress of Sport Psychology*, ed. G. S. Kenyon. Chicago: Athletic Institute.

Bruce, R. 1966. The effects of variations in ball trajectory upon catching performance of elementary school children. Doctoral dissertation, University of Wisconsin.

Byrne, D. G. 1975. Note on decision time/movement time relationships in normal and depressed subjects. *Perceptual and Motor Skills* 41:907-910.

———. 1976. Choice reaction times in depressive states. *British Journal of Social and Clinical Psychology* 15:149-156.

Cattell, J. McK. 1947. The influence of the intensity of the stimulus on the reaction time. *Brain* 9:512-515.

Christina, R. W., and Buffan, J. L. 1976. Preview and movement as determiners of timing a discrete motor response. *Journal of Motor Behavior* 8:101-112.

Clarke, H. H. 1971. *Physical and motor tests in the Medford boys' growth study*. Englewood Cliffs, N.J.: Prentice-Hall.

Clarkson, P. M., and Kroll, W. 1978. Practice effects on fractionated response time related to age and activity level. *Journal of Motor Behavior* 10:275-286.

Colbert, J., and Harrow, M. 1969. Psychomotor retardation in depressive syndromes. *Journal of Nervous and Mental Diseases* 145:405-419.

Cratty, B. J., and Martin, M. M. 1969. *Perceptual-motor efficiency in children*. Philadelphia: Lea & Febiger.

Crawford, A. 1962. The perception of light signals: The effect of the number of irrelevant lights. *Ergonomics* 5:417-428.

Czudner, G., and Rourke, B. P. 1972. Age differences in visual reaction of brain damaged and normal children under regular and irregular preparatory interval conditions. *Journal of Experimental Child Psychology* 13:516-526.

Dingman, H. F., and Silverstein, A. B. 1964. Intelligence, motor abilities and reaction time in the mentally retarded. *Perceptual and Motor Skills* 19:791-794.

Drowatzky, J. N. 1971. *Physical education for the mentally retarded*. Philadelphia: Lea & Febiger.

Dunham, P., Jr. 1977. Age, sex, speed, and practice in coincidence-anticipation performance of children. *Perceptual and Motor Skills* 45:187-193.

Ellis, N. R., and Sloan, W. 1957. Relationship between intelligence and simple reaction time in mental defectives. *Perceptual and Motor Skills* 7:65-67.

Fitts, P. M., and Posner, M. I. 1967. *Human performance*. Monterey, Calif.: Brooks/Cole.

Fitts, P. M., Bukrich, H. P., Noble, M. E., and Briggs, A. E. 1961. *Skilled performance*. New York: John Wiley and Sons.

Fuchs, A. H. 1962. The progression-regression hypothesis in perceptual motor skill learning. *Journal of Experimental Psychology* 63:177-182.

Gibson, M. A., Karpovich, P. V., and Gollnick, P. D. 1961. Effect of training upon reflex and reaction time. Unpublished paper, Department of Physiology, Springfield College, Springfield, Mass. Cited by H. T. A. Whiting, *Acquiring ball skill: A psychological interpretation*, Philadelphia: Lea & Febiger, 1969.

Grose, J. E. 1967. Timing control and finger, arm and whole body movements. *Research Quarterly* 38:10-21.

Guilford, R. N. 1963. Tracking performance of the human operator with advanced and delayed visual displays. Master's thesis, University of California, Los Angeles.

Hale, D. J. 1967. Sequential analysis of effects of time uncertainty on choice reaction time. *Perceptual and Motor Skills* 25:285-288.

Halsey, E., and Porter, L. 1968. *Physical education for children*. Englewood Cliffs, N.J.: Prentice-Hall.

Harris, G., and Lown, B. 1968. Interitem time distribution and response compatibility in the short term serial retention of digits. *Psychonomic Science* 10:295-296.

Harrison, J. S. 1960. Psychological refractoriness and the latency time of two consecutive motor responses. *Research Quarterly* 31:590-600.

Hawkins, W. F., Baumeister, A. A., and Holland, J. M. 1965. Reaction time in retardates following variations in warning signal intensity and preparatory interval. *American Journal of Mental Deficiency* 70:135-138.

Henry, F. M. 1958. Specificity vs. generality in learning motor skills. *National College Physical Education Association for Men Proceedings* 61:126-128.

———. 1960. Influence of motor and sensory sets on reaction latency and speed of discrete movements. *Research Quarterly* 31:459-468.

———. 1961*a*. Reaction time-movement time correlations. *Perceptual and Motor Skills* 12:63-66.

———. 1961*b*. Stimulus complexity, movement complexity, age, and sex in relation to reaction latency and speed in limb movements. *Research Quarterly* 32:353-366.

Henry, F. M., and Rogers, D. E. 1960. Increased response latency for complicated movement and a "memory drum" theory of neuromotor reaction. *Research Quarterly* 31:448-458.

Hermelin, B. 1964. Effects of variations in the warning signal on reaction time of severe subnormals. *Quarterly Journal of Experimental Psychology* 16:241-249.

Hodgkins, J. 1963. Reaction time and speed of movement in males and females of various ages. *Research Quarterly* 34:335-343.

Holden, E. A., Jr. 1965. Reaction time during unimodal and trimodal stimulation in educable retardates. *Journal of Mental Deficiency Research* 9:183-190.

Hovland, C. I. 1938. Experimental studies in rote learning theory: II. Reminiscence with varying speeds of syllable presentation. *Journal of Experimental Psychology* 22:338-353.

Hubbard, A. W., and Seng, C. N. 1954. Visual movements of batters. *Research Quarterly* 25:42-57.

Hyman, R. S. 1953. Stimulus information as a determinant of reaction time. *Journal of Experimental Psychology* 45:188-196.

Jersild, A. T. 1968. *Child psychology*. Englewood Cliffs, N.J.: Prentice-Hall.

Karlin, L. 1959. Reaction time as a function of foreperiod duration and variability. *Journal of Experimental Psychology* 58:185-191.

Kellas, G. 1967. The effects of warning signal duration on the reaction times of mental defectives. Master's thesis, University of Alabama.

Keller, L. P. 1940. The relation of quickness in bodily movement to success in athletics. Doctoral dissertation, New York University.

Kephart, N. C. 1964. Perceptual motor aspects of learning disabilities. *Exceptional Children* 31:201-206.

Knapp, B. 1961. Simple reaction time of selected topclass sportsmen and research students. *Research Quarterly* 32:409-412.

Kroll, W. 1961. Relationship of interval of time between paired auditory and visual stimuli and reaction time. *Research Quarterly* 32:367-381.

Lehman, J. 1971. Visual perception and information processing in the cerebral palsied as contrasted with normal and mentally retarded children. Master's thesis, University of Toledo.

Leonard, J. A. 1953. Advance information in sensori-motor skills. *Quarterly Journal of Experimental Psychology* 5:141-149.

Lotter, W. S. 1960. Interrelationships among reaction times and speed of movement in different limbs. *Research Quarterly* 31:147-155.

Lueft, R. J. 1970. The effect of experimental design upon expectancy and speed of response. In *Contemporary psychology of sport: Proceedings of the Second International Congress of Sport Psychology*, ed. G. S. Kenyon. Chicago: Athletic Institute.

McCormack, P. D., Binding, F. R. S., and McElhearn, W. G. 1963. Effects on reaction time of partial knowledge of results of performance. *Perceptual and Motor Skills* 17:279-281.

McLellan, J. C. 1978. Information processing ability of the cerebral palsied individual as a function of increasing age and stimulus complexity. Ph.D. dissertation, University of Toledo.

Martin, I., and Rees, L. 1966. Reaction times and somatic reactivity in depressed patients. *Journal of Psychosomatic Research* 9:375-382.

Mendryk, S. 1960. Reaction time, movement time, and task specificity relationships at ages 12, 22, and 48 years. *Research Quarterly* 31:156-162.

Miller, R. G., and Shay, C. T. 1964. Relationship of reaction time to the speed of a softball. *Research Quarterly* 35:433-437.

Moss, E. 1956. *Lawn tennis: How to discover and correct faults*. London: Link House Publications.

Mowrer, O. H. 1941. Preparatory set (expectancy)—further evidence of its central locus. *Journal of Experimental Psychology* 28:116 133.

Nash, E. L., Phelan, J. G., Demas, G., and Bittner, A. 1966. Effects of manifest and induced anxiety and experimenter variability on simple reaction time. *Perceptual and Motor Skills* 22:483-487.

Nettelbeck, T., and Lally, M. 1979. Age, intelligence, and inspection time. *American Journal of Mental Deficiency* 83:398-401.

Noble, C. E. 1966. Selective learning. In *Acquisition of skill*, ed. E. A. Bilodeau. New York: Academic Press.

Noble, D. 1966. Unpublished data, Loughborough University of Technology. Cited by H. T. A. Whiting, *Acquiring ball skill: A psychological interpretation*. Philadelphia: Lea & Febiger, 1969.

Norrie, M. L. 1967. Practice effects on reaction latency for simple and complex movements. *Research Quarterly* 38:79-85.

Osgood, C. E. 1964. *Method and theory in experimental psychology*. New York: Oxford University Press.

Pascal, G. R. 1953. The effect of a disturbing noise on the reaction time of mental defectives. *American Journal of Mental Deficiency* 57:691-699.

Pierson, W. R. 1959. The relationship of movement time and reaction time from childhood to senility. *Research Quarterly* 30:227 231.

Posner, M. I. 1966. Components of skilled performance. *Science* 152:1712-1718.

Poulton, E. C. 1952*a*. Perceptual anticipation in tracking with two pointer and one pointer displays. *British Journal of Psychology* 43:222-229.

———. 1952*b*. The basis of perceptual anticipation in tracking. *British Journal of Psychology* 43:295-302.

Raab, D. H., Fehrer, E., and Hershenson, M. 1961. Visual reaction time and the Broca-Sulzer phenomenon. *Journal of Experimental Psychology* 61:193 199.

Scott, W. S. 1940. Reaction time in young intellectual deviates. *Archives of Psychology* 35:1 64.

Simon, J. R., and Slaviero, D. P. 1975. Differential effects of a foreperiod countdown procedure in simple and choice reaction time. *Journal of Motor Behavior* 7:9 14.

Slater-Hammel, A. T. 1952. Reaction time and speed of movement. *Perceptual Motor Skills Research Exchange* 4:110-113.

———. 1955. Comparisons of reaction time measures to a visual stimulus and arm movement. *Research Quarterly* 26:470 479.

———. 1958. Psychological refractory period in simple paired response. *Research Quarterly* 29:468 481.

Smith, L. E. 1961. Reaction time and movement time in four large muscle movements. *Research Quarterly* 32:88 92.

Stadulis, R. E. 1971. Coincidence anticipation behavior of children. Doctoral dissertation, Teachers College, Columbia University.

Terrell, C., and Ellis, N. R. 1964. Reaction times in normal and defective subjects following varied warning conditions. *Journal of Abnormal and Social Psychology* 69:449 452.

Underwood, B. J. 1966. *Experimental psychology*. 2d ed. New York: Appleton-Century-Crofts.

Welford, A. T. 1958. *Aging and human skill.* Westport, Conn.: Greenwood Press.

Whiting, H. T. A. 1969. *Acquiring ball skill: A psychological interpretation*. Philadelphia: Lea & Febiger.

Whitley, J. D. 1966. Faster reaction time through increasing intent to respond. *Perceptual and Motor Skills* 22:663 666.

Williams, H. G. 1967. The perception of moving objects by children. Unpublished manuscript, University of Toledo.

———. 1968. The effects of systematic variation of speed and direction of object flight and of skill and age classifications upon visuo-perceptual judgments of moving objects in three-dimensional space. Doctoral dissertation, University of Wisconsin, Madison.

Wilson, D. J. 1959. Quickness of reaction and movement related to rhythmicity or nonrhythmicity of signal presentation. *Research Quarterly* 30:101 109.

Woodworth, R. S., and Schlosberg, H. 1954. *Experimental psychology*. Rev. ed. New York: Holt, Rinehart and Winston.

Young, J. D., and Skemp, M. G. 1959. A comparison of peripheral vision reaction time of athletes and nonathletes in relationship to the colors of red and green. Master's thesis, University of Wisconsin.

Zahn, T. P., Rosenthal, D., and Shakow, D. 1963. Effects of irregular preparatory intervals on reaction time in schizophrenia. *Journal of Abnormal and Social Psychology* 67:44 52.

6 Information Processing

In our day-to-day lives, we are vitally concerned with receiving input from the environment and using that input to form a response to deal with or modify the environment. Many linguistic, occupational, sports, and recreational skills can be classed as information-processing skills. Information is received from the environment in the form of physical energy (light, pressure, etc.), which is transduced by the sense organs into neural excitation, is stored in memory, and finally is transformed into overt responses. Most information processing results in movement, whether it be fine movement (such as the motions involved in writing and speaking) or gross movement (involving the large muscles of the body).

Fitts and Posner (1967) have specified three forms of information-processing activity:

1. the conservation or transmission of information
2. the reduction of information
3. the creation or elaboration of information

Information conservation is processing in which information received from external stimuli is communicated by the subject's response. In some information conservation tasks, output (e.g., speech or movements) transmits received information so completely that the stimulus can be inferred precisely from the response. Examples include a secretary taking dictation or transcribing a letter and a coach scouting a game, making diagrams on paper, and translating the diagrams into formations on the field.

Information reduction is processing in which only a portion of the received information is selected for attention while the rest is ignored. It is perhaps best illustrated by the example of writing a book report or an abstract of an article. Thinking, reasoning, decision making, and problem solving all require information reduction. For example, a tennis player pays attention only to certain aspects of the environment during a match. A coach uses information reduction to write a scouting report, and a teacher uses it to guide students toward correct performances.

The creation or elaboration of information is processing in which the subject's immediate experience of a stimulus is augmented by information that has been stored in memory. For example, a performer creates information during a performance as he or she brings order out of an existing array of information. A coach builds on existing information, obtained from scouting reports and game films, to construct a game plan.

THE SENSORIMOTOR SYSTEM

A skilled performer can be viewed as a functional system, receiving information, processing it, and developing appropriate responses. Welford (1976) attempted to integrate research on the principal mechanisms of skill. His diagram of a hypothetical human sensorimotor system (see Figure 6.1) includes representations of identifiable body structures as well as functions that cannot presently be located in particular sites in the brain. The left side of the diagram represents the sense organs, which receive information from both the external and the internal environment. Input ranges from visual and auditory signals to proprioceptive signals to internal states of blood chemistry. The sense organs transduce the received energy into neural impulses. The right side of the diagram represents the effectors, which include voluntary muscles, involuntary muscles, glands, and other response mechanisms that are not normally under voluntary control.

Welford suggested that various mechanisms (i.e., the central nervous sytem) mediate between sensory input and effector output. These central mechanisms deal with the formation of perceptions, the

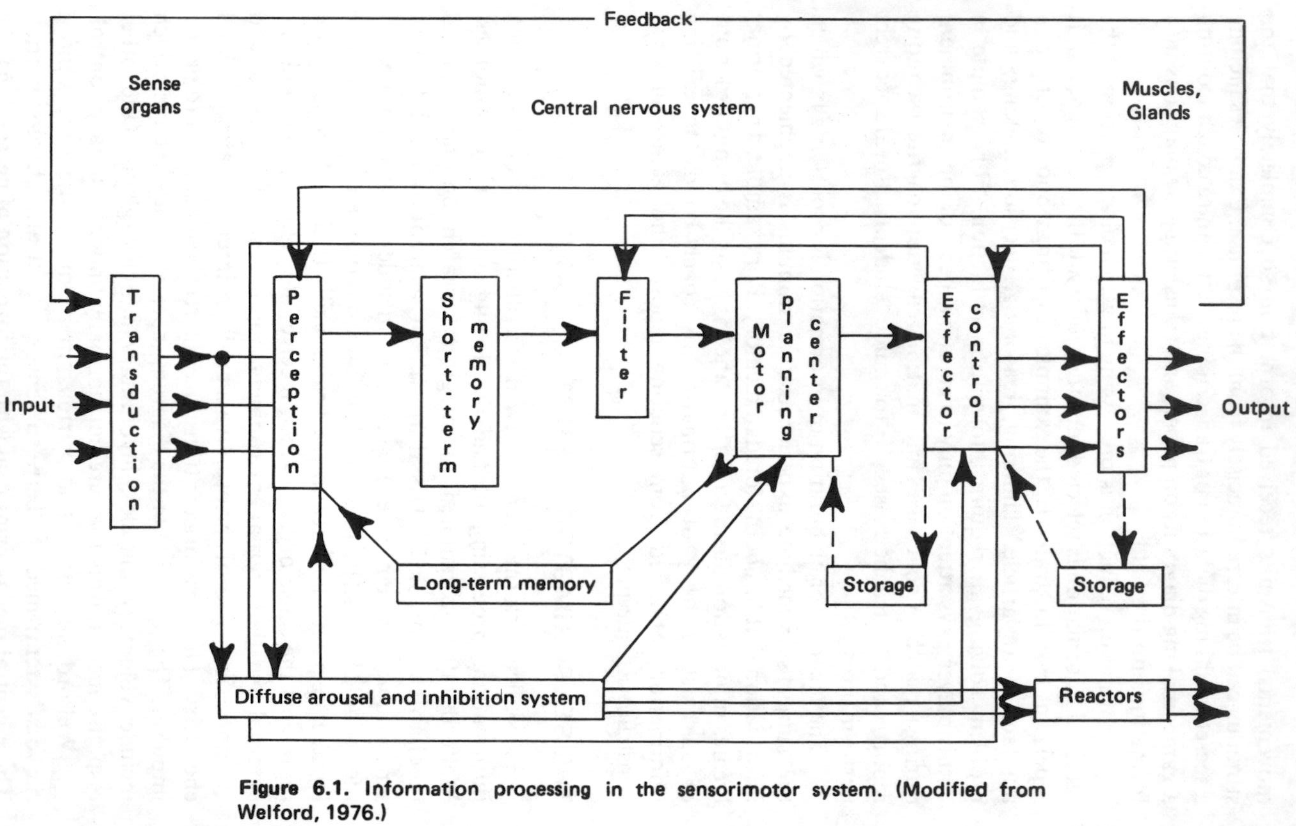

Figure 6.1. Information processing in the sensorimotor system. (Modified from Welford, 1976.)

translation of perception into action, and the control of action. They are actively involved in the conservation, reduction, and creation of information. Sensations acquire meanings and thereby become perceptions, information is stored in memory, the motor planning center translates perceptions into choices of responses, and effector control is maintained by central mechanisms.

Limits of Information Processing

Our ability to perform is limited. In spite of the remarkable feats of memory demonstrated by mnemonists and the great capacity for movement control exhibited by outstanding artists and athletes, their performances are limited. Human performance is constrained by limitations of time and limitations of space (Posner and Keele, 1970; Keele, 1973; Posner, 1973).

Limitations of time affect the storage of information in memory. Information can be held in either short-term sensory storage, short-term memory, or long-term memory. Short-term sensory storage lasts for a few seconds, short-term memory persists for 10 or 20 seconds, and long-term memory is more permanent. A second temporal limitation relating to storage arises from the fact that some time is required for information to be transformed from one form into another.

Other time limitations are imposed on the retrieval of information from memory. The minimum reaction time which elapses from the presentation of a signal to the initiation of a response, is approximately 0.15 seconds. Any complications, such as choices or unfavorable conditions, increase the latency period.

Finally, any movement requires time for performance. Controlled movements and complicated movements take more time than ballistic movements or simple movements do.

Limitations of space also affect information processing. Psychologists determine that a task requires neural space if it cannot be performed simultaneously with another. Performance of the one task interferes with the processing required for the other. Some tasks involve no such interference, in which case one or both of them require no neural space. For example, walking can be carried on simultaneously with talking. Intensive sports competition or typing, however, interfere with conversation. Interference occurs despite the fact that these tasks use different sensory and motor systems. Therefore, it is inferred that the interference occurs at a central level and that some process in both activities takes space, so that simultaneous performance without interference is impossible (Keele, 1973).

Attention imposes similar limitations on information processing. If a person directs attention to one thing, he or she cannot simultaneously pay attention to another. Therefore, tasks that demand attention interfere with each other during simultaneous performances.

MENTAL OPERATIONS

To make responses that depend on thought, we must be able to reorganize information, use representations that have been stored in memory, and develop new structures to interpret the world around us. These processes are called *mental operations*. Posner (1973, p. 92) defined them as "an internal transformation of information from one form into another." Transformation does not destroy existing structures. It creates new structures, which are coded in persistent, abstract representations and placed in memory. Piaget and Inhelder (1969) have argued that mental operations are reversible in principle but that reversal may not be possible in practice because of forgetting.

Current psychological research measures and traces the sequence of mental operations because of their relevance to temporal and spatial requirements for the processing of information. Many of these studies involve rather complicated reaction time paradigms.

Mental operations can be considered to have four stages (see Figure 6.2):

1. The stimulus is abstracted, and a representation of it is formed.
2. The memory is searched, as the abstraction is checked.
3. The appropriate response is chosen.
4. The response is initiated.

Abstraction of the Stimulus

A stimulus can be abstracted in at least two ways. A performer can select one part of the input to attend to and ignore other parts. A performer can also classify the input into general rather than specific categories. Very complex manipulations of visual operations can be performed, and the time required for the manipulation depends on the task (Shepard and Metzler, 1971).

The qualitative form of stored information is called *coding*. *Images* are internal representations, which closely correspond to sensory experiences. Images in the visual modality are *iconic codes* and auditory images are *echoic codes*. Memory codes for motor activity have been called *enactive codes* (Bruner, Oliver, and Greenfield, 1966), *memory drum* (Henry and Rogers, 1960), and *motor programs* (Keele, 1968).

Search of Memory

The simplest mental operation is recognition. For example, incoming visual information interacts with previously formed iconic concepts, and in the process new iconic concepts are formed and modified. The visual form thus produces the experience of recognition. That is, we recognize the form without knowing its name. Apparently, the iconic code is contacted, but the association with a name is not activated. Such associations are often believed to involve verbal descriptions of information.

Operations that are more complex than recognition involve a search of either short-term or long-term memory. A performer's efficiency often depends on the rapidity with which information about the appropriate response can be retrieved from memory. Thus, the time and attention required for retrieval influence one's efficiency.

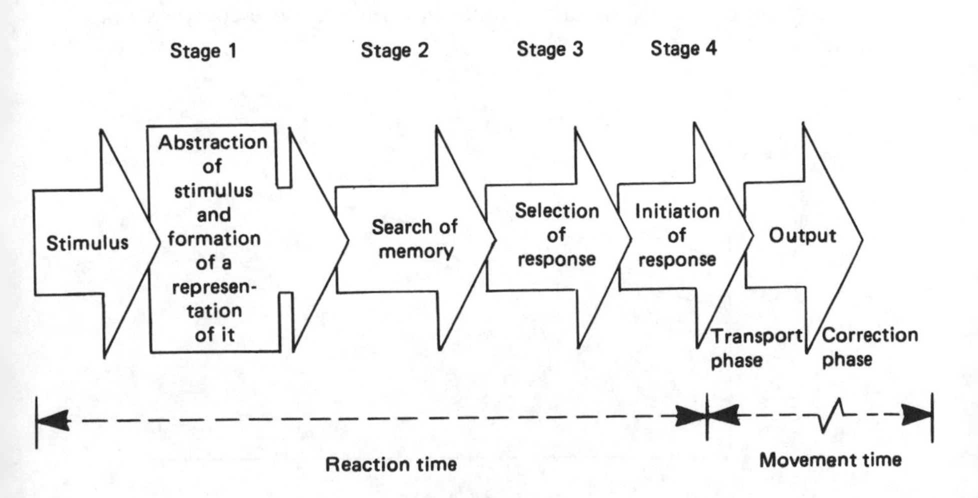

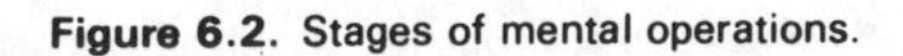
Figure 6.2. Stages of mental operations.

Search can involve finding and identifying a pattern out of an array of stimuli, or it can involve matching a pattern in the input with one that is stored and linked to a response. A performer must initially search through the stimuli in the visual field and then search through his or her memory for an appropriate association. Chase and Posner (1965) compared rates of visual field search with rates of memory search and found that they are just about the same (see Figure 6.3). As the size of the visual array increases, reaction time increases for both visual field searches and memory searches (Hick, 1952).

As a performer becomes familiar with the stimuli level, overlearned sets are placed into memory, and the search process tends to become increasingly rapid. The duration of the search does not appear to increase as the number of items to be searched increases (Neissen, Novick, and Lazar, 1963). This reduced search requirement for highly skilled persons is one factor that contributes to their exceptional performances.

Selection of a Response

In the formation of motor responses, incoming data are treated in both spatial and temporal terms, apparently in a single operation (Welford, 1976). This ordering allows complex data to be processed as a unitary whole and improves the ability to discriminate a pattern from the irrelevant background (Thierman, 1968). One type of ordering is the recombination of several simple cues into fewer, more complex ones (Fuchs, 1962).

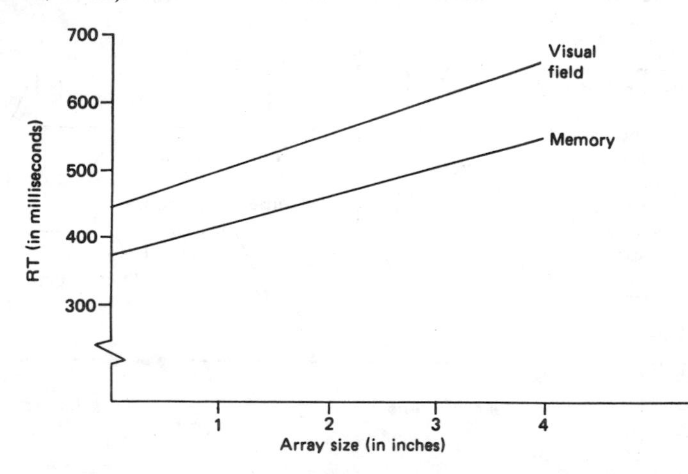

Figure 6.3. A comparison of visual field search and memory search in arrays of increasing size. (Modified from Chase and Posner, 1965.)

The incoming data are then compared with information stored in the memory, and some familiar category is applied to them. If the category appears to fit the data adequately, the responses associated with the stored information are selected and carried out. People can make an amazing variety of responses. In fact, Paillard (1960) indicated that our responses are never identical and that no two movement patterns, repeated twice in succession, are strictly superposable. The selection of a particular response pattern probably depends on the recency of its use, the degree of learning, and other factors.

Initiation of the Response

The exact manner in which a given response is selected and initiated from the great variety of potential responses is not well understood. Some authors have suggested that voluntary movements can be viewed in terms of hierarchical organization (Bryan and Harter, 1899; Welford, 1968; Easton, 1972, 1975). According to one version of this hypothesis, reflex patterns could form the basis for voluntary movements. Elemental reflexes that approximate desired movements might be coupled with adjusting reflexes, which introduce biasing and fine adjustments. This hypothesis indicates that the reflex substrate can be initiated either by a command issued centrally or by peripheral input (Hayes and Marteniuk, 1976).

The hypothesis of motor programming is another attempt to explain the selection and initiation of responses (Keele, 1968, 1973; Henry and Rogers, 1960; Schmidt, 1975; Lashley, 1917). A motor program is defined as a well-coordinated sequence of subroutines that operate together to control movement and are not dependent on feedback (Hayes and Marteniuk, 1976). According to Keele (1973), when neither visual nor kinesthetic feedback is used, movement patterns are represented centrally in the brain or, sometimes, in the spinal cord. These internal representations are motor programs.

No matter which of the two hypotheses we accept, responses can result from activity that is initiated either centrally or peripherally. The existence of motor programs and the manner in which responses are initiated is still open to debate (Drowatzky and McLellan, 1978; Pew, 1974; Schmidt, 1975; Adams, 1976; Drowatzky, 1976). These authors generally view motor responses as feedback-controlled movements based on a reference mechanism that provides general direction and extent. This reference system is generally believed to involve some type of verbal mediation that links feedback with movements.

MOTOR CONTROL

Mental operations begin when a stimulus is detected and end when the response is initiated. After the response has begun, the problem remains for the performer to control the movement until it is completed. Motor control is better understood in its physiological-anatomical aspect than in its psychological-cognitive aspect.

Open-Loop Control and Closed-Loop Control

The motor program hypothesis is one theoretical model to explain how we control our movements. According to this theory, a motor program is a central representation of movements, by which a movement sequence can be initiated and carried out without subsequent kinesthetic feedback, in the absence of error. Some skills are thought to be directly programmed, and subsidiary programming might be used to produce precise termination of movements. For human skills, however, the environment is unpredictable and performance less than perfect. Therefore, feedback remains a part of the picture, and motor programs are best viewed as schema of possible movements and expected feedback (Keele and Summers, 1976).

Controls such as motor patterns have been described as *open-loop systems:* they do not use feedback or other mechanisms for the regulation of errors. Information enters as input, the system effects its transformations on the input, and the system produces output. Motor programs have been proposed to explain the performance of everyday skills. They include event-to-event structures (formed through direct associations in simple skills) and high-order, or hierarchical, structures (formed in complex situations). Timing, in the form of rhythm, plays a role in motor programs, although speed does not. Rhythms are defined as symmetrical, hierarchical patterns in which elements of the response occur at equal time intervals (Martin, 1972).

Closed-loop systems, which incorporate feedback through verbal mediation or verbal responses, have also been proposed to account for motor control. For example, Adams (1971, p. 115) noted that "humans covertly guide their motor behavior with verbal responses. . . . That we talk to ourselves, form hypotheses and instruct ourselves is a kind of covert guidance which fails to fit the S-R [open-loop] model." Feedback, error detection, and error correction are key elements of Adams's closed-loop system. Output, in the form of feedback, is compared with a reference, or model, so that errors (deviations from the model) can be detected and corrected. A closed-loop system is thus self-regulating. Knowledge of results and a memory trace based on such knowledge are necessary for the initiation of a movement. After the movement has begun, perception and feedback regulate it.

Research

Some form of storage code or memory code is important in response selection and control. Manis (1966) indicated that not only do we use symbolic representations of our problems, but we also form symbolic representations of possible responses. In this manner we try out various behaviors before taking any overt action. Thus, movements are produced and controlled through one or more memory codes.

Posner (1973) has distinguished several types, including iconic, echoic, enactive, imagery, and symbolic codes. Iconic codes are associated with visual modalities, echoic codes with auditory modalities. Enactive codes are motor programs, also called schemata (Pew, 1966, 1974), that is, codes that preserve motor activity. In adults, it is difficult to isolate motor codes from other types of codes. Imagery codes are internal representations that closely resemble the sensory experiences that produced them. Symbolic codes stand for or suggest something else by reason of an arbitrary relationship rather than by reason of resemblance; language is a prime example.

On the basis of a series of reaction time experiments, Henry and Rogers (1960) proposed the memory drum model for movement control. According to this view, a reaction must be viewed as a whole; it cannot be separated into a series of successive mental and motor acts. A well-learned response is controlled by a stored program. An unlearned response does not have a stored program but is "carried out under conscious control in an awkward, step-by-step, uncoordinated manner" (p. 449). Consequently, reaction time is longer for poorly learned responses than for well-learned ones and longer for responses that require complex movements than for those that are composed of simple movements. Henry and Rogers argued that well-learned programs are more readily selected than poorly learned ones and that complex programs require more time for processing than simple ones.

Henry and Rogers supported this model with an examination of reaction times. According to the memory drum theory, processing time would increase with an increase in the complexity of the task. This increase in reaction time was observed at all age levels (see Table 6.1). The relation between reaction time and task complexity is preserved despite the fact that adults' reactions are faster than younger subjects'.

Table 6.1. Mean Reaction Time for Tasks of Increasing Complexity

AGE (IN YEARS)	REACTION TIME (IN MILLISECONDS)		
	Task A (Least Complex)	Task B (Moderately Complex)	Task C (Most Complex)
8	226.0	264.0	282.5
12	168.5	207.5	220.0
24	151.0	191.5	206.0

Data from Henry and Rogers, 1960.

The faster reactions of adults were attributed to their greater experience and better developed programs. Other studies (Harrison, 1960; Henry and Harrison, 1961; Williams, 1971, 1973, 1975) have provided further support for the memory drum theory under different conditions. Once a response has been selected, control is exercised through the memory drum in open-loop fashion.

Pew (1966) described a gradual shift in control of the visual system during the learning of a tracking skill. Early in practice subjects appeared to use a closed-loop control, which was highly dependent on feedback. After a few weeks of practice, however, they appeared to adopt an open-loop control, in which movement apparently was not under visual control, although visual feedback was used periodically to make corrections. Other subjects adopted a type of control that Pew termed *modulation,* by which rapid, regular movements are somewhat modulated. The important aspect of this study is that more than one method was used to control movements.

Similar results have been reported by others. Laszlo and Manning (1970) found that subjects use all available information during learning. These authors reported that the presence or absence of positive feedback results in the use of two separate closed-loop units and that subjects use different strategies, depending on which loop is available. This study also indicated that learning does occur under the control of central mechanisms, independently of the peripheral feedback loops, but that positive feedback does not affect performance if the peripheral loops are eliminated.

Kerr (1975) argued that motor programs must be redefined to include skills that require feedback and processing capacity. In a study of the execution phase of the movement of a stylus through a semicircular track, she concluded that if the route signal is known prior to initiation of a movement, the processing demands during the execution for one- and two-choice conditions do not differ. Subjects select and organize their response prior to the execution phase, with no further capacity requirements. The movement of the stylus through the track to a stop was not automated, however.

Looking at the control of aimed movements, Klapp (1975) concluded that long movements are controlled by feedback while short movements are predominantly ballistic and programmed. This conclusion was based on the observation that for movements through a short distance, reaction times decrease with increases in the size of the target; for greater movement lengths, however, reaction time is not affected by target size (see Table 6.2). Klapp further suggested the possibility that both programming and feedback control are involved in short movements.

After a review of literature, Welford (1976) suggested that two control processes or phases of movement should be distinguished. First is the transport phase, in which distance-covering movements are initiated. These pick up speed as they proceed, until the onset of the correction phase, in which movements become slower as they are guided toward contact with the target (see Figure 6-4).

Welford's view is congruent with an earlier proposal by Megaw (1972), who found that both the central and peripheral controls guide short-duration ballistic movements after they are selected. Megaw suggested two levels of response control. The first level produces muscle activity sequencing, and the second controls the fine details of the activity.

Miles and Evarts (1979) reported that the oculomotor system is subject to both open-loop and closed-loop control. These independent

Table 6.2. Reaction Times for Various Target Sizes and Movement Lengths (in milliseconds)

	MOVEMENT LENGTH			
TARGET DIAMETER	2 mm	11 mm	70 mm	336 mm
Small (2 mm, 4 mm)	374	347	322	327
Medium (8 mm, 16 mm)	327	336	318	329
Large (32 mm, 64 mm)	304	299	307	323

Data from Klapp, 1975.

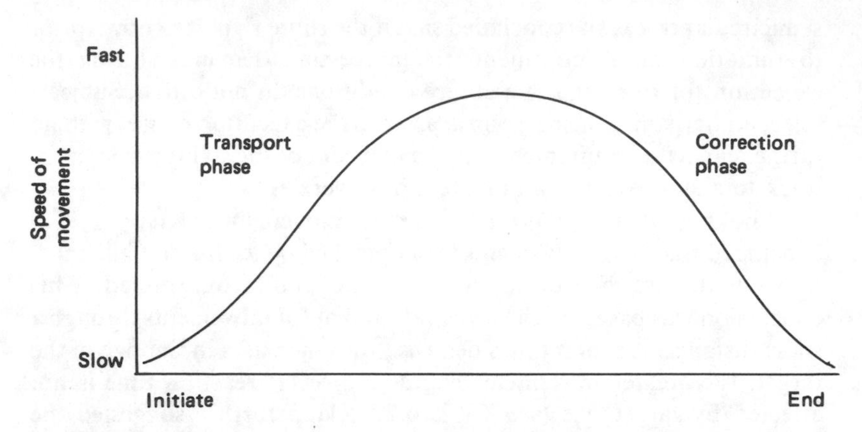

Figure 6.4. Relationship between the phase of movement and speed of movement.

and complimentary controls are mediated by two different modalities. The open-loop system deals with images that shift at high velocities (for example, images received as the head turns) and provides coarse control. The closed-loop system is slower and provides fine control by its sensitivity to low-velocity shifts in residual images. This arrangement enables the oculomotor system to take advantage of the speed of open-loop control and eliminates its disadvantage of lack of immediate error correction. The closed loop provides correction, and its slowness in reaction is overcome by the use of the open-loop system.

This brief survey of research literature indicates that both open-loop control (motor programs) and closed-loop control are involved in the initiation and control of movement. Recent studies suggest the possibility of an interaction of the two systems, for example, in oculomotor control.

A CONTROL MODEL

Responses can be either stereotyped or varied. Some can be performed simultaneously with others, and some can only be performed singly. Any model of human behavior must be able to accommodate all the possibilities of human movement. A control model must therefore include both open-loop and closed-loop control.

Figure 6.5 proposes such a model. The top half of the diagram shows open-loop control, which has been observed in ballistic movements and movements of short duration and limited extent. The bottom half shows closed-loop control, which is seen in tracking and other movements that require involved sequences or accuracy. Input from the sensory organs enters both control loops, and output from both loops activates the effectors. An integrator meshes output from the two control loops, to result in skilled, coordinated movement.

The assumption underlying this model is that our responses are stimulus-dependent. The increased reaction time observed for tasks of greater complexity reflects the stimulus dependency of responses. Further, the stimulus includes all key aspects of the situation, both the "start" stimulus and the "termination" stimulus, or target. Table 6.3 lists types of reaction time, in order of increasing latency, according to the difficulty of decision making for different tasks. The difficulty increases with the number of decisions that must be made.

Movement control is accomplished by the open loop for movements of short duration and limited extent (approximately 200 milliseconds and 10 millimeters or less). In movements of greater complexity or longer duration, the open loop controls the brief, initial (transport) phase of the movement, and the closed loop controls the terminal and sequencing (correction) phases. Thus, a performer first determines the moment when a movement is to be initiated and then begins to move under open-loop control, guiding the general direction

Table 6.3. Reaction Time (RT) in Order of Increasing Difficulty of Decision Making

	LEAST DIFFICULT				MOST DIFFICULT
	1	2	3		4
Type of RT	Simple RT	RT with movement	Simple RT with catch	*or* Choice RT	RT with movement and catch
Example of task	Finger lift, performed each trial	Movement, performed each trial	Finger lift, not performed each trial	One of two movements, performed each trial	Movement not performed each trial
Decisions	When to move	When and where to move	Whether and when to move	Which movement to make and when to move	Whether, when, and where to move

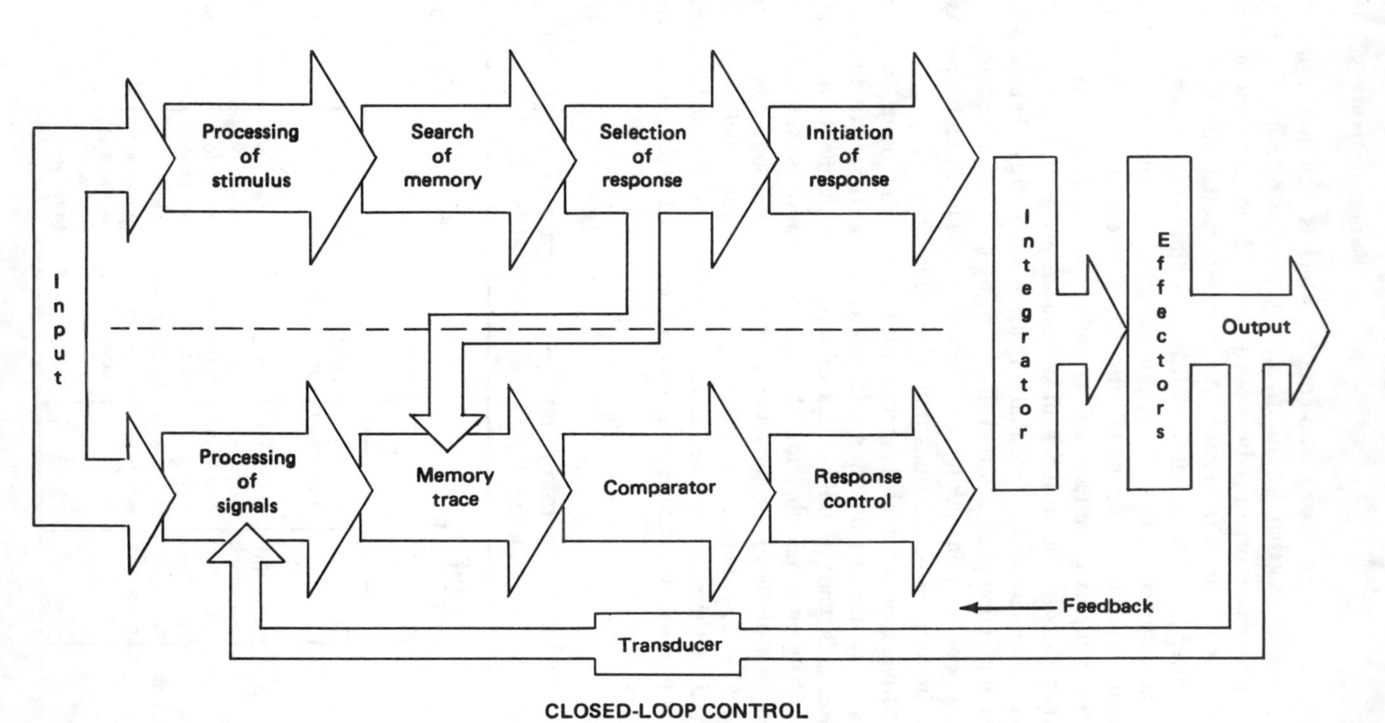

Figure 6.5. A model of movement control.

and extent of the movement. This phase is followed by closed-loop control, in which adjustments for accuracy and appropriate variations are made.

The four stages of information processing in open-loop control are identical to those proposed by Posner (1973) and discussed earlier in this chapter. The stimulus is received and processed, the memory is searched, the appropriate response is selected, and subsequently the response is initiated. The response that is selected is also transformed into a memory trace, which is stored for use in the closed-loop sequence.

During the closed-loop phase of movement control, part of the output from the effectors is returned as feedback. This feedback initially passes through a transducer, which monitors actual performance and sends negative feedback into the closed-loop control system. Negative feedback (amount of disparity) indicates the extent to which the sensorimotor system is carrying out instructions. This feedback is processed and, in conjunction with a memory trace of the movement that was selected, is sent to a comparator. The function of this unit is to compare the actual ongoing performance with the desired output. Once this comparison is accomplished, a response control unit issues commands to correct errors. These commands are sent to the integrator, so that a modified response can be superimposed upon or exchanged for the original responses.

GUIDING PRINCIPLES FOR THE TEACHER

1. Four mental operations are involved during information processing: (*a*) abstraction and representation of the stimulus; (*b*) memory search, to evaluate the abstraction; (*c*) selection of an appropriate response; and (*d*) initiation of the response.

2. A motor program is a representation in the central nervous system, by which a movement sequence can be initiated and carried out without subsequent kinesthetic feedback, in the absence of error. Such a control system is called an open-loop system.

3. Closed-loop control systems use feedback to allow the detection and correction of errors. Such systems also incorporate feedback through verbal mediation and verbal responses.

4. Except for short, ballistic movements, most responses probably involve both motor programming and feedback. Motor programming controls the initial phase of movement, and feedback controls accuracy and the termination of movement.

SUMMARY

One factor that determines the speed with which we can respond to situations is the amount of information that must be processed. The more complex the information to be processed, the longer the latent period before a response can be initiated. The complexity of any given situation depends on a number of factors, for example, the nature of the stimulus, the type of movement to be performed, and the compatibility of the stimulus and the movement.

In some situations, responses are subject to open-loop control, producing movements that appear to be programmed. The concept of a motor program has been devised to explain open-loop control. In other situations, movements are subject to closed-loop control, using negative feedback for error correction. Teachers and coaches must help students recognize appropriate stimulus-response frameworks and also must help them recognize and use appropriate feedback to correct errors in movement performance.

REFERENCES

Adams, J. A. 1971. A closed-loop theory of motor learning. *Journal of Motor Behavior* 3:111–149.

———. 1976. Issues for a closed-loop theory of motor learning. In *Motor control: Issues and trends*, ed. G. E. Stelmach. New York: Academic Press.

Bruner, J. S., Oliver, R. R., and Greenfield, P. M. 1966. *Studies in cognitive growth*. New York: John Wiley and Sons.

Bryan, W. L., and Harter, N. 1899. Studies on the telegraphic language: The acquisition of a hierarchy of habits. *Psychological Review* 6:345–375.

Chase, W. G., and Posner, M. I. 1965. The effect of auditory and visual confusability on visual and memory search tasks. Unpublished paper. Cited by P. M. Fitts and M. I. Posner, *Human performance*. Monterey, Calif.: Brooks/Cole, 1967.

Drowatzky, J. N. 1976. Mediation: The precursor of skilled performance. In *Physical education, sports and the sciences*, ed. J. Broekhoff. Eugene, Oreg.: Microform Publications.

Drowatzky, J. N., and McLellan, J. C. 1978. Henry's "memory drum" theory of neuromotor reaction revisited. *Abstracts of research papers*. Washington, D.C.: AAHPER.

Easton, T. A. 1972. On the normal use of reflexes. *American Scientist* 60:591–599.

———. 1975. Reflexes and fatigue: New directions. In *Psychological aspects and physiological correlates of work and fatigue*, ed. E. Simonson. Springfield, Ill.: Charles C. Thomas.

Fitts, P. M., and Posner, M. I. 1967. *Human performance*. Monterey, Calif.: Brooks/Cole.

Fuchs, A. H. 1962. The progression-regression hypothesis in perceptual-motor skill learning. *Journal of Experimental Psychology* 63:177–182.

Harrison, J. S. 1960. Psychological refractoriness and the latency time of two consecutive motor responses. *Research Quarterly* 31:590–600.

Hayes, K. C., and Marteniuk, R. G. 1976. Dimensions of motor task complexity. In *Motor control: Issues and trends*, ed. G. E. Stelmach. New York: Academic Press.

Henry, F. M., and Harrison, J. S. 1961. Refractoriness of a fast movement. *Perceptual and Motor Skills* 13:351–354.

Henry, F. M., and Rogers, D. E. 1960. Increased response latency for complicated movements and a "memory drum" theory of neuromotor reaction. *Research Quarterly* 31:448–458.

Hick, W. E. 1952. On the rate of gain of information. *Quarterly Journal of Experimental Psychology* 4:11–26.

Keele, S. W. 1968. Movement control in skilled motor performance. *Psychological Bulletin* 70:387–403.

———. 1973. *Attention and human performance*. Pacific Palisades, Calif.: Goodyear Publishing.

Keele, S. W., and Summers, J. J. 1976. The structure of motor programs. In *Motor control: Issues and trends*, ed. G. E. Stelmach, New York: Academic Press.

Kerr, B. 1975. Processing demands during movement. *Journal of Motor Behavior* 7:15–27.

Klapp, S. J. 1975. Feedback versus motor programming in the control of animal movements. *Journal of Experimental Psychology* 104:147–153.

Lashley, K. S. 1917. The accuracy of movement in the absence of excitation from the moving organ. *American Journal of Psychology* 43:169–194.

Laszlo, J. I., and Manning, L. C. 1970. The role of motor programming, command, and standard in the central control of skilled movement. *Journal of Motor Behavior* 2:111–124.

Manis, M. 1966. *Cognitive processes*. Belmont, Calif.: Wadsworth.

Martin, J. G. 1972. Rhythmic (hierarchical) versus serial structure in speech and other behavior. *Psychological Review* 79:487–509.

Megaw, E. D. 1972. Direction and extent uncertainty in step-input tracking. *Journal of Motor Behavior* 4:171–186.

Miles, F. A., and Evarts, E. V. 1979. Concepts of motor organization. In *Annual review of psychology*. Vol. 30, ed. M. R. Rosenzweig and L. W. Porter. Palo Alto, Calif.: Annual Reviews.

Neissen, U., Novick, R., and Lazar, R. 1963. Searching for ten targets simultaneously. *Perceptual and Motor Skills* 17:955–961.

Paillard, J. 1960. The patterning of skilled movements. In *Handbook of physiology*. Sec. 1., vol. 3, ed. H. W. Magoun. Washington, D.C.: American Physiological Society.

Pew, R. W. 1966. Acquisition of hierarchical control over temporal organization of a skill. *Journal of Experimental Psychology* 71:764–771.

———. 1974. Human perceptual-motor performance. In *Human information processing: Tutorials in performance and cognition*, ed. B. H. Kantowitz. New York: Erlbaum.

Piaget, J., and Inhelder, B. 1969. *The psychology of the child*. Translated by H. Weaver. New York: Basic Books.

Posner, M. I. 1973. *Cognition: An introduction*. Glenview, Ill.: Scott, Foresman.

Posner, M. I., and Keele, S. W. 1970. Time and space as measures of mental operations. Paper presented at the 78th annual convention of the American Psychological Association, Division 3.

Schmidt, R. A. 1975. A schema theory of discrete motor skill learning. *Psychological Review* 82:225–260.

Shepard, R. N., and Metzler, J. 1971. Mental rotation of three-dimensional objects. *Science* 171:701–703.

Thierman, T. 1968. A signal detection approach to the study of set in tachistoscopic recognition. *Perceptual and Motor Skills* 27:96–98.

Welford, A. T. 1968. *Fundamentals of skill*. London: Methuen.

———. 1976. *Skilled performance: Perceptual and motor skills*. Glenview, Ill.: Scott, Foresman.

Williams, L. R. T. 1971. Refractoriness of a long movement. *Research Quarterly* 42:212 219.

———. 1973. Psychological refractoriness of two serial motor responses. *Research Quarterly* 44:24 33.

———. 1975. Effects of complexity on movement refractoriness. *Research Quarterly* 46:177 183.

7 Transfer

Transfer is the process in which a person uses learning that he or she has acquired in one situation by applying it to a new or different situation. It is an important part of educational training. This process occurs often and widely. It is well known that people can transfer much of what they have learned in one situation to many others. For example, knowledge of some components of field hockey, such as an understanding of the players' positions on the field, can help a performer in soccer. The transfer of other principles, however, such as knowledge of the players' positions during an end-line out-of-bounds play in field hockey, can interfere with the learning of play at the end line of the soccer field. This tendency to use past experiences in new situations was noted by Thorndike, who called it the *spread of effects*. Skinner prefers the term *generalization*. The Gestalt school referred to the process as *transposition*. Regardless of the term used to describe transfer, all theories recognize the same tendency: the attempt to apply learning from past experiences to new situations.

Although the problem of transfer initially arose in the context of educational psychology, it has been a fundamental area of study for psychologists, therapists, physical educators, and coaches as well. McGeoch and Irion (1952, pp. 346–347), for example, stated that

> after small amounts of learning early in the life of the individual, every instance of learning is a function of the already learned organization of the subject; that is, all learning is influenced by transfer. . . .
>
> The learning of complex, abstract, meaningful materials and the solution of problems by means of ideas (reasoning) are to a great extent functions of transfer. Where the subject "sees into" the fundamental relations of a problem or has "insight," transfer seems to be a major contributing condition. It is, likewise, a basic factor in originality, the original and creative person having, among other things, unusual sensitivity to the applicability of the already known to new problem situations. Perceiving, at whatever level, is probably never free of the influence of transfer. In a word, there is no complex psychological function or event which is not in some way a function of transfer of training.

This statement does not restrict the phenomenon of transfer to "purely academic" pursuits, nor should it. For example, baseball players readily acquire the skills that are necessary for success in handball and golf. A few years ago, a famous, successful basketball coach, faced with a big, awkward college team, attempted to capitalize on the transfer effect by enrolling the players in a local ballet school. Educators once advocated that all students should study Latin because the practice would train the mind for later use. Fortunately for today's students, research projects have indicated that "mental training" from the study of Latin or from practice in memorization does not transfer to other areas of endeavor. Transfer involves specific skills more than general abilities.

Consequently, we cannot always readily distinguish new learning from learning that has been acquired through transfer. Nor can we be certain about which information will transfer in new situations and which will not. Most studies of this process have used subjects of various ages and have paid little regard to the nature and extent of early experiences, particularly during the preschool years, which may have a greater and more generalized effect than we currently realize. Early motor experience may be more important in transfer than many other types of experience.

This chapter describes types of transfer, the major techniques used to study it, factors that affect it, and the implications of transfer for the acquisition of skilled motor performance.

TYPES OF TRANSFER

Transfer can have either positive or negative effects. Consider two situations that a swimming instructor might encounter. Assume that one student swims the crawl stroke with a variation of the scissors kick rather than the flutter kick. If our instructor attempted to teach this student to swim the sidestroke and perform certain lifesaving carries that involve the scissors kick, the student probably would readily acquire the new skills. *Positive transfer* would take place: the skills that the student originally learned apply equally well to the new skills. If our instructor atempted to teach the student to swim the breaststroke, however, the student probably would continue to use the scissors kick rather than incorporate the new whip kick into the stroke. This is an example of *negative transfer:* the skills that the student originally learned are not compatible with those required for the breaststroke.

In general, positive transfer occurs if previously acquired learning benefits learning or performance in a new situation. Negative transfer occurs if it hinders new learning or performance. A third effect, *zero* or *neutral transfer,* occurs if the original learning appears neither to help nor to hinder in a new situation.

Psychologists have classified transfer as proactive and retroactive. In *proactive transfer,* learning acquired in the initial task affects the subsequent learning or performance of a new task. In the previous example, the initial acquisition of the scissors kick has a proactive transfer effect on learning the frog kick later. *Retroactive transfer* is illustrated by the following example. Suppose that a person learns tennis during the summer but, after the weather turns cold, moves indoors for racquetball. Next summer, the player finds that the winter of racquetball has affected his or her tennis skills. The transfer effect in this example is retroactive: practicing the second task influences performance in a task that was learned earlier.

MEASUREMENT OF TRANSFER

The basic experimental design for transfer studies involves an experimental group, which learns an initial task and then a transfer task, and a control group, which learns only the transfer task (see Table 7.1). The amount and direction (positive or negative) of transfer can be ascertained by measuring and comparing the performances of the groups during the transfer requirement stage. According to Ellis (1965),

Table 7.1. Basic Experimental Design for Transfer Studies

	INITIAL REQUIREMENT	TRANSFER REQUIREMENT
Experimental group	Learn Task 1	Learn Task 2
Control group	Rest	Learn Task 2

the simplest type of transfer study is one in which the responses required by the initial task and the transfer task are the same but the stimuli involved in the tasks are different.

McGeoch and Irion (1952), however, pointed out that the basic experimental design suffers from two deficiencies. First, it contains no adequate basis for matching the experimental group and the control group. This problem can be overcome by the random assignment of subjects to the two groups. The second problem is that this method makes no provision for a warm-up effect, and this deficiency appears to be more serious. Thune (1950) reported that learning is enhanced if subjects warm up by practicing some different task prior to the learning trials. The initial task in the basic experimental design (Task 1) may serve as a warm-up for the transfer task (Task 2), but this effect would not be apparent from the experiment.

Other experimental designs have been developed in attempts to eliminate these weaknesses (Ellis, 1965; Woodworth and Schlosberg, 1954; McGeoch and Irion, 1952). These are summarized in Table 7.2. In the first of these designs, subjects are tested on a part of Task 2 prior to their assignment to either the experimental group or the control group. The experimenter can therefore match the two groups on the basis of the pretest scores and can nearly equalize possible warm-up effects on both groups.

The second design requires that half of the subjects learn Task 1 and then Task 2 while the other half learn them in the reverse sequence. This approach has been used to study transfer from one sensory system to another, but there is no assurance that the practice effects in the experimental sequence are the same as those in the control sequence.

The third design requires that the experimental group learns Task 1 and then Task 2 while the control group learns Task 1 and then Task 2*a*, which is similar to but not identical with Task 2. This design controls factors such as warm-up and learning to learn, but it is difficult to insure that Task 2 and Task 2*a* are sufficiently similar.

Table 7.2. Additional Experimental Designs for Transfer Studies

DESIGN	GROUP		INITIAL REQUIREMENT	TRANSFER REQUIREMENT
1	Experimental	Pretest on Task 2*a*	Learn Task 1	Learn Task 2
	Control	Pretest on Task 2*a*	Rest	Learn Task 2
2	Experimental		Learn Task 1	Learn Task 2
	Control		Learn Task 2	Learn Task 1
3	Experimental		Learn Task 1	Learn Task 2
	Control		Learn Task 1	Learn Task 2*a*
4	Experimental and control		Learn Task 1	Learn Task 2
			(Variable time intervals)	

Modified from Ellis, 1965.

The fourth design requires all subjects to learn Task 1 and then Task 2, but different time intervals elapse between the tasks for the two groups. In addition, a control group that learns only Task 2 is sometimes also used. This design is particularly useful in investigating the effects of time on transfer.

Consequently, the evaluation of transfer studies must take into account both the skills being tested and the research design. Designs must be appropriate for the problem and situation under investigation. The compatibility of experimental and control groups, the elimination of a warm-up effect, and other extraneous factors must be properly controlled if transfer is to be adequately determined.

Measures of the Transfer Effect

Measurements must be taken to ascertain the amount of transfer that occurs in any situation. The most frequently used measures include

1. the number of trials necessary for a subject to attain the required proficiency
2. the amount of time necessary to attain the required proficiency
3. the level of proficiency reached after a given amount of time has passed or a given number of trials have been performed

4. the number of errors made as a subject attains the required level of proficiency

Scores can be translated into a percentage of transfer index through the following formula, for purposes of comparison.

$$\text{Percentage of transfer} = \frac{\text{transfer score} - \text{initial control score}}{\text{final control score} - \text{initial control score}} \times 100$$

Several other transfer formulas, reported by Ellis (1965) may be appropriate in different circumstances. He also compared the transfer percentages obtained from different formulas, to aid one in choosing the most appropriate approach.

Savings Scores

Another method used to assess the transfer effect employs savings scores, which measure how much work on the criterion task is saved by preliminary training. A control group learns the criterion task and attains a particular level of proficiency after a specified number of trials. An experimental group receives preliminary training and then practices the criterion task until it is as proficient as the control group. If the control group practices for 20 trials and the experimental group requires only 12 to attain the same level of proficiency, the transfer effect amounts to a savings of 8 trials out of 20, or 40 percent.

The savings method can be extended by the use of successive performance criteria. The number of trials required to reach criterion by the control group and the experimental group are counted, and the percentage of savings is computed at each criterion level. Thus the transfer effect can be traced throughout the entire learning process.

FACTORS INFLUENCING TRANSFER

We have considered general principles of transfer and methods used to study it, but important theoretical aspects still remain for our consideration. How is transfer influenced by prior experience and learning? How do different tasks and materials relate to transfer? Does the degree of initial learning affect transfer? What other factors may be involved in transfer?

Prior Experience

Recall that two stages of learning, primary and later learning, have been postulated. Primary learning is the stage in which our environment becomes meaningful. Later learning is characterized by the formation of associations and new concepts. Later learning is highly efficient and rapid, because it takes advantage of the learner's prior experience. Hebb (1949) supported this statement with the clinical findings of Senden and the results of investigations by Riesen. According to Senden's (1932) report, persons born with cataracts who have them removed in later life are, for all practical purposes, blind. Extremely long periods of time are required before such patients can learn to see effectively. This report was supplemented by the findings of Riesen (1947, 1950). His observations of chimpanzees reared in darkness also indicate the need for past experience in learning and transfer. Studies by Clarke et al. (1951), Nissen, Chow, and Semmes (1951), Hebb (1937), and Towne (1954) also illustrate the importance of prior experience in transfer.

General experience with environmental stimuli is important, but some specific experience with the task at hand or similar tasks apparently is also required before transfer occurs. In a classical study, Harlow (1949) offered monkeys a choice between two objects varying in color, texture, size, shape, and other characteristics. The monkeys were rewarded each time they selected one of the objects. In a series of comparisons, the monkeys became better and better at discriminating between the objects, until the task no longer presented any difficulty and the problem was solved in one trial. Harlow obtained similar results with children and brain-damaged monkeys as subjects in further studies. These results have been replicated by several investigators in varying situations (Messick and Solly, 1957; Nissen and McCulloch, 1937; Shepard, 1957; Stevenson and Zigler, 1958; Zeaman and House, 1963).

These studies emphasize that the facility for transfer of learning requires more than the general experiences that attach meaning to the environment. In addition to these, subjects must experience different types of problems. This requirement is not restricted to exposure to original learning situations. Frequently, the solution to a problem requires that an old learning set be discarded and a new one acquired. The data presented in Figure 7.1 are representative of the acquisition of a learning set (learning to learn). The learning curve rises gradually and gives an S-shaped appearance in the first series of discriminations. As the learning set is practiced, the curve becomes steeper and steeper until the second choice is nearly 100 percent correct.

Stimulus and Response Similarity

One of the most important factors in determining the nature and amount of transfer is the degree of similarity between stimuli and

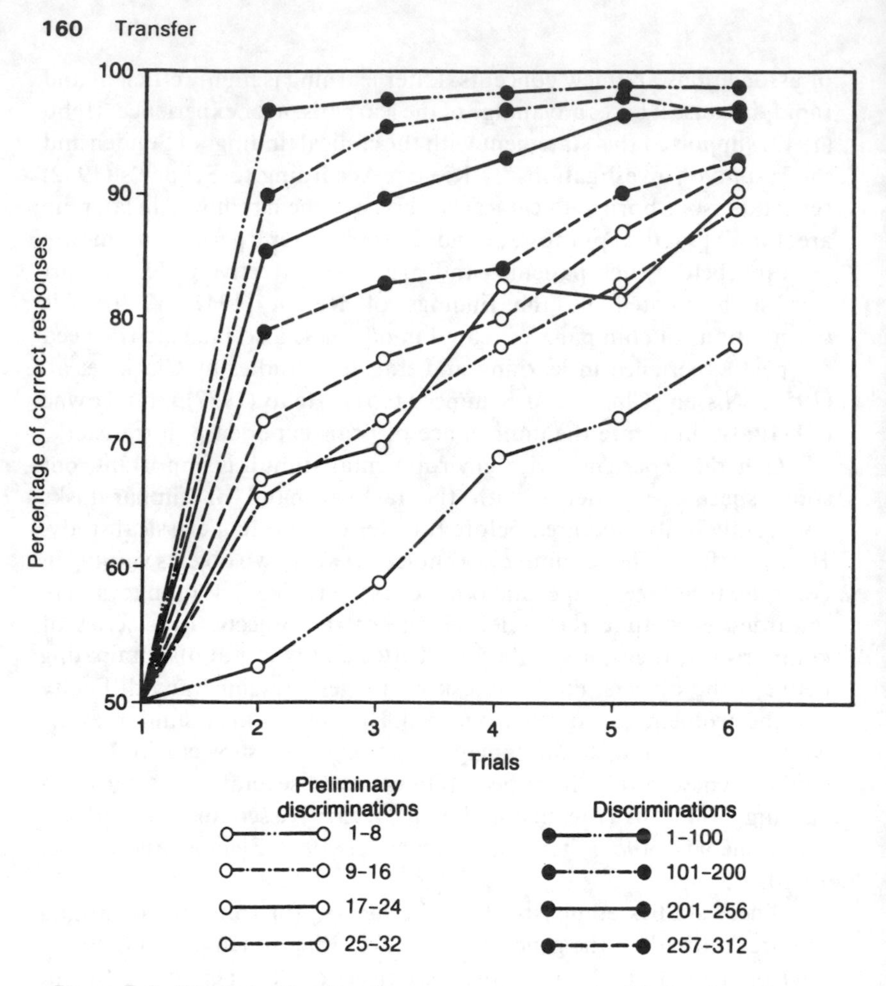

Figure 7.1. Discrimination learning curves on successive blocks of problems; the acquisition of a learning set. (Modified from Harlow, 1949.)

between responses in the two tasks. Perhaps the best illustration of the effect of stimulus and response similarity comes from a study conducted by Bruce (1933). Paired-associate lists—stimulus-response pairs of nonsense syllables—were presented to subjects, who learned one list (initial task) and then another (transfer task). The following experimental conditions were set up:

1. In the first set of lists, the stimuli for the initial task were different from the stimuli for the transfer task, but the responses were identical.

2. In a second set of lists, the stimuli were identical and the responses were dissimilar.
3. In a third set, the stimuli were similar and the responses were identical.
4. In a fourth set, the stimuli were identical and the responses were similar.

The results of this study (summarized in Table 7.3) indicate that transfer can be either positive or negative, according to the degree of stimulus similarity and the degree of response similarity.

The effects of stimulus and response similarity on transfer have been summarized by Morgan and King (1966, p. 130):

> 1. Learning to make identical responses to new stimuli results in *positive transfer* (conditions 1 and 3 of the Bruce experiment).
>
> 2. Learning to make new (dissimilar, opposite, or antagonistic) responses to similar or identical stimuli results in *negative transfer* (condition 2 of the Bruce experiment).
>
> 3. The amount of transfer, regardless of whether it is positive or negative, is a function of stimulus similarity. The greater the stimulus similarity between tasks 1 and 2, the greater the amount of transfer.
>
> 4. Whether transfer is positive or negative is largely dependent upon response similarity.

Table 7.3. Effects of Stimulus-Response Relationships on Transfer

CONDITION	STIMULUS-RESPONSE RELATIONSHIPS	DIRECTION OF TRANSFER
1	Stimuli dissimilar—responses identical	Slightly positive
2	Stimuli identical—responses dissimilar	Negative
3	Stimuli similar—responses identical	Very strongly positive
4	Stimuli identical—responses similar	Slightly positive

Modified from Bruce, 1933.

The influence of stimulus and response similarity on transfer is graphically summarized in Figure 7.2. This contingency table indicates that positive transfer results if the new task requires a response that is similar to a previously acquired response. If a dissimilar response must be made to familiar patterns of stimulation, learning is subject to interference. Totally new situations, involving dissimilar stimuli and dissimilar responses, are not subject to either facilitation or interference.

Similar findings have been reported by Singer and Pease (1978). They found that transfer in gross motor skills is most effective if the learning conditions are similar for the initial task and the transfer task. In other words, transfer leaning is greatest if the testing method used in the second task is similar to the learning method invovled in the initial task. Similarity between tasks was reported to be the most important factor.

Osgood (1949), in an attempt to diagram the relationship between similarity and transfer, devised the Osgood transfer surface (see Figure 7.3). The direction and amount of transfer are represented by the vertical dimension of the form. The width of the form represents stimulus similarity, and its length represents response similarity. Osgood believed that this surface shows transfer as a smooth, unbroken sequence, with facilitative functions rising above the median plane and interfering functions falling below it.

Results of experiments in motor learning led Irion (1969, pp. 20–21) to conclude that

> except under very carefully controlled and arranged conditions, positive transfer appears to be much more likely to

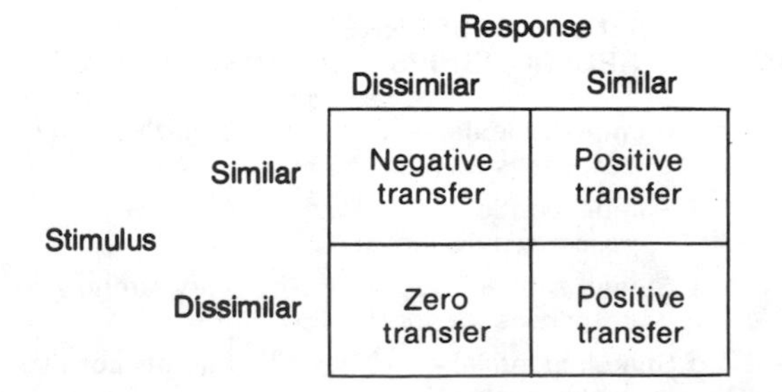

Figure 7.2. The influence of stimulus-response similarity on transfer.

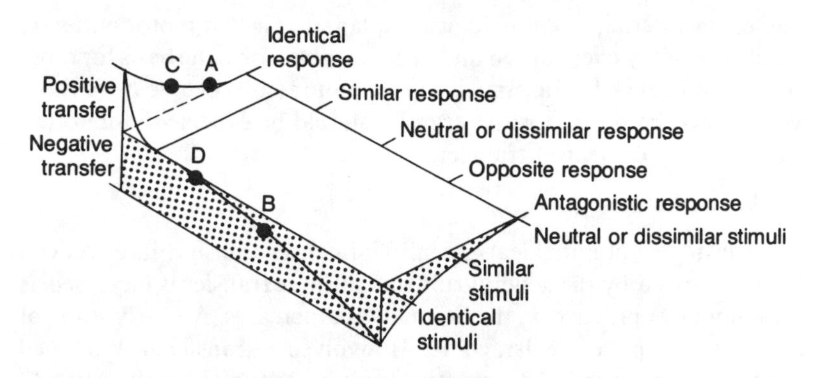

Figure 7.3. The Osgood transfer surface. The amount and direction of transfer depends on the similarity of stimuli and of responses in the learning task and the transfer task. Response similarity decreases from upper left to lower right along the response axis. Stimulus similarity decreases from lower left to upper right along the stimulus axis. The vertical axis represents the amount of transfer. (Negative transfer is shown in the shaded area.) Points *A, B, C,* and *D* mark the amount and direction of transfer resulting from the four stimulus-response combinations (conditions 1, 2, 3, and 4, respectively) of Bruce's (1933) experiment. (Modified from Osgood, 1949.)

> occur than negative transfer. Even when optimum conditions for the production of interference are arranged, the negative transfer effects seem to be somewhat weak, quite transitory, and very apt to shift to facilitation during relearning. . . In short, interference and negative transfer effects are difficult to produce in skills situations. Those who favor an interference theory of forgetting can take some meager comfort from the fact that motor skills seem to be impervious to both interference and forgetting.

The studies reviewed deal primarily with fine, rather than gross, motor skills. Although gross motor skills present considerable difficulty in control, the stimulus-response situations are different enough that they merit special study to see whether Irion's statement applies to them. Open skills and serial responses to serial stimuli particularly deserve further study.

In any event, it is likely that rules obtained from verbal and perceptual studies are difficult to apply to motor learning. One possible explanation for this disparity is that rules of transfer are applicable only in highly structured environments, such as those in which most of these studies are conducted, but not in less controlled situations, such as classrooms. Perhaps a more logical explanation is that motor patterns, which are highly overlearned and generalizable, form the basis for most of our physical skills. Inasmuch as new motor skills evolve from these well-learned patterns, positive transfer should be expected more often than negative or neutral transfer.

Initial Learning

The degree of initial learning also influences transfer. Its effect can be summarized by the general rule that positive transfer is increased as the amount of practice on the original task increases. An early study of this effect (Siipola and Israel, 1933) involved a transfer task learned after a varying number of practice trials on the initial task. After 12 practice trials, slight positive transfer occurred. After 26 trials, there was negative transfer. After 96 trials and again after 208 trials, increased amounts of positive transfer were recorded. Underwood (1951) also tested the hypothesis that transfer is directly related to the degree of initial learning. His findings show the importance of a high degree of initial learning in verbal learning and the role of task similarity in the facilitation of high positive transfer. The findings of these investigators have received further support from the results of animal studies conducted by Bruner et al. (1958) and Reid (1953).

The implications of these studies are of utmost importance to physical educators and coaches: a little practice can be dangerous. In view of the fact that the greatest amount of negative transfer appears to occur after relatively little practice on the original task, extensive practice is necessary to insure a minimum of negative transfer and a maximum of positive transfer (see Figure 7.4). Thus, these findings about initial learning further emphasize the need for general prior experience and underscore the influence of learning to learn as a factor affecting transfer.

Other Factors

Although elements of a familiar task that most closely resemble the elements of a new task are transferred most readily, other factors are also important in the transfer of learning. One of these is the emotional and attitudinal state of the students. For example, Norcross (1921) and Denny and Reisman (1956) pointed out the importance of the emotional state in the transfer of learning. Subjects with high anxiety states were observed to perform more poorly on transfer tasks than persons who were not anxious. The effects of attitudes were

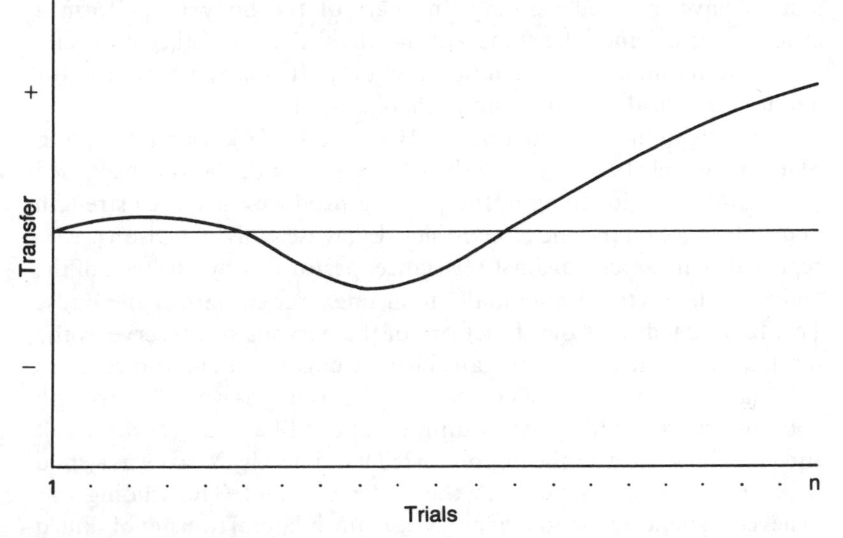

Figure 7.4. Hypothetical curve showing the relationship between direction of transfer and amount of practice.

summarized by Cratty (1967) and Lewis, Smith, and McAllister (1952). They included attitudinal states in algebraic summations of the tendencies to make appropriate responses (positive transfer), to inhibit inappropriate responses, and to make inappropriate responses (negative transfer).

Zeaman and House (1963) discovered through their work with retarded children that attention plays an important role in transfer. In retarded individuals, attention was found to facilitate transfer if the initial training occurs on an easy task and then task difficulty is increased. It was necessary for each subject to learn to attend to the relevant characteristics of the task each time, but the subjects were able to reverse the role of positive and negative cues and learn new pairs of relevant dimensions. These authors concluded that the attention theory can explain much of the data obtained in transfer studies. Their findings need to be compared to investigations using normal subjects to determine the relevance of attention to transfer in general.

TRANSFER AND MOTOR LEARNING

The majority of studies investigating the transfer of gross motor skills have been concerned with bilateral transfer. Typically, these studies have involved training one part of the body to perform a criterion task and then measuring the effect on the opposite, unpracticed limb. These studies are of particular importance for adaptive physical education and rehabilitation.

Investigations by Hellebrandt, Houtz, and Krikorian (1950) and Slater-Hammel (1950) indicate that if one side of the body is exercised until it increases in strength, the training produces increased strength and endurance on the unexercised side. Likewise, Sills and Olson (1958) reported that exercise against resistance, performed by one part of the body, elicits electrical potentials in an unexercised part of the body. This finding indicates that functions of the nervous sytem serve as the mechanism for the bilateral transfer of strength and endurance.

Bilateral transfer occurs in motor skill training as well as in strength and endurance training. According to Thorndike et al. (1928), adult subjects can write with the nonpreferred hand nearly as easily as a child of 8 or 9 years can write with the preferred hand. This finding was believed to indicate the role of practice in the bilateral transfer of skilled motor learning. Hellebrandt and Waterland (1962) indicated that practice limited to one muscle group improves the performance of muscle groups on the opposite side of the body. Walter (1955) concluded that the greatest bilateral transfer of a motor skill is obtained through practice with overload. Short-term practice periods, however, may not produce any such effects. Walker, DeSoto, and Shelly (1959) observed that short warm-up periods with the right hand did not serve as a warm-up for skills to be performed with the left hand. Likewise, Dunham (1977) did not find bilateral transfer in the performance of a coincidence anticipation timing task.

These and other studies show that bilateral transfer can be important in therapy and rehabilitation. One can retain some degree of muscle tone in immobilized extremities through exercise of the opposite member of the body, as long as the neural connections are still operative in the immobilized limb. The observation (Caplan, 1976) that fatiguing leg exercise impairs output of the arms is consistent with this principle. Heavy exercise appears to have a general effect on muscle tone throughout the body.

Motor skill transfer also appears to have a general, pervasive influence among muscles. Investigations by Black (1949) and Hellebrandt and Waterland (1962) indicate that practice influences the performance of muscle groups that are not commonly used in the task, as well as those that are directly involved. Cratty (1962) discovered that prior experience with a small maze results in initial positive transfer to a similarly patterned large maze, while practice on a reverse-patterned small maze produces initial negative transfer. Apparently, transfer involves factors other than the acquisition of specific muscular movement.

Lindeburg (1949) trained subjects in table tennis, special arm exercises, and other physical education activities, to determine the effects of training on their speed in operating a finger press and shifting pegs. His results indicate no transfer effect from one activity to another and support the theory that the transfer of motor skill elements is highly specific. He concluded that transfer occurs only if the practice units or parts are identical to parts of the criterion task. Crafts (1935) also reported a close relationship between the amount of transfer and the number of common elements in motor tasks. Thus, motor learning appears to transfer readily, but within rather specific limits.

Knowledge of relationships between different tasks seems likely to facilitate the transfer of learning. There is some scientific evidence in support of this conclusion. According to Barker (1932), knowledge of relationships between maze patterns has a positive transfer effect. Judd (1908) and Hendrickson and Schroeder (1941) hypothesized that knowledge of the principles involved in a task facilitates positive transfer of a sensorimotor skill, and both studies found support for the hypothesis. It appears that subjects do not always need to recognize that the tasks are alike in principle. Woodward (1943) studied transfer between two tasks requiring identical patterns of movement but involving different materials. The subjects were not told of the relationship between the tasks. Transfer effects were apparent, although none of the subjects realized that the tasks were alike in principle.

Reaction time, movement time, and coordination are important elements of many motor and athletic skills, but little research has been conducted to ascertain transfer effects from training programs dealing with these abilities. This type of problem was investigated by Fairclough (1952), who reported that motivated improvement in the speed of hand movement resulted in a significant improvement in the speed of foot movement. Improvements in reaction time appear to transfer more readily than improvements in movement time. According to Hopper (1962), eye-hand and eye-foot coordination training on one side of the body result in transfer to members on the opposite side, but training in eye-hand coordination appears to have a negative transfer effect on eye-foot coordination. Some of the results obtained in this study could be predicted from principles of bilateral transfer, but a great deal of further study is needed in this area.

One area of interest to coaches and athletes is the value of overload (using additional weight for practice) on the acquisition and performance of motor skills. A thorough search of the literature produced only one study of the transfer effects of overload on motor skill performance. Egstrom, Logan, and Wallis (1960) conducted practice with projectiles of varying weights in an attempt to identify its effect on the throwing accuracy of college students. They found that subjects who practiced with a light ball experienced positive transfer to throwing accuracy with a heavier ball, but practice with a heavier ball did not transfer to throwing performance with a lighter ball. Presently, therefore, no evidence exists to support the value of overload in motor skill learning. Additional inquiry into the value of this practice is needed.

TRANSFER OF PSYCHOLOGICAL FACTORS

Transfer is not limited to verbal and motor skills. Psychological aspects of performance and learning, such as attitudes, expectancies, ideals, prejudices, and motives, are all subject to transfer. These cognitive attributes are actively involved in setting one's goals and shaping one's course of activity. Persons who have been successful in the past expect to be successful in the future. Conversely, students who have had unpleasant experiences in physical education courses approach physical activities with distaste. Attitudes toward study, methods of study, and methods of adjustment transfer from one subject to another and from one situation to another. Indeed, transfer involves far more than the acquisition of skills; it involves every aspect of one's life and determines how a person will respond to new situations.

A teacher cannot expect transfer to occur as a matter of course. The transfer of ideals, attitudes, knowledges, and principles must be taken into account in course and teaching objectives. Lesson plans should include ways in which the teacher can draw on past experiences and students' attitudes to facilitate positive transfer. The desire to learn and participate must be encouraged before students begin a task, rather than after it has been completed.

Participation depends on students' motives. Grades, prizes, and other awards are often used to encourage students, but these devices soon lose their appeal if the motives behind them do not transfer from situation to situation. In physical education, some motives are intrinsic to the activity, as chasing and fleeing games, but others must be transferred from past training and participation. Students readily learn when their past experience enables them to see present situations as having worthy goals and skills to be learned.

Since transfer depends on experience, a greater potential for transfer exists in students who are more intelligent, have a greater range of past experience, and are older. Severely retarded children, for example, may have greatly restricted potential for transfer. Students in elementary school have less potential for transfer than those in secondary school. The characteristics of students, as well as the material being presented, must be taken into account in planning teaching units and picking instructional methods.

TEACHING FOR TRANSFER

Transfer can be beneficial for both students and teachers. Through positive transfer, it is possible to avoid costly practice, secure valuable concomitants, and speed up reinforcement. To ensure positive transfer, a teacher must carefully plan so that conditions are appropriate for the students in the class. In the organization of groups, such as physical education classes, specific hypotheses must be developed about the relation of the activity to the desired behavioral changes. Changes are more likely to be encouraged if hypotheses are explicitly stated and revised as the teacher evaluates the effectiveness of instruction. Such evaluation requires clear and specific statements of the desired behavioral changes as well as comparisons of several classroom stiuations. The following guidelines can be used in planning, so that what is taught will be more likely to transfer to new learning situations.

First, teaching conditions should be as similar as possible to ultimate testing conditions. Identical items are most likely to transfer from one situation to another. The first step in attaining this goal is to answer two questions: What do I want my students to know? and, How can this knowledge (skill) be used in the future? As a result of this step, drills become similar to games—in a very real sense. If a drill is to be an effective teaching device, it must contribute to success in the actual game. The drill must pose the problems, as well as the skill requirements, that are encountered in the game. If the game requires performance with spectators and crowd noise, the training must provide for this experience at some point.

Next, students must have adequate experience with the original task. Limited practice can produce negative or neutral transfer to subsequent tasks, whereas extensive practice on the original task increases the likelihood of positive transfer. Successful coaches believe in the use of extensive drills and overlearning, but limited or scarce practice sessions are all too characteristic of physical education classes. An interesting variety of drills that progressively improve the students' skills is one necessary requirement of successful programs.

Teachers must provide for a variety of examples and situations that present concepts and principles. Exposure to a large variety of stimuli is an important factor leading to positive transfer in open skills and games that require performers to make choices. To this end, successful basketball coaches use three-on-two, two-on-two, two-on-one, and similar drills to teach for positive transfer in game situations. Football coaches use movies of opponents' games to give players some concepts of the teamwork and strategy they are likely to encounter. Good coaching is accomplished through effective teaching. Classroom teachers must conduct their courses with the same planning and enthusiasm if an effective job is to be accomplished.

Teachers must label or identify the important features of a task. Labeling helps to distinguish important features and aids subsequent learning, although research does not indicate whether the improvement results from the increased attention given to these features or from the label itself. One way to help defensive football players distinguish between pass plays and draw plays is to identify the crucial differences between the two. The identification of subtle differences in any sports situation improves the performances of participants.

Finally, teachers must ensure that general principles are understood before they expect much transfer. For example, striking patterns all have important common characteristics. The use of an implement as an extension of the arm, such as a bat or a tennis racket, increases the effective radius of rotation. This knowledge and an understanding of its value can aid performers in progression from sport to sport. Strategy in games can be presented in several ways, and the students can be requested to list strengths and weaknesses. Drills or subgames can be employed to see whether teaching tactics are effective.

GUIDING PRINCIPLES FOR THE TEACHER

1. Transfer is the process in which learning acquired in one situation is applied to a new or different situation. The process is related

to cognitive learning. Positive transfer occurs if the skills used in one situation apply equally well in a new situation. Negative transfer occurs if the original skills interfere with performance in a new situation.

2. The ability to use transfer depends on an extensive background of general experience, experiences with tasks related to the criterion task, the degree of initial learning, attention, and an understanding of the principles required by the task. The amount of transfer depends on stimulus similarity: the greater the similarity, the greater the amount of transfer. Response similarity determines whether transfer is positive or negative: learning to make a dissimilar response to the same or similar stimuli produces negative transfer, and learning to make an identical response to new stimuli produces positive transfer.

SUMMARY

This chapter has summarized studies of transfer. Three kinds of transfer were noted: positive transfer, which facilitates new learning; negative transfer, which hinders it; and neutral transfer, which neither helps nor hinders.

Transfer plays an important role in motor learning, as it does in all learning situations. Motor skills transfer from one task to another, transfer bilaterally, and exhibit mostly positive or neutral transfer effects. Reaction time appears to be affected by transfer more than movement time is, although this may be due to varying complexities of the tasks used in the study. No support has been found for the practice of overloading during practice in attempts to improve performance in motor skills.

Transfer influences more than motor skills and academic skills. Motives, attitudes, and expectations are also subject to transfer. In physical education, for example, some motives are intrinsic to the games, but others must be acquired from training and past experiences.

Thus, teachers must be concerned with knowledges, skills, and attitudes. Too often, students are told to read from a textbook or are given a demonstration without being shown the implications for other situations. If transfer is to occur, teachers must actively plan for it.

Factors that influence transfer transfer include the following.

Past Experience. Experience in both general learning situations and in situations that are specifically related to the new task apparently facilitates transfer. Many experiences that occur during initial learning appear to facilitate positive transfer. A person must learn how to learn and how to solve problems.

Stimulus and Response Similarity. Transfer is greatest if the stimuli and responses for the initial task are highly similar to the stimuli and responses for the transfer task. If the new task requires the same response to new stimuli, positive transfer occurs in proportion to the degree of similarity of the stimuli. If the new task requries a different response to the same or similar stimuli, negative transfer results. Negative transfer in motor skills may be transitory and is difficult to produce.

Initial Learning. Two aspects of initial learning are important: exposure to a wide variety of experiences and the degree of original learning. Generally, the higher the degree of initial learning, the more likely positive transfer is to occur.

Attitude and Anxiety. Transfer tasks are performed poorly by persons who have high anxiety. Important attitudes include tendencies to make appropriate or inappropriate responses.

Attention. Attention plays an important role. It is necessary for an individual to learn the relevant characteristics of a task before transfer can occur.

Knowledge of Principles. Transfer appears to be positive and more pronounced if the individual understands the principles, rules, or relationships governing the task. These do not always need to be consciously recognized before the transfer effect is produced.

Transfer appears to depend on both general and specific factors in the learning situation. The amount of transfer varies according to the difficulty of the material, the similarity of stimuli and of responses, and characteristics of the learner.

Transfer is not automatic. Teachers cannot expect it to occur as a matter of course. Lesson plans should include ways in which the teacher can draw on past experiences and the students' attitudes to facilitate positive transfer. Although factors other than specific muscular movements appear to transfer, it is difficult to predict what elements will transfer or what the transfer effect will be.

Perhaps the best summary for this discussion comes from Thompson (1962, p. 216): "Arranging environmental conditions so that they promote maximum positive transfer and minimum conflict among the generalized response tendencies is largely an educational art." Teachers should plan to incorporate methods that facilitate positive transfer. The process offers much for the educational setting.

REFERENCES

Barker, R. G. 1932. Factors influencing transfer between finger mazes. *Journal of General Psychology* 6:115-132.

Black, J. 1949. An experimental study of the learning of a fine motor skill. Master's thesis, Pennsylvania State University.

Bruce, R. W. 1933. Conditions of transfer of training. *Journal of Experimental Psychology* 16:343-361.

Bruner, J. S., Mandler, J. M., O'Dowd, D., and Wallach, M. A. 1958. The role of overlearning and drive level in reversal learning. *Journal of Comparative and Physiological Psychology* 51:607-613.

Caplan, C. S. 1976. Fatigue transfer in endurance performance. *Research Quarterly* 47:603-609.

Clarke, R. S., Heron, W., Fetherstonhaugh, M. L., Forgays, D. G., and Hebb, D. O. 1951. Individual differences in dogs: Preliminary report on the effects of early experience. *Canadian Journal of Psychology* 5:150-156.

Crafts, L. W. 1935. Transfer as related to number of common elements. *Journal of General Psychology* 13:147-158.

Cratty, B. J. 1962. Transfer of small-pattern practice to large-pattern learning. *Research Quarterly* 33:523-535.

———. 1967. *Movement behavior and motor learning.* Philadelphia: Lea & Febiger.

Denny, M. R., and Reisman, J. M. 1956. Negative transfer as a function of manifest anxiety. *Perception and Motor Skills* 6:73-75.

Dunham, P., Jr. 1977. Effect of bilateral transfer on coincidence/anticipation performance. *Research Quarterly* 48:51-55.

Egstrom, G. H., Logan, G. A., and Wallis, E. L. 1960. Acquisition of throwing skill involving projectiles of varying weights. *Research Quarterly* 31:420-425.

Ellis, H. C. 1965. *The transfer of learning.* New York: Macmillan.

Fairclough, R. H. 1952. Transfer of motivated improvement in speed of reaction and movement. *Research Quarterly* 23:20-27.

Harlow, H. F. 1949. The formation of learning sets. *Psychological Review* 56:51-65.

Hebb, D. O. 1937. The innate organization of visual activity: II. Transfer of response in the discrimination of brightness and size by rats reared in total darkness. *Journal of Comparative Psychology* 24:277-299.

———. 1949. *The organization of behavior.* New York: John Wiley and Sons.

Hellebrandt, F. A., Houtz, S. J., and Krikorian, A. M. 1950. Influence of bimanual exercise on unilateral work capacity. *Journal of Applied Physiology* 2:446-452.

Hellebrandt, F. A., and Waterland, J. 1962. Indirect learning: The influence of unimanual exercise on related muscle groups of the same and opposite side. *American Journal of Physical Medicine* 41:45-55.

Hendrickson, G., and Schroeder, W. H. 1941. Transfer of training in learning to hit a submerged target. *Journal of Educational Psychology* 32:205-213.

Hopper, L. 1962. A study of transfer of training in eye-hand and eye-foot coordinations. Master's thesis, Smith College.

Irion, A. L. 1969. Historical introduction. In *Principles of skill acquisition,* ed. E. A. Bilodeau and I. McD. Bilodeau. New York: Academic Press.

Judd, C. H. 1908. The relation of special training to general intelligence. *Educational Review* 36:28-42.

Lewis, D., Smith, P. N., and McAllister, D. E. 1952. Retroactive facilitation and interference in performance on the two-hand coordinator. *Journal of Experimental Psychology* 44:44-50.

Lindeburg, F. A. 1949. A study of the degree of transfer between quickening exercises and other coordinated movements. *Research Quarterly* 19:180 195.
McGeoch, J. A., and Irion, A. L. 1952. *The psychology of human learning.* 2d ed. New York: Longmans, Green.
Messick, S. J., and Solley, C. M. 1957. Probability learning in children: Some exploratory studies. *Journal of Genetic Psychology* 90:23 33.
Morgan, C. T., and King, R. A. 1966. *Introduction to psychology.* 3d ed. New York: McGraw-Hill.
Nissen, H. W., Chow, K. L., and Semmes, J. 1951. Effects of restricted opportunity for tactual, kinesthetic, and manipulative experiences on the behavior of chimpanzees. *American Journal of Psychology* 64:485 507.
Nissen, H. W., and McCulloch, T. L. 1937. Equated and nonequated stimulus situations in discrimination learning by chimpanzees: III. Prepotency of response to oddity through training. *Journal of Comparative Psychology* 23:377 381.
Norcross, W. H. 1921. Experiments on the transfer of training. *Journal of Comparative Psychology* 1:317 363.
Osgood, C. E. 1949. The similarity paradox in human learning: A resolution. *Psychological Review* 56:132 154.
Reid, L. S. 1953. The development of noncontinuity behavior through continuity learning. *Journal of Experimental Psychology* 46:107 112.
Riesen, A. H. 1947. The development of visual perception in man and chimpanzee. *Science* 106:107 108.
. 1950. Arrested vision. *Scientific American* 183 (July): 16 19.
Senden, M. von. 1932. *Raumund gestaltauffassung bei operieten blindgegorenen vor und nach der operation.* Leipzig: Barth.
Shepard, W. O. 1957. Learning set in preschool children. *Journal of Comparative and Physiological Psychology* 50:15 17.
Siipola, E. M., and Israel, H. E. 1933. Habit interference as dependent upon stage of training. *American Journal of Psychology* 45:205 227.
Sills, F. D., and Olson, A. L. 1958. Action potentials in unexercised arm when opposite arm is exercised. *Research Quarterly* 29:213 221.
Singer, R. N., and Pease, D. 1978. Effect of guided vs. discovery learning strategies on initial motor task learning, transfer, and retention. *Research Quarterly* 49:206 217.
Slater-Hammel, A. T. 1950. Bilateral effects of muscle activity. *Research Quarterly* 21:203 209.
Stevenson, H. W., and Zigler, E. G. 1958. Probability learning in children. *Journal of Experimental Psychology* 56:185 192.
Thompson, G. G. 1962. *Child psychology: Growth trends in psychological adjustment.* 2d ed. Boston: Houghton Mifflin.
Thorndike, E. L., Bergman, E. O., Tilton, J., and Woodyard, E. 1928. *Adult learning.* New York: Macmillan.
Thune, L. E. 1950. The effect of different types of preliminary activities on subsequent learning of paired-associate material. *Journal of Experimental Psychology* 40:423 438.
Towne, A. L. 1954. A study of figural equivalence in the pigeon. *Journal of Comparative and Physiological Psychology* 47:283 287.
Underwood, B. J. 1951. Associative transfer in verbal learning as a function of response similarity and degree of first-list learning. *Journal of Experimental Psychology* 42:44 54.
Walker, L. G., DeSoto, C. B., and Shelly, M. W. 1957. Rest and warm-up in bilateral transfer on a pursuit rotor task. *Journal of Experimental Psychology* 53:394 397.
Walter, C. E. 1955. The effect of overload on bilateral transfer of a motor skill. *Physical Therapy Review* 35:567 569.

Woodward, P. 1943. An experimental study of transfer of training in motor learning. *Journal of Applied Psychology* 27:12–32.
Woodworth, R. S., and Schlosberg, H. 1954. *Experimental psychology*. Rev. ed. New York: Holt, Rinehart and Winston.
Zeaman, D., and House, D. J. 1963. The role of attention in retardate discrimination learning. In *Handbook of mental deficiency: Psychological theory and research*, ed. N. R. Ellis. New York: McGraw-Hill.

8 Perception

The stimulation of the sensory organs produces sensations, which provide us with contact with our world. Sensation by itself does not carry sufficient information for understanding and interpreting our world, however. Understanding and interpretation come about through perception—a higher-order process in which sensations arising from more than one source are integrated and past experiences are correlated and compared with present events. The process is learned and subject to the same laws of learning that were described earlier.

Perceptions used in reaching and grasping are developed from visual information, and somesthetic sensations are merged time and time again. We acquire expectations that certain responses and situations lead to certain goals. The world about us gains stability as we develop the ability to perceive constancy and identity. Constancy refers to the recognition that objects have constant, unchanging characteristics, such as size, shape, and color, although these may appear to change as surrounding conditions vary (e.g., amount of light, position of view, and distance). Identity develops as one acquires the ability to generalize or group objects on the basis of their similarities and discriminate objects or emphasize their differences.

The real world is not exactly as we perceive it. The world as we perceive it, however, is fundamentally stable and predictable. We can choose between alternative behaviors and strive for meaningful goals. Perceptions vary from person to person, and consequently different persons behave differently in the same situation. The perceptual differences among people are a product of different sensory capacities and different personal characteristics and histories. Perception is a wholly subjective, individual experience (Weintraub and Walker, 1966).

This chapter presents a brief overview of the sensory and neurological mechanisms involved in perception, followed by a discussion of perception from a behavioral point of view, with emphasis on vision, kinesthesis, and balance in motor learning and motor performance.

PERCEPTUAL MECHANISMS

Perception involves the integration of sensory information from more than one type of sense organ. This discussion deals mainly with the two sensations that are relied on most heavily for motor performance: somesthetic sensations (generalized sensations from the body, such as temperature, pressure, and position) and visual sensations. The general concepts concerning the relationship between sensation and perception are similar for the different sensory systems, although different receptors, pathways, and areas of the brain may be involved. It is important to be aware that impairment of the senses can produce movement and motor disturbances (Morris and Whiting, 1971).

Not only do sensations arise from different areas of the body, but the impulses also travel to different areas of the nervous system. Some of the sensory nerve branches end in the lower levels of the spinal cord to cause cord reflexes. Others terminate in higher levels of the spinal cord or in the brain. Sensory pathways to the brain have been observed to terminate in localized areas. These include (1) sensory areas in the brainstem, such as the bulboreticular formation, (2) the cerebellum, (3) the thalamus, and (4) the cerebral cortex (Guyton, 1974; Morgan, 1965). Figure 8.1 displays the various somesthetic receptors and nerve pathways to the brain.

Signals transmitted to the cerebellum and the reticular formation are subconscious and result in subconscious motor activity, such as a

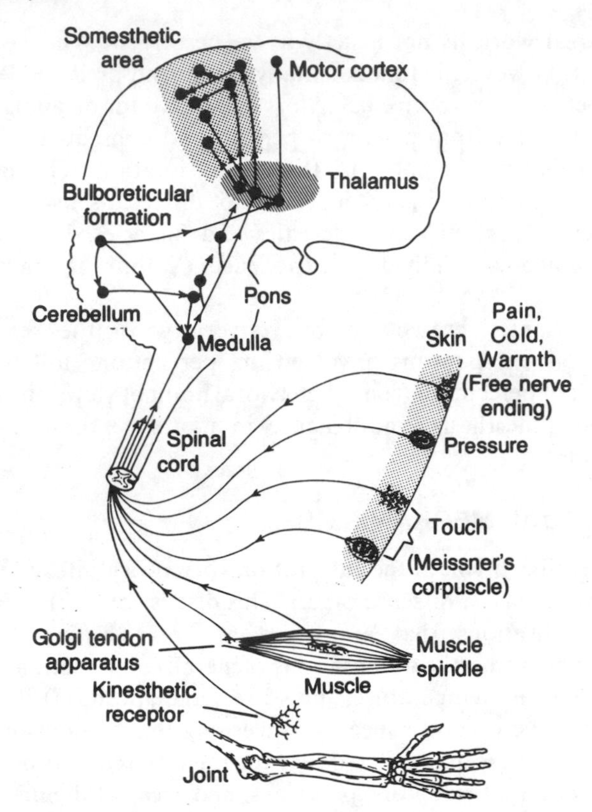

Figure 8.1. Sensory receptors and nerve pathways for transmission of sensory signals to the brain and spinal cord. (Redrawn from A. C. Guyton, *Function of the human body,* 4th ed., Philadelphia: W. B. Saunders, 1974, p. 273.)

knee jerk in response to a patellar tap. Sensory input to the brainstem produces motor reactions that are more complex and of a higher level than cord reflexes, such as walking. Signals that reach the thalamus and the cerebral cortex enter consciousness. They are also crudely localized according to point of origin and type of sensory receptor stimulated. It then remains for a collation of the signal with past experiences stored in the cortex, in order for interpretation to be achieved.

Somesthetic Sensation

According to Guyton (1974), somesthetic sensations are generally subdivided into exteroceptive, proprioceptive, and visceral sensations.

This is largely an academic distinction, as there is much overlap among these different types. Touch, pressure, heat, cold, and pain—all normally felt from the skin—are exteroceptive sensations. Sensations such as tension of the muscles or tendons, angulation of the joints, and deep pressure from the bottom of the feet are proprioceptive. They provide the brain with information about the physical state of the body. Visceral sensations, such as pain, fullness, and sometimes heat, come from the internal organs. Overlap among these three types of somesthetic sensations can be observed in cases of pressure, pain, and heat.

Williams (1969) identified four types of sensory receptors in the muscles, tendons, and joints, which provide proprioceptive input. These include the muscle spindles; Golgi tendon organs; joint receptors, or Pacinian corpuscles; and free nerve endings.

Muscle spindles and Golgi tendon organs transmit proprioceptive information from the muscles. Muscle spindles, consisting of muscle fibers innervated by sensory nerve endings, are found in the equatorial region of the muscles. These receptors are sensitive to muscle stretch and transmit this information to the central nervous system. Golgi tendon organs are sensitive to the overall tension applied to a tendon and inform the central nervous system of the effective muscle contractile strength.

Pacinian corpuscles are sensitive to deep pressure, as they become excited by deformation of the tissue in which they are housed. They provide information about the degree of angulation of joints and the rate at which the angulation changes. Two classes of joint receptors have been proposed: fast-adapting and slow-adapting receptors. The former discharge only if movement is present in the joint. The latter respond to position as well as movement.

The free nerve endings detect sensations of touch, pressure, pain, heat, and cold, but only in a very crude sense. Not much is known about these sensory receptors, because they sometimes interconnect extensively and are not always specific to the type of sensation transmitted. It is known that the free nerve endings provide the general background functions of sensation, while more specific discriminations are provided by more specialized receptors.

Once somesthetic impulses have left a sense organ and traveled up a peripheral nerve, they enter the spinal cord and are transmitted to the brain over either the dorsal column system or the spinothalamic system. The dorsal column system transmits highly localized and finely graded touch sensations, phasic sensations (vibrations), kinesthetic sensations, muscle sensations, and finely graded pressure sensations. The spinothalamic system conducts such sensations as pain, temperature, crude touch and pressure, tickles, itches, and sexual arousal. Most of the nerve fibers in the spinothalamic system terminate in the brainstem.

Visual Sensation

Vision has probably received more study than any of the other senses, and enough material has been gathered to fill a book. The following treatment is brief, emphasizing the points that aid in understanding how visual perception is accomplished.

Perhaps the most outstanding anatomical feature of the eye is its construction, which enables it to function as a camera does. Light passes through a small opening, the pupil, and then through a lens, which focuses the light on the retina. The retina is a photosensitive structure, which translates images into nerve impulses. These impulses are transmitted via the optic nerve to the brain.

The optic nerves, one from each eye, meet in the optic chiasm, located at the base of the brain, and part of the fibers of each nerve cross over to the other side of the brain. In humans, the lateral half of the right retina is connected to the right hemisphere of the brain, and the lateral half of the left retina to the left hemisphere. The medial half of each retina is connected to the hemisphere on the opposite side (see Figure 8.2). Many of the fibers synapse in the lateral geniculate body on their way to the visual cortex. Other fibers terminate in the thalamus, the midbrain, and various subcortical structures. The fact that synapses are located in different areas allows discrimination among certain qualities of the visual display.

The retina provides the central nervous system with two components of information: a visual pattern and changes in light intensity. A visual pattern is provided when light areas are stimulated and dark areas are not. Changes in light intensity are detected because the retina responds strongly when it is first stimulated, but then its response quickly drops to a low level. Through this type of response, our vision is more sensitive to movement than to stationary objects. The lateral geniculate body of the thalamus interprets other aspects of the visual display. It is believed to be involved in depth perception and color vision (Guyton, 1974).

Sensory information from the eyes is also provided from sources other than the retina. Each eye is positioned by three pairs of muscles:

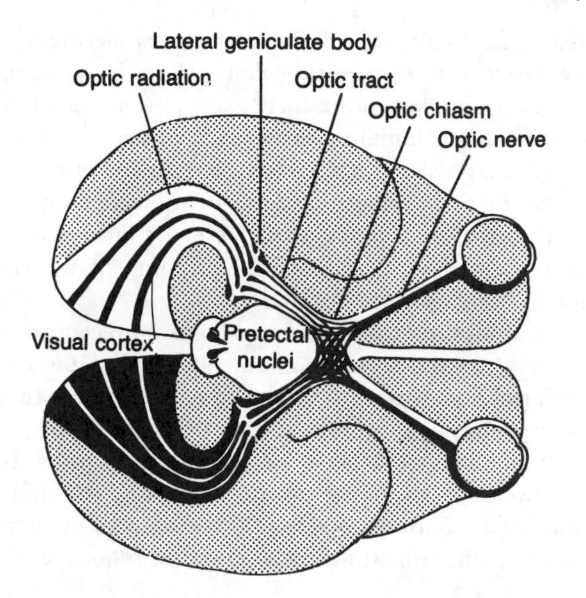

Figure 8.2. Pathways for the transmission of visual signals from the retinas of the two eyes to the visual cortex.

one for horizontal movement, the second for vertical movement, and the third for rotation of the eye in either direction. These muscles are used to move the eyes so that they focus on the target, fuse the image on the corresponding portions of both retinas, and provide kinesthetic cues about eye position. Guyton (1974) has suggested that the minute adjustments of the eyes' position are so important to vision that large parts of the visual association areas in the cortex are concerned with eye movements.

Interpretation by the Brain

Two types of sensory information, diffuse and discrete, are sent to the brain. Diffuse information follows collateral branches of a pathway that directs impulses through the reticular activating system (RAS) to the cerebral cortex. It provides the central nervous system with arousal or alerting information—it tells the brain to get ready for something. Discrete information follows the sensory tract to the appropriate locations in the brain. It is specific information, transmitted to specific locations in the brain (French, 1957, 1960).

The various sensations are transmitted from the receptor organs to small, localized areas of the cortex called projection areas, or primary cortical areas (see Figure 8.3). The primary somesthetic area lies immediately posterior to the central sulcus. The primary visual area is located in the posterior part of the cortex, as a part of the occipital lobe.

At the point when impulses arrive at a primary cortical area, a person is aware that a signal has arrived, but a perception is yet to be formed. Formation of a perception occurs in a second, adjacent area of the cortex called the association area. Here the interrelationships of objects, identity of objects, and overall meaning of the stimuli are comprehended.

The information supplied from several sensory receptors is merged in the common integrative area (Magoun, 1963; John, 1967). From this point, the information is sent to the premotor area and an area that Luria (1966) described as a motor analyzer, or the motor planning area. Here kinesthetic, proprioceptive sensations are integrated with information about spatial and temporal aspects of the environment, into what has been described as a spatial synthesis of movement. The final movement plan, consisting of a temporal sequence of links, is

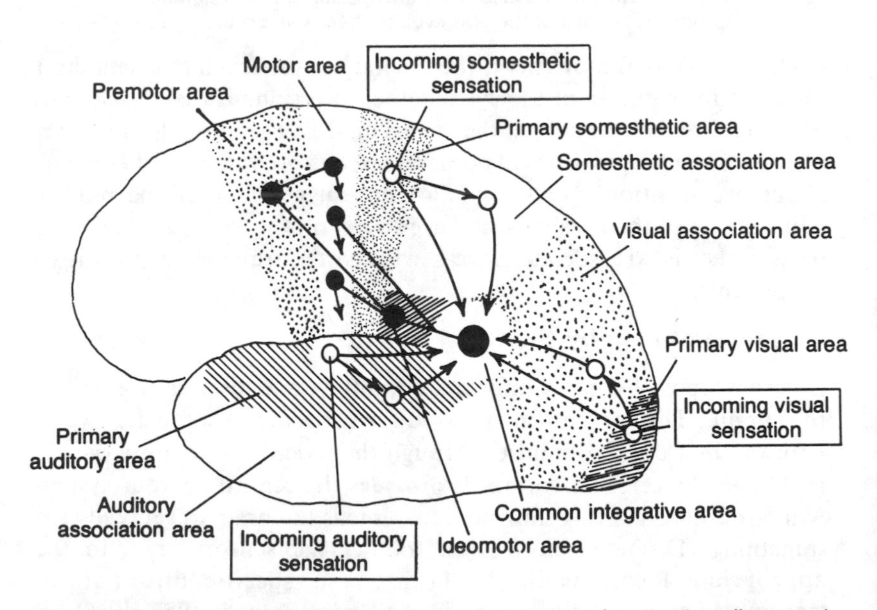

Figure 8.3. Primary cortical areas and association areas for visual, auditory, and somesthetic sensations. Sensory signals from several different sources are merged into a single impulse by the common integrative area. (From A. C. Guyton, *Function of the human body,* 4th ed., Philadelphia: W. B. Saunders, 1974, p. 283.)

formed. This sequence, or motor plan, is a complex system of successive innervations and denervations that take place as the appropriate segments of the series are performed. Once single motor responses have been converted and organized into serial movements that reflect time and the general tonic state of the person, the movement plan is sent to the motor area of the cortex and other areas, such as the cerebellum, for execution.

Paillard (1960) has described the cortical participation in the formation of voluntary responses. He believed that three factors are integrated to form voluntary patterns: afferent input with its spatio-temporal characteristics, individual characteristics of the nervous system, and the ability ("will," or "mind") to control and modify input and output. These factors allow a great plasticity of response. They continuously adapt motor responses to new situations by inventing novel coordinating patterns and fixing them in memory. In fact, the spatial and temporal characteristics of movement are such that a given motor response cannot be performed exactly the same at different times. One act becomes the signal that brings the next one into play.

Information can be filtered to a degree at the peripheral level as well as in the cerebral cortex. This process, called adaptation, occurs as sensory receptors respond vigorously at first but progressively less and less with continued stimulation. Adaptation occurs in varying degrees and with varying speeds. Sensations of light and some types of pressure adapt very quickly, but proprioceptive sensations have a long period of persistence. This characteristic of proprioceptive stimulation enables the brain to know the physical status of the body parts at all times rather than only immediately after movements have ocurred.

This overview of the functions of the nervous system in perception has been provided to illustrate the complex nature of perception. It has emphasized that perceptions are highly individualistic and are acquired only after long periods of learning. The remainder of this chapter looks at perception from a behavioral rather than a neurological approach. Visual perception, kinesthetic perception, and balance will be discussed with emphasis on their relevance to motor learning and motor performance.

PERCEPTUAL ORGANIZATION

Individuals adopt a perceptual attitude or personal outlook on the world, called perceptual organization, which provides an organizing theme through which the individual tests reality. Types of perceptual organization were studied by Drowatzky and Slobof (1967) to determine their role in learning. They observed that the mode of perceptual organization used by college men has no effect on learning a mirror-tracing skill. In a similar study conducted with college women as subjects, however, Drowatzky (1968) observed an interaction between perceptual organization and learning a mirror-tracing task. The interaction is most apparent in the middle of a series of practice trials. Further investigations of perceptual organization have indicated that it is a factor in learning gross motor skills. In a study of catching performance among high school students, MacGillivary (1979) reported that field-independent perceptual organization is related to greater rates and greater amounts of learning.

Three perceptual types were proposed by Petrie (1967) to describe the ways in which different individuals interpret the sensory environment. Reducers are persons who consistently reduce the intensity of perceived stimuli. Augmenters consistently augment the intensity of what they perceive. Moderators neither reduce nor augment their perceptual experiences. Ryan and Kovacic (1966) found that athletes commonly possess characteristics such as pain tolerance, intolerance of sensory deprivation, and extroversion, which are common to reducers.

In a study of perceptual types and athletic participation, Ryan and Foster (1967) reported significant differences between the characteristics of athletes and nonathletes. Athletes in contact sports tolerate the most pain, make the greatest underestimates of time, and reduce their kinesthetic estimations. Nonathletes tolerate the least pain, overestimate time, and augment their kinesthetic estimations. The responses of athletes in noncontact sports are intermediate between those of the other two groups. No differences between the groups were observed in reaction time and movement time.

Another category, the stimulus-governed type, was postulated by Petrie (1967). Stimulus-governed persons either augment or reduce their perceptions, depending on how the stimuli are presented. Petrie suggested that this type is atypical and is either very immature or brain damaged. In a later study, however, Hoff (1979) reported that a large proportion of her sample was stimulus-governed persons. She therefore concluded that this type should be considered a part of the normal population, with its own particular perceptual style, rather than immature or neurologically damaged.

The studies summarized suggest that various aspects of perception affect performance and perhaps learning. Much research needs to be conducted before any definitive statements can be made.

VISUAL PERCEPTION

Improved visual perception has been reported in highly skilled performers. The relationship between athletic ability and the capacity to perceive, analyze, interpret, and react quickly to visual cues was assessed in champion, near-champion, and low-skilled performers by Miller (1960). She found that the visual perceptual abilities of championship-caliber players are measurably superior to those of persons with low levels of motor skill.

Krieger (1962) evaluated the influence of figure-ground perception on the ability of beginning and intermediate tennis players to orient the racket for successful ball contact. Her findings indicate a relationship between figure-ground perception and the ability to make spatial adjustments.

Drowatzky (1967) investigated the relationship of size constancy (a form of perceptual organization) to performance in eight different motor skills. He reported significant relationships for the more complex motor skills, which required movement in more than one plane of action.

Gallahue (1968) investigated the relationship between figure-ground perception and performance on gross motor tasks by kindergarten pupils. His findings suggest that the accuracy of performance on such tasks is influenced by the composition of various figure-ground patterns of the tasks. A study by Fleishman and Rich (1963) reported that sensitivity to spatial visual cues is important in early stages of learning.

Two visual abilities that contribute to motor skill performance deserve particular attention: depth perception and peripheral vision.

Depth Perception

Our world is a three-dimensional space filled with objects located at different distances, but we can perform exceedingly difficult acts requiring precise judgments of depth, such as hitting a pitched ball, driving a car, or landing an aircraft. Observations of highly skilled sports performers illustrate the need for accuracy in judgments of depth.

Depth perception is accomplished through the precision engineering of the eye. Two classes of information, primary cues and secondary cues, are used by the central nervous system to perceive depth. Primary cues are provided by accommodation, convergence, and binocular disparity. Accommodation, or changes in the shape of the lens as an image is focused on the retina, provides kinesthetic sensations if objects are very close. Convergence, or the inward rotation of the eyes, also provides kinesthetic sensations, originating in the external eye muscles. Binocular disparity, or retinal disparity, is the difference between the two images presented to the retinas, as a result of seeing with two eyes, which view objects from slightly different angles (Vernon, 1963). Binocular disparity probably provides more important cues than either accommodation or convergence.

A large number of secondary or learned cues are also used in depth perception. These present information about such characteristics as size, color, partial overlap, texture, shadow, and perspective (Weintraub and Walker, 1966). As these cues are learned, they can become highly important in motor performance. There are professional athletes who, having lost the use of primary cues as a result of blindness in one eye, are still highly successful in performances requiring depth perception. They have developed a reliance on secondary depth cues instead of primary cues.

In a review of research conducted during the 1952 Olympics, Graybiel, Jokl, and Trapp (1955) reported moderate correlations between athletic performance and depth perception. The relationship between ability and depth perception was especially evident with tennis and soccer players. A comprehensive investigation by Miller (1960) indicated that depth perception is one of the main factors differentiating outstanding sports performers from low-skilled persons. These studies are typical of research conducted to assess depth perception and motor performance. Their weakness is that they investigated static depth perception, with tests using stationary elements. Two studies by Williams (1967, 1968), however, using a dynamic measure of depth perception, indicated similar differences between skilled and unskilled performers. She further reported that depth perception is rather well developed by 12 years of age.

Attempts have been made to improve depth perception and other visual capacities of young children through sensorimotor training programs. These efforts have not met with apparent success, however. Newmeister (1977) indicated the 5-year-old children did not improve their depth perception after 30 days of practice. It is logical to expect that brief programs have little impact on long-term developmental changes.

Peripheral Vision

Peripheral vision refers to the ability to receive and use visual cues that originate in the periphery of the retina. This capacity also enters into skilled sports performance. In the review cited earlier, Graybiel, Jokl, and Trapp (1955) found that the elimination of peripheral vision in skilled athletes causes a greater disturbance in performance than the elimination of central vision and in some cases the elimination of all vision.

Williams and Thirer (1975) reported that the vertical and horizontal visual fields of college athletes are larger than those of nonathletes. They observed no sex differences for the horizontal field but found that women have a greater high vertical range. McCain (1950), however, found little difference in the peripheral vision of high school athletes and nonathletes. The difference in the results of these two studies can probably be explained by the caliber of the athletes involved.

Sills and Troutman (1965) investigated the relation between perceptual vision and accuracy in shooting a basketball. They reported no influences on shooting accuracy for peripheral sightings as much as 10° from the basket. As the angle of peripheral sightings increased to 20° and 30° from the basket, accuracy in shooting decreased.

The role of peripheral vision in sports performance has not received extensive investigation, and thus only the most general and tentative conclusions can be drawn. Peripheral vision affects performance, and its importance apparently increases with skill level.

Eye Movement

The position and movement of the eyes are controlled by several mechanisms. As mentioned earlier (see chapter 6), an open-loop system provides coarse control for rapid eye movement as the head moves, and a closed-loop system provides fine control for slow eye movements. Sudden acceleration and deceleration of the head, however, can stimulate the semicircular canals of the inner ear, distorting sensations of the upright position and causing rotational and postrotational nystagmus. To prevent these problems, dancers, divers, skaters, and gymnasts avoid sudden movements of the head and maintain a fixed visual reference. Head movements and changes in visual field are restricted to one quick motion for each revolution (Leukel, 1976).

Movement of the eyes can also cause changes in the center of gravity if the gaze is shifted. Closing the eyes facilitates vestibular influences, as the use of the visual system modifies vestibular effects on posture. Fixation of the visual system is more important for postural stabilization than the retinal input is (Gurfinkel and Shik, 1973).

Finally, tracking is accomplished by two optical movement systems: the smooth pursuit system, which matches the velocity of eye movements with the velocity of the target, and the saccadic eye movement system, which detects and corrects for differences between the location of the target and the fixation point of the eyes. Williams and Helfrich (1977) found that high school girls with faster saccadic eye movements are better batters than girls with slower saccadic eye movements. Training programs were reported to improve batting performance and increase the speed of saccadic eye movement. According to Festinger and Cannon (1965), a target is located accurately on the basis of saccadic movements, followed by the less accurate pursuit movements. Thus, improvement in saccadic accuracy and speed should enhance ball skills and other activities involving targets.

Effects of Activity on Visual Perception

Few studies have evaluated the effects of physical activity on visual perception, and research on this problem has yielded mixed results. The effects appear to depend on the type of perception involved.

Tussing (1940) investigated the effects of athletic participation on the depth perception of college athletes. Varsity basketball players and freshman football players tested before and immediately after practice sessions showed no significant changes in depth perception as a result of practice. In a similar but better controlled study, Schwartz (1968) found no significant differences in depth perception between a nonexercising control group and a group that performed progressively more strenous exercise. Further, no differences were obtained between the initial and final depth perception scores for either group.

Other types of visual perception are affected by physical activity. Tussing (1941) reported that physical fatigue from athletic practice and isotonic exercise causes increases in fluctuations in visual illusions. The same effect was reported by Hollingworth (1939), after observing subjects exposed to a rigorous work program.

Several investigators have evaluated the effects of fatigue on flicker fusion frequency (FFF), which is the rate at which successive flashes from a stationary light source appear as a steady beam rather than a flicker. Brozek and Keys (1944) reported small decreases in FFF in men after exposure to prolonged stress, such as varying work loads. Increases in FFF after static exercise and decreases after dynamic exercise were observed by Simonson, Enzer, and Benton (1943). Likewise, Arnold (cited in Simonson and Brozek, 1952) observed a decrease in FFF after various types of work, such as lifting or riding a bicycle ergometer with different work loads. After 5 or 10 minutes of recovery, the decrease in FFF was followed by an increase.

In addition to its long-term role in the development of perception, motor activity can have acute, short-term influences on some aspects of vision. Few studies have been conducted to assess the acute effects of activity, but at least two types of visual perception, illusions and FFF, have been observed to change somewhat after strenuous physical work. Other perceptual capabilities, such as depth perception, are not affected in the same manner. There has not been enough comprehensive study of the short-term effects of physical activity on perception to merit any further generalizations.

KINESTHETIC PERCEPTION

Knowledge of the orientation of the body in space and of spatial relations between body parts depends on information from proprioceptive, vestibular, and visual receptors. Kinesthesis—the proprioceptive sense of position and movement of the joints—depends on the input of receptor organs located in the joints (Rose and Mountcastle, 1959). In behavioral terms, physical educators refer to kinesthesis as a general ability by which one knows the position of the body and its parts. Most studies, however, have indicated that kinesthesis is not a general ability but is highly specific to the body part and the movement involved (Fleishman, 1958; Scott, 1955; Wiebe, 1954; Young, 1945).

Some researchers have suggested that kinesthesis is used in learning. Perhaps the most comprehensive investigation of this theory was conducted by Honzik (1936). He found that white rats cannot learn to traverse a maze on the basis of kinesthesis alone. Consequently, he concluded that kinesthesis becomes important in motor learning only after other types of sensory information have begun the learning process. Other studies with rats by Ingebritsen (1932) and Lashley and Ball (1929) also indicate that kinesthesis is not a primary factor in maze learning. It appears that the correct "feel" experienced by performers must be acquired with other aspects of performance. This position is supported by Fleishman and Rich (1963), who found that as performance on skills with complex movements improves, so does kinesthesis. Tracking tasks are performed best if a variety of kinesthetic cues are available (Notterman and Page, 1962).

It also appears that skilled movements do not require kinesthesis, however (Taub and Berman, 1968; Bossom and Ommaya, 1968; Wilson, 1961; Lazlo, 1966; Lashley, 1951). In a study of the ability to recall from visual and short-term memory, Wilberg (1969) found differences in visual and kinesthetic memory images: performances based on visual input exceed those based on kinesthetic sources, and kinesthetic input was not usable in some situations. Phillips and Summers (1954) observed a relationship between the acquisition of bowling skill and kinesthesis and believed that the kinesthetic sense is more important during the early stages of skill learning than later. Their finding conflicts with other research, probably because bowling involves a familiar arm movement, which is easily transferred. This interpretation is supported by their observation that the preferred arm has more kinesthetic sensitivity than the nonpreferred arm. Using a two-hand coordination task, Fleishman and Rich (1963) observed that sensitivity to proprioceptive cues is important in later perceptual-motor learning. This finding appears to be more consistent with the overall trend of the literature.

Several studies have reported little or no relationship between kinesthesis and motor learning. Rollo (1959) compared the effectiveness of the traditional method of teaching beginning golf skills with instruction through kinesthetic perception. She observed no differences between the two approaches. After evaluating simple and complex motor learning tasks, Hill (1964) reported that kinesthetic tests had zero correlation with either type of learning. Likewise, Sisley (1963) reported a negligible relationship between kinesthesis and skill level in basketball, bowling, and tennis. Finally, a study of elementary school boys and girls by Witte (1962) showed no relationship between ball-rolling skills and kinesthesis. No differences between boys' and girls' performances on the kinesthetic task were observed in this study. Thus, there is no documented basis for the use of kinesthesis as the primary, initial teaching technique. It appears to be of greater value once the initial acquisition of a task has been accomplished.

BALANCE

Balance, or equilibrium, is related to kinesthesis and proprioception but requires special attention because of its important role in motor activity. Balance is controlled by the central nervous system through sensations originating in the vestibular apparatus of the inner ear, the visual system, and the muscles of equilibrium (see Figure 8.4). From these sources, nerve impulses travel to the lower brainstem, which performs two motor functions: it supports the body against gravity and

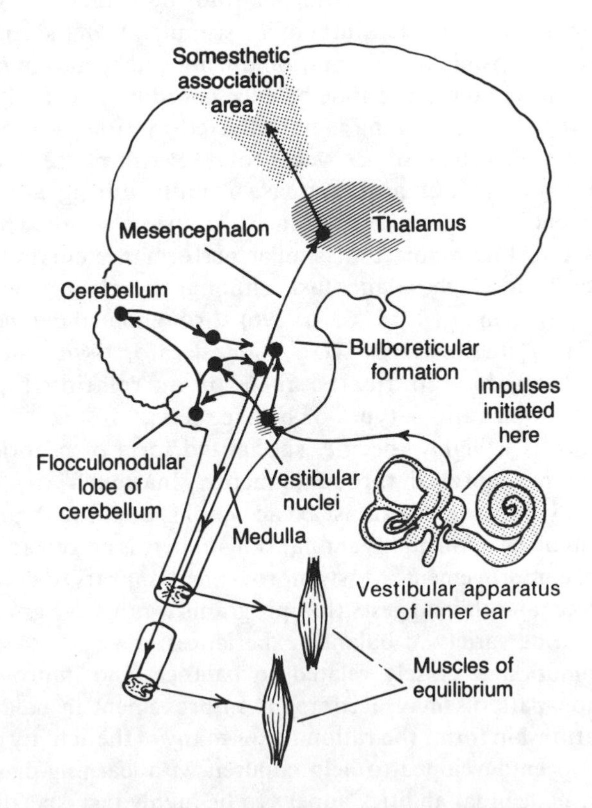

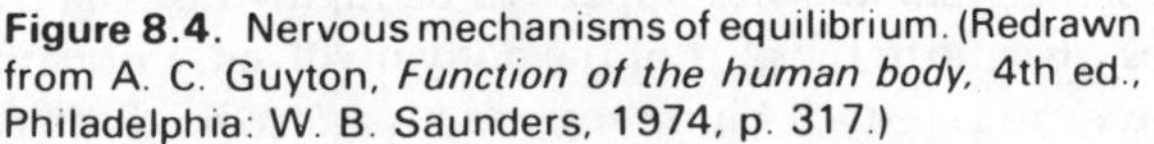
Figure 8.4. Nervous mechanisms of equilibrium. (Redrawn from A. C. Guyton, *Function of the human body,* 4th ed., Philadelphia: W. B. Saunders, 1974, p. 317.)

maintains equilibrium. These functions become integrated with rhythmic circuits in the central nervous system for locomotion. Other components of the central nervous system, such as the cerebellum, are also involved in balance and locomotion. The maintenance of equilibrium is not a simple neurological process.

Various classifications have been applied to types of balance, but most commonly it has been viewed as either static or dynamic. Dynamic balance is involved in the maintenance of equilibrium during motion, and static balance relates to postural orientation when one is motionless (Bass, 1939; Seashore, 1947). Some investigators (Travis, 1945) define balance as reflecting the relationship of the body to gravity. Equilibrium apparently is not the only factor responsible for body orientation in all activities. Results of a study by Tillman (1964) suggest that experience and practice, rather than stimulation of the semicircular canal, are responsible for orientation during rotary movements.

Bachman (1961) found that balance coordination can be learned and that the rate of learning is not affected by either age or sex, for subjects between 6 and 26 years old. Performance levels vary considerably with age and increase rapidly during adolescence. Improvement with practice on balance tasks was also noted by Wyrick (1969). She further reported dissimilar performance curves for a low-balance task and a high-balance task, although correlations between the two tasks were high (from .63 to .96) throughout the experimental period. Other studies (Drowatzky and Zuccato, 1967; Sanborn and Wyrick, 1969) have indicated little or no relationship among performances on various types of balance tests.

Balance is a highly specific, specialized form of proprioception, which can be improved through practice. Inasmuch as it is highly specific, any improvement must be accomplished through practice on the skill involved or on highly similar skills. There is no general program for balance improvement. Most improvement appears to occur during adolescence, and this suggests that programs for this age group should contain a wide variety of balance experiences.

Locomotion is closely related to balance, and improvement in locomotion patterns may accompany improvement in balance. This close relationship forms the rationale for many of the activity programs that have been developed to help children with learning disabilities.

Most perceptual abilities appear to be highly task-specific and, in some cases, specific to the part of the body involved. Little relationship among the various tests of kinesthesis and balance has been reported in the literature. One possible exception to the specificity of perception occurs with mentally retarded children. Significant correlations have been reported between some motor abilities and perceptual abilities in these children (Malpass, 1963). A number of researchers believe that perceptual defects and motor performance or motor learning are linked. Bateman (1964), Kephart (1964), Hammill and Bartel (1971), and Myers and Hammill (1969) provide examples of this approach to learning disabilities.

GUIDING PRINCIPLES FOR THE TEACHER

1. Perception is a process that correlates past experiences with present events and integrates sensations from more than one sensory source. The process is thus of a higher order than sensation. Perceptions are learned and consequently are subject to the laws of learning. Perception is a subjective process.

2. Our world acquires stability through perceptual constancy and identity. Constancy refers to the knowledge that objects have constant, unchanging characteristics, such as size, shape, and color. Identity comes when objects can be grouped on the basis of their similarities (generalization) or differences (discrimination).

3. Highly skilled performers generally have superior visual abilities; differences have been found in figure-ground relations, depth perception, peripheral vision, and the rapidity with which they can perceive, analyze, and interpret visual cues.

4. Highly skilled performers have better static and dynamic depth perception than low-skilled performers. Persons who have lost the use of primary depth cues, however, can learn to rely on secondary cues and still perform successfully.

5. Peripheral vision is more important in the performances of highly skilled individuals than in the performances of beginners. Its importance appears to increase with increasing skill levels, as performers become more familiar with cues in their central vision and can pay more attention to subtle cues and peripheral cues.

6. Participation in strenuous physical activities causes acute (short-term) changes in visual illusions and flicker fusion frequency but does not affect depth perception.

7. Kinesthesis is the ability to perceive the orientation of the body in space and spatial relations between body parts. It is based on input

from proprioceptive and vestibular receptors. It is not a general ability but is highly specific to the body part and the movement involved.

8. Kinesthesis alone does not provide enough information for learning new skills. It becomes important after other sensory sources have initiated the learning process and after the performer has acquired the correct kinesthetic "feel."

9. Balance, or equilibrium, is a specialized aspect of proprioception. It requires information from the vestibular apparatus of the inner ear and the muscles of equilibrium. Visual information also contributes to balance. Balance reflects the relationship of the body to gravity in static positions and during movement.

10. Balance is not a general factor; it is highly specific to the position or movements involved. Performance levels vary greatly with age and improve most rapidly during adolescence.

SUMMARY

Perception is the process through which our world acquires stability and meaning. It is dependent on learning. Perception involves the integration of two or more kinds of sensory information. Meanings are bestowed on present events as they are integrated with memories of past experiences stored in the central nervous system. Some interpretation of stimulus events can occur at the sensory receptor through adaptation. Constancy, generalization, and discrimination are perceptual processes that confer stability on the world.

This chapter discussed the two types of perception that are most involved in motor performance: somesthetic or proprioceptive perception and visual perception. Balance, or equilibrium, was discussed as a special type of proprioception. The general theme of perceptual integration with motor activity stresses the finding that we use different types of perception at different stages of learning. For most tasks, it appears that visual perception is most important early in the acquisition period, while kinesthetic perception becomes more important later. The studies reviewed here indicate that kinesthesis alone is not adequate for the learning of new skills.

Depth perception and peripheral vision are two important contributors to successful performance. Depth perception, which depends on both primary and secondary cues, is apparently well developed by 12 years of age. There are differences in the depth perception of skilled and unskilled performers. Peripheral vision acquires greater importance in motor performance among highly skilled performers. The elimination of peripheral vision can seriously disrupt the performance of highly skilled athletes. The use of peripheral vision at angles greater than 10° appears to decrease accuracy in tasks such as shooting a basketball.

Most perceptual abilities seem to be highly task-specific and, in some cases, specific to certain parts of the body, except perhaps among mentally retarded children. The specificity of perception requires teachers to plan for improvement in many specific abilities rather than one general ability.

REFERENCES

Bachman, J. C. 1961. Motor learning and performance as related to age and sex in two measures of balance coordination. *Research Quarterly* 32:123-137.

Bass, R. I. 1939. An analysis of the components of tests of semicircular canal functions and a static and dynamic balance. *Research Quarterly* 10:33-52.

Bateman, B. 1964. Learning disabilities—yesterday, today and tomorrow. *Exceptional Children* 31:167-177.

Bossom, J., and Ommaya, A. K. 1968. Visuo-motor adaptation (to prismatic transformation of the retinal image) in monkeys with bilateral dorsal rhizotomy. *Brain* 91: 161-172.

Brozek, J., and Keys, A. 1944. Changes in flicker fusion frequency (FFF) under experimental stress. *Federation Proceedings* 3:6.

Drowatzky, J. N. 1967. Relationship of size constancy to selected measures of motor ability. *Research Quarterly* 38:375-379.

———. 1968. Effects of modes of perceptual organization upon the acquisition of a perceptual motor skill by college women. Unpublished manuscript. University of Toledo.

Drowatzky, J. N., and Slobof, H. 1967. Influence of modes of perceptual organization upon the acquisition of perceptual motor skill. *Abstracts of research papers.* Washington, D.C.: AAHPER.

Drowatzky, J. N., and Zuccato, F. C. 1967. Interrelationships between selected measures of static and dynamic balance. *Research Quarterly* 38:509-510.

Festinger, L., and Cannon, L. K. 1965. Information about spatial location based on knowledge about efference. *Psychological Review* 72:373-384.

Fleishman, E. A. 1958. An analysis of positioning movements and static reaction. *Journal of Experimental Psychology* 55:13-24.

Fleishman, E. A., and Rich, S. 1963. Role of kinesthetic and spatial visual abilities in perceptual motor learning. *Journal of Experimental Psychology* 66:6-11.

French, J. D. 1957. The reticular formation. *Scientific American* 195 (May): 54-50.

———. 1960. The reticular formation. In *Handbook of physiology*. Sec. 1, vol. 2, ed. H. W. Magoun. Washington, D.C.: American Physiological Society.

Gallahue, D. I. 1968. The relationship between perceptual and motor abilities. *Research Quarterly* 39:948-952.

Graybiel, A., Jokl, E., and Trapp, C. 1955. Russian studies of vision in relation to physical activity and sports. *Research Quarterly* 26:480-485.

Gurfinkel, V. S., and Shik, M. L. 1973. The control of posture and locomotion. In *Motor control*, ed. A. A. Gydikov, N. T. Tankov, and D. S. Kosarov. New York: Plenum Press.

Guyton, A. C. 1974. *Function of the human body*. 4th ed. Philadelphia: W. B. Saunders.

Hammill, D. D., and Bartel, N. R., eds. 1971. *Educational perspectives in learning disabilities.* New York: John Wiley and Sons.
Hill, R. E. 1964. The relationship between selected measures of kinesthesis, general motor ability, and rates of learning simple and complex motor movements. Doctoral dissertation. University of Iowa.
Hoff, P. A. 1979. Kinesthetic augmentation and reduction in adult females. *Perceptual and Motor Skills.* 48:711-720.
Hollingworth, H. L. 1939. Perceptual fatigue as a fatigue function. *Journal of Experimental Psychology* 24:511-519.
Honzik, C. H. 1936. The role of kinesthesis in maze learning. *Science* 84:373.
Ingebritsen, O. C. 1932. Maze learning after lesion in the cervical cord. *Journal of Comparative Psychology* 14:279-294.
John, E. R. 1967. *Mechanisms of memory.* New York: Academic Press.
Kephart, N. C. 1964. Perceptual motor aspects of learning disabilities. *Exceptional Children* 31:201-206.
Krieger, J. C. 1962. The influence of figure ground perception on spatial adjustments in tennis. Master's thesis, University of California, Los Angeles.
Lashley, K. S. 1951. The problem of serial order in behavior. In *Cerebral mechanisms in behavior: The Hixon Symposium,* ed. L. A. Jeffres. New York: John Wiley and Sons.
Lashley, K. S., and Ball, J. 1929. Spinal conduction and kinesthetic sensitivity in the maze habit. *Journal of Comparative Psychology* 9:71-101.
Lazlo, J. I. 1966. The performance of a simple motor task with kinaesthetic sense loss. *Quarterly Journal of Experimental Psychology* 18:1-8.
Keukel, F. 1976. *Introduction to physiological psychology.* 3d ed. St. Louis: C. V. Mosby.
Luria, A. R. 1966. *Human brain and psychological processes.* New York: Harper & Row.
McCain, S. H. 1950. A comparison of the motion perception fields of athletes and nonathletes. Master's thesis. University of Alabama.
MacGillivary, W. W. 1979. Perceptual style and ball skill acquisition. *Research Quarterly* 50:222-229.
Magoun, H. W. 1963. *The waking brain.* 2d ed. Springfield, Ill.: Charles C. Thomas.
Malpass, L. F. 1963. Motor skills in mental deficiency. In *Handbook of mental deficiency: Psychological theory and research,* ed. N. R. Ellis. New York: McGraw-Hill.
Miller, D. M. 1960. The relationship between some visual perceptual factors and the degree of success realized by sports performers. Doctoral dissertation, University of Southern California.
Morgan, C. T. 1965. *Physiological psychology.* 3d ed. New York: McGraw-Hill.
Morris, P. R., and Whiting, H. T. A. 1971. *Motor impariment and compensatory education.* Philadelphia: Lea & Febiger.
Myers, P. I., and Hammill, D. D., eds. 1969. *Methods for learning disorders.* New York: John Wiley and Sons.
Newmeister, G. H. 1977. Effects of a visually directed sensory motor training program on depth perception of children. *Research Quarterly* 48:129-133.
Notterman, J. M., and Page, D. E. 1962. Evaluation of mathematically equivalent systems. *Perceptual and Motor Skills* 15:683-716.
Paillard, J. 1960. The patterning of skilled movements. In *Handbook of physiology.* Sec. 1, vol. 3, ed. H. W. Magoun. Washington, D.C.: American Physiological Society.
Petrie, A. 1967. *Individuality in pain and suffering.* Chicago: University of Chicago Press.
Phillips, M., and Summers, D. 1954. Relation of kinesthetic perception to motor learning. *Research Quarterly* 25:456-469.
Rollo, E. T. 1959. A comparison of two methods of teaching selected golf strokes. Master's thesis. University of Iowa.

Rose, J. E., and Mountcastle, V. B. 1959. Touch and kinesthesis. In *Handbook of physiology*. Sec. 1, vol. 1, ed. H. W. Magoun. Washington, D.C.: American Physiological Society.

Ryan, E. D., and Foster, R. 1967. Athletic participation and perceptual augmentation and reduction. *Journal of Personality and Social Psychology* 6:472-476.

Ryan, E. D., and Kovacic, C. R. 1966. Pain tolerance and athletic participation. *Perceptual and Motor Skills* 22:383-390.

Sanborn, C., and Wyrick, W. 1969. Prediction of Olympic balance beam performance from standardized and modified tests of balance. *Research Quarterly* 40:174-184.

Schwartz, R. M. 1968. The effects of various degrees of muscular work upon depth perception. Master's thesis, University of Toledo.

Scott, M. G. 1955. Measurement of kinesthesis. *Research Quarterly* 26:324-341.

Seashore, H. G. 1947. The development of a beam walking test and its use in measuring development of balance in children. *Research Quarterly* 18:246-259.

Sills, F. D., and Troutman, D. C. 1965. Peripheral vision and accuracy in shooting a basketball. *National College Physical Education Association for Men Proceedings* 69:112-114.

Simonson, E., and Brozek, J. 1952. Flicker fusion frequency—background and applications. *Physiological Review* 32:349-378.

Simonson, E., Enzer, N., and Benton, R. W. 1943. The influence of muscular work and fatigue on the state of the central nervous system. *Journal of Laboratory and Clinical Medicine* 28:1555-1567.

Sisley, H. L. 1963. Kinesthesis in relation to skill level in basketball, bowling and tennis. Master's thesis, University of North Carolina.

Taub, E., and Berman, A. J. 1968. Movement and learning in the absence of sensory feedback. In *The neuropsychology of spatially oriented behavior*, ed. S. J. Freedman. Homewood, Ill.: Dorsey.

Tillman, T. N. 1964. A preliminary study of the measurement of human orientation ability during rotation. Master's thesis, Michigan State University.

Travis, R. C. 1945. Experimental analysis of dynamic and static equilibrium. *Journal of Experimental Psychology* 35:216-234.

Tussing, L. 1940. The effect of football and basketball on vision. *Research Quarterly* 11:16-18.

———. 1941. Perceptual fluctuations of illusions as a possible fatigue index. *Journal of Experimental Psychology* 29:85-88.

Vernon, M. D. 1963. *The psychology of perception*. New York: Penguin.

Weintraub, D. J., and Walker, E. L. 1966. *Perception*. Monterey, Calif.: Brooks/Cole.

Wiebe, V. R. 1954. A study of tests of kinesthesis. *Research Quarterly* 25:222-230.

Wilberg, R. B. 1969. Response accuracy based upon recall from visual and kinesthetic short term memory. *Research Quarterly* 40:407-414.

Williams, H. G. 1967. The perception of moving objects by children. Unpublished manuscript, University of Toledo.

———. 1968. The effects of systematic variation of speed and direction of object flight and of skill and age classification upon visual perceptual judgments of moving objects in three dimensional space. Doctoral dissertation. University of Wisconsin, Madison.

———. 1969. Neurological concepts and perceptual motor behavior. In *New perspectives of man in action*, ed. R. C. Brown, Jr. and B. J. Cratty. Englewood Cliffs, N.J.: Prentice-Hall.

Williams, H. G., and Helfrich, J. 1977. Saccadic eye movement speed and motor response execution. *Research Quarterly* 48:598-605.

Williams, J. M., and Thirer, J. 1975. Vertical and horizontal peripheral vision in male and female athletes and nonathletes. *Research Quarterly* 46:200-205.

Wilson, D. M. 1961. The central nervous control of flight in a locust. *Journal of Experimental Biology* 38:471-490.

Witte, F. 1962. Relation of kinesthetic perception to a selected motor skill for elementary school children. *Research Quarterly* 33:476-484.

Wyrick, W. 1969. Effects of task height and practice on static balance. *Research Quarterly* 40:215-221.

Young, O. G. 1945. Study of kinesthesis in relation to selected movements. *Research Quarterly* 16:277-287.

9 Personality and Performance

Personality refers to the unique characteristics of individuals. It may determine what acitivities one chooses to participate in, social contacts, and many patterns of behavior. No one set of personality traits is common to athletes or groups of athletes, so that teachers and coaches must be able to meet many and diverse needs.

What is personality? The overriding theme of this book is that teachers must be sensitive to individual differences among students. Personality is one way to describe and assess individual differences. According to McKeachie and Doyle (1966, p. 410), personality refers to "the unique organization of relatively enduring psychological characteristics possessed by an individual, as revealed by his interaction with the environment." Drever (1964, p. 208) gave this definition:

> A term used in various senses, both popularly and psychologically, the most comprehensive and satisfactory being the integrated and dynamic organization of the physical, mental, moral, and social qualities of the individual, as that manifests itself to other people, in the give and take of social life; on further analysis it would appear in the main to comprise the natural and acquired impulses and habits, interests, and

> complexes, the sentiments and ideals, the opinions and beliefs, as manifested in his relations with his social milieu.

Efforts by psychologists to arrive at a more precise definition have generally been unsuccessful. Personality theorists do not agree on more specific aspects of the subject (as, similarly, their colleagues disagree about precise definitions of intelligence or physical fitness). The difficulties, however, do not prevent us from working with the general concept as we endeavor to sharpen our understanding of it.

The term *personality* is sometimes used synonymously with *character* or *temperament*. *Character* is most commonly used to describe a person's volitional qualities or acts that one performs voluntarily and willfully. *Temperament* most commonly refers to emotional qualities. According to the definitions presented above, personality includes both character and temperament as well as abilities, interests, and appearance.

These definitions emphasize the individual nature of persons. No two people are exactly alike: each possesses a unique set of psychological characteristics. Further, although personality is relatively stable and endures through time, it is continually developing and evolving—a dynamic rather than a static, unchanging dimension. Finally, personality is disclosed in the way one interacts with the environment; inferences about an individual's personality are based on either observable behavior or responses on standardized tests.

Personality can be described in terms of either types or traits. Personality types are general categories that classify individuals according to various qualities. For example, one may be described as an athletic type, an artistic type, or an integrated type. Jung (1933) proposed introversion and extroversion as two basic personality types. Sheldon's somatotype and personality type systems describe persons as cerebrotonic, viscerotonic, and somatotonic (Sheldon, Stevens, and Tucker, 1940; Sheldon and Stevens, 1942).

Classification according to personality types has not proved to be as useful in scientific research as classification by personality traits. In this approach, personality is regarded as a composite of a relatively large number of narrowly defined traits. These are not discrete categories to which a person does or does not belong, but rather they are dimensions that characterize an individual in a high, low, or moderate degree. For example, one may be described as very honest, somewhat selfish, or quite brave. Psychologists have defined personality traits that can be measured on quantitative scales. One problem is that so many traits have been identified; Allport and Odbert (1936) estimated that between 3,000 and 5,000 trait names have been used to describe personal qualities. Different psychologists have selected sets of traits for study, and the proliferation of personality tests is a consequence of their attempts to measure them.

Personality tests sometimes give an impression of consistency of personality. That is, there is a tendency to assume that individuals display the same traits from time to time and from situation to situation. Such consistency, however, is not truly characteristic of personality. For example, Andersen (1973), in an investigation of swimmers' personalities, indicated that the situation in which persons find themselves has an important influence on the traits that are observed. The swimmers in his study tended to set goals considerably below the reference norm for unfamiliar tasks but slightly above their reference for familiar tasks.

Much of the research on personality assessment has been generated by agencies dealing with individuals who have personality problems or inadequacies. Consequently, there are many more tests for maladjustment than for adjustment. In fact, problem areas such as neurotic tendencies, can be measured much more successfully than positive qualities such as leadership. Interpretation of the results of research and attempts to generalize findings must therefore consider the purpose for which a given test was developed.

MEASUREMENT OF PERSONALITY

The concept of traits enables us to compare one person or group of persons with another and thus measure personality. Various methods of personality assessment have been used for research on individual differences. Each method has been subjected to statistical analysis to evaluate validity and reliability. Validity, in relation to personality assessment, requires that a test actually measures the traits that it is supposed to measure. Reliability requires that a test produces about the same results for the same subjects in different trials; a reliable test gives stable results. In addition, the instrument must be sensitive enough to discriminate among people. This requirement is closely related to validity and reliability. Reliability combined with sensitivity should produce stability in test scores obtained under the same conditions, if there has been no true change in the trait that is being measured.

The quantitative assessment of personality has generally been based on one of four principal methods. The first is a rating technique, in which an observer assigns a value on a scale from 1 to 5 or from 1 to 7, representing the degree to which the subject displays a particular trait. This method is not widely used in research today because of reliability problems; ratings are often confounded, as they are partly determined by the personality of the rater, as well as the personality of the subject. Another problem is that they represent the image the subject shows to the rater, which may not reflect the subject's real self. This type of rating is still used informally by most of us in our day-to-day dealings with others, however.

The second type of personality assessment involves the use of questionnaires or self-report inventories, in which subjects respond to questions about their activities, preferences, and feelings. Scores on this type of instrument depend a great deal on the subject's honesty in answering the questions. Special keys have been developed to indicate whether a person has tried to project a good or bad image, but doubts remain about the meaning of self-reports.

Perhaps the most widely used testing questionnaire is the Minnesota Multiphasic Personality Inventory (MMPI), which was originally developed "to assay those traits that are commonly characteristic of disabling psychological abnormality" (Hathaway and McKinley, 1967, p. 1). It has been used and evaluated in more than 1,500 published studies. The MMPI covers a variety of content areas, such as health, psychosomatic symptoms, neurological disorders, and motor disturbances; sexual, political, religious, and social attitudes; educational, occupational, family, and marital status: and neurotic and psychotic behavior manifestations (obsessive and compulsive states, delusions, hallucinations, ideas of reference, phobias, and sadistic and masochistic trends). Responses to 550 true-false items (for example, "My sex life is satisfactory" and "I am often afraid of the dark") are evaluated on 10 clinical scales, which indicate hypochondriasis, depression, hysteria, psychopathic deviance, masculinity-feminity, paranoia, psychasthenia, schizophrenia, hypomania, and social introversion. The clinical scales cannot be literally interpreted, as normal people can score as high on a given scale as abnormal people do. Although the MMPI and similar instruments are easily administered, proper interpretation requires considerable psychological sophistication and should be undertaken only by trained specialists.

A similar invention, developed on the model of the MMPI but for use with normal populations, is the California Personality Inventory (CPI). Eighteen scales have been developed from its 480 true-false items, to assess sense of well-being, good impression, communality, dominance, sociability, self-acceptance, responsibility, socialization, self-control, achievement-via-conformance, achievement-via-independence, femininity, capacity for status, social presence, tolerance, intellectual efficiency, psychological-mindedness, and flexibility (Gough, 1960). This inventory has evolved through continuous improvement and technical development. It has been subjected to extensive research, which has produced a series of regression equations that are useful in predicting various aspects of personality.

Factor-analytic techniques have been used to develop other questionnaires and inventories having some consistency, generality, and stability. An example is the Sixteen Personality Factor Questionnaire (16PF), which has been extensively used with athletes. It provides scales for sociability, intelligence, ego-strength, dominance, surgency, conscientiousness, adventurousness, realism, protension, bohemianism, shrewdness, insecurity, radicalism, self-sufficiency, will power, and tenseness (Cattell and Eber, 1970).

The problem with inventories such as the 16PF is that they were developed through statistical techniques and give no clear picture of what the traits are or how they appear in real-life situations. The trait names were derived from attempts by different researchers to describe clusters of items that are statistically related. Thus, although both the CPI and the 16PF contain scales for dominance, there is no reason to believe that these scales measure the same or related personality characteristics. Each test stands alone and must be interpreted on its own terms. This is the case for each of the many questionnaire inventories in use today.

A third technique of personality assessment is the projective or expressive method. This method presents a relatively unstructured task and brief, general instructions to elicit an almost unlimited variety of responses. The underlying assumption is that the way in which an individual interprets or structures the test materials reflects fundamental aspects of his or her psychological functioning. Projective tests are often regarded as especially effective in revealing unconscious aspects of personality. They are predominantly clinical tools, which require special training and skill. Perhaps the most familiar example is the Rorschach inkblot test, in which subjects tell what each of ten test blots represents (Rorschach, 1942). A more highly structured stimulus situation, requiring more complex verbal responses, is used in the Thematic Apperception Test (TAT) (Murray et al., 1938). Subjects are asked to make up a story about each of 19 picture cards and to give details about what led to the situation, what is happening, and what each character in the picture is feeling and thinking. One blank card is also displayed, and subjects are asked to imagine and describe a picture on it. This test and its many adaptations have been developed for various special purposes.

The fourth commonly used method of personality evaluation, called the objective method, involves the measurement of behavioral or physiological responses. This method has not been widely used because of difficulties in administration, interpretation, and reliability. With improved statistical and analytical techniques, however, it may be more widely used in the future.

Personality assessment instruments tend to be designed and validated for use with specific age groups (children, adolescents, college-students, adults, or some combination of these). Results of personality studies therefore should not be generalized beyond the population from which the data are derived. Conclusions drawn from a study of preadolescent children should be helpful in understanding that group, if the subjects in the study are representative of preadolescents. Similar limitations are imposed on conclusions from studies of other age groups. It is likely that there are important relationships between personality and performance of physical skills at each maturation or age level, but these relationships are not likely to be the same at all levels. At the present time, little is known about the effects of aging on these relationships. Understanding the changing nature of relationships between personality and performance as age advances would be an important asset to physical educators, since it would give them firm grounds for designing programs that are suitable for students at different levels of maturity.

PERSONALITY THEORIES

Psychologists have developed personality theories to interpret their observations of human behavior. Any personality theory includes certain assumptions about human nature and the theorist's beliefs about what is desirable or undesirable behavior. An accurate theory would have a complex range of personality categories. Complexity is not necessarily desirable, however, and it makes behavior difficult to predict. Conversely, simplicity of classification would miss the richness of the range of possible emotions and expressions. Personality theories thus represent compromises in attempts to minimize these disadvantages and yet reflect theorists' observations of and beliefs about human behavior.

Maslow's self-actualization approach is one example of a personality theory. It represents a departure from tradition in that Maslow has considered motivation in terms of growth and striving for happiness and satisfaction rather than avoidance of pain and reduction of tension (Maslow, 1970). According to his theory, human needs are arranged in a hierarchy, with the lower needs having greater potency and thus priority over the higher needs. At the lowest level are physiological needs, followed by needs for safety, love and belonging, and esteem. Only when all these are at least partially gratified can a person begin to experience the higher, self-actualizing needs—needs to develop one's individual nature and fulfill one's potential. The most human condition is thus expressed in the pursuit of self-actualization.

Maslow described needs as deficit states. That is, a need is a lack of something, which serves as an impelling force. A motive, in contrast, is a conscious desire, a felt impulse, or an urge for a specific object. Therefore, he viewed needs as the basic ends and motives as the specific means to fulfill the needs. Life offers many more motives than needs.

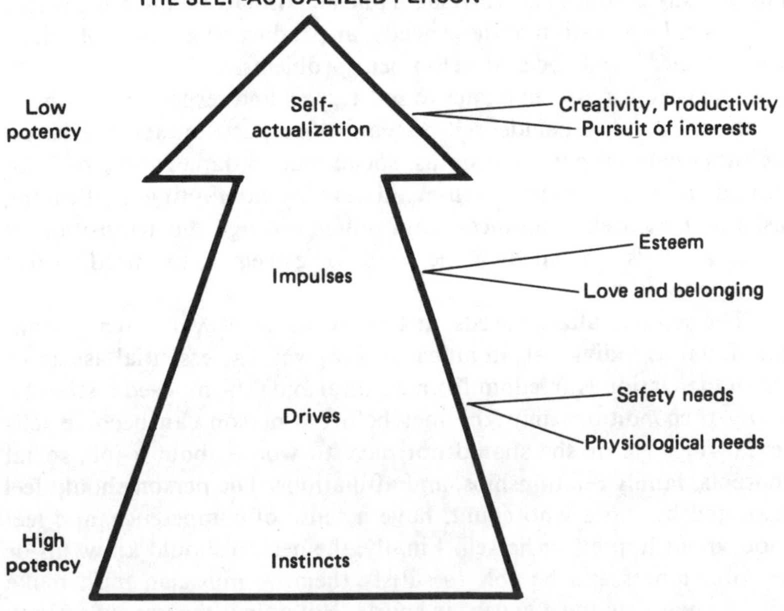

Figure 9.1. Maslow's hierarchy of human needs.

Two people may have the same need for respect, but one may attempt to obtain it through sports while the other chooses music or art as the means of gratification.

The most potent needs in Maslow's scheme are the physiological needs. When these are deprived for long periods of time, other needs fail to appear or recede from view. Yet the physiological needs are the least significant for a self-actualizing person.

Safety needs include the need for security, stability, order, protection, and dependency. These are all related to preserving of the status quo—conserving and maintaining order and security. Although many persons declare their desire for greater independence, they find it hard to accept freedom and lack of structure. Children are particularly vulnerable to fear-producing situations because of their great lack of control over their surroundings. The best climate for children is a structured environment, imposed to promote security and healthy growth, with freedom and self-control provided in measured dosages that the children can handle.

Needs for love and belonging take different forms throughout life. Infants require physical demonstrations of affection. Teenagers want love in the form of respect, understanding, and appreciation. Young adults desire emotional involvement and an intimate relationship with a loved one. Deprivation of these needs can produce a variety of physical, psychological, and social development problems.

The need for esteem relates to self-respect and respect from others. On the one hand, it includes self-esteem, self-respect, and self-regard; on the other hand, reputation, status, social success, fame, and glory. An individual may engage in self-evaluation by attempting challenging tasks or may seek assurances from others through the acquisition of status symbols. Included in the need for esteem is the need to feel superior to others.

The self-actualizing needs, at the highest level, vary greatly from individual to individual. In all cases, however, the essential aspect of self-actualization is freedom from cultural and self-imposed restraints. Many preconditions must be met before a person can become self-actualizing. He or she should not have to worry about a job, social contacts, family relationships, and affiliations. The person should feel respected by those who count, have a sense of competence, and feel good about himself or herself. Finally, the person should know his or her preferences and be able to satisfy them. A musician must make music, an athlete must engage in sports. Not only is the type of activity important, but also the manner of performing it counts.

CHANGES IN PERSONALITY WITH AGE

Unique personality traits, which mark an individual as different from others, emerge very early, and yet children also acquire similar characteristics at a young age. *Socialization* is the means by which conventional or similar patterns of behavior are acquired. This is a learning process through which a child adopts the manners and customs of his or her family, community, and society. Even the most basic drives are subject to socialization; eating, sleeping, and other body functions are regulated by it.

Through socialization, children learn roles, or the customary behavior that society expects of them. Roles change from situation to situation: a child may be a daughter in a family, a pupil in school, and a peer in a play group, and in each case is expected to act differently. Roles are shaped by adults expectancies, although the child is free to accept or reject them. Further, society is in a constant state of change, as our culture faces different needs and conditions. Cultural changes may also modify the roles passed to children through socialization.

Although socialization tends to impose similarities on children, they remain individuals. Each accepts only certain aspects of socialization, according to his or her past experiences and constitutional background. What emerges from this interactive process is the child's own personality, which is a unique pattern of tendencies. Through this process the personality meets each new situation as a dynamic organization, which modifies the individual's particular way of reacting to the situation.

Just as they represent periods of rapid physical growth, childhood and adolescence are also periods of rapid psychological and personality development. Children become aware of themselves as persons and become socially aware of others. The self becomes intimately intertwined with its social aspect as self-awareness and social-awareness become an inseparable unity.

Gesell has developed an elaborate theory of the personality growth of children during their first 16 years (Gesell, Halverson, and Amatruda, 1940; Gesell and Ilg, 1943, 1946; Gesell, Ilg, and Ames, 1956). It describes stages of personality organization, which are sequential with age. According to this theory, children move through general developmental stages, which can sometimes result in drastic changes in their behavioral organization. The stages are characterized by general descriptions of behavioral organization, such as motor characteristics, personal hygiene, emotional expression, fears and dreams, self and sex, interpersonal relations, play and pastimes, school life, ethical sense, and philosophic outlook. The theory outlines the general characteristics of children of a given age, but it does not attempt to explain the underlying factors that produce personality change. Further, it does not facilitate an understanding of individual children or predictions of an individual's behavior.

Gesell's theory does illustrate that while personality maintains a high degree of consistency and stability from year to year, many changes can also be noted. Most changes occur when a child discovers new resources or must deal with new stresses for which he or she is not prepared (Jersild, 1963). Thus, although personality is characterized by stability and consistency, it also shows a great capacity for flexibility and change.

PERSONALITY AND PHYSICAL ACTIVITY

Physical educators have attempted to determine whether certain traits are related to, or formed by, participation in sports and other types of physical activity. The following studies illustrate research that has been conducted on individual differences in personality, with respect to motor learning and physical activity.

Physical Fitness and Activity

Personality has been suggested as a factor that determines one's choice of life-style. For example, Friedman and Rosenman (1958) proposed two personality types related to risk of heart attack. A Type A person has a high sense of time urgency and other characteristics that increase the probability of heart attack. A Type B person, with opposite personality characteristics, has a reduced risk.

In a study of extreme physical activity in junior and senior high school boys, Ruffer (1965) found that physically active subjects, having been brought up with less severe, sobering standards, are more social and less excited and tense than inactive subjects. Likewise, Harris (1963, 1965) reported personality differences between women with high physical fitness indices and women with low indices. In the first of these studies, she reported that women who are fit appear more stable and less anxious than unfit women. In Harris' second study, high-fitness women tested on the Edwards Personal Preference Schedule scored above the norms for autonomy and heterosexuality and below the norms for deference and dominance. Low-fitness groups scored higher than the norm for abasement and lower than the norm for deference.

Regular and nonregular adult exercisers were observed over a 4-year period by Young and Ismail (1977). They reported a stable relationship between physical fitness and self-confidence, as the regularly active adults were more confident in all testing periods. Personality differences between fit and unfit junior and senior high school students were reported by Tillman (1965), who found the fit groups to be more social, less tense, and more ascendant than the unfit groups. Tillman reported no changes in personality after participation in a 9-month fitness improvement program. Similar differences between high-fit and low-fit adults were reported by Young and Ismail (1976). They described the high-fit groups as more intellectually inclined, emotionally stable, composed, self-confident, easygoing, and relaxed and less ambitious and unconventional than the low-fit groups. They also reported that personality characteristics did not change over a 4-month period, in spite of fitness gains.

Whiting and Stembridge (1965) looked at the personalities of "persistent" nonswimmers. They observed that college and junior high nonswimmers are more introverted than those who learned to swim, and that junior high nonswimmers were also more neurotic than swimmers of the same age. Behrman (1967) described nonswimmers as more submissive, introverted, hypersensitive, and self-centered than swimmers. Other differences suggest that nonswimmers may be less aggressive in sports situations involving an element of danger and therefore lack the "will to win," or the positive, courageous attitude required in such activities.

These studies support the belief that successful teachers must individualize their instruction in recognition of differences among students. The suggestion from these studies is that unfit persons do not participate in regular physical activity because the activities do not meet their personality needs. Programs and activities must be developed to meet their needs as well as the needs of people who are already active. For example, persons who fail to learn to swim must be approached in a manner that is supportive of their needs. Such an approach should be followed in all instructional programs.

Athletes and Nonathletes

Some personality characteristics of athletes are measurably different from those of nonathletes, as these two classifications are presently defined. Usually, athletes are described as individuals who regularly engage in programs of highly organized athletic competition (interscholastic, intercollegiate, amateur athletic union, or professional), and nonathletes are those who are not or have not been engaged in such programs. Since the latter group might be physically active outside of organized athletic competition, it is probably more accurate to describe these "nonathletes" as nonparticipants in athletic programs.

The research literature is generally consistent in reporting personality differences between participants and nonparticipants. Cooper (1969) summarized a series of studies of the personalities of athletes and nonparticipants, according to which athletes can be described as follows:

1. They are more outgoing and socially confident.
2. They are more socially aggressive, dominant, and leading.
3. They are better adjusted socially.
4. They have greater prestige and higher social status.
5. They are less anxious, more self-confident, and more emotionally stable.

The preceding summary is based on studies of male subjects, but other research indicates that the same types of statements apply to female athletes:

1. They are more extroverted, optimistic, and energetic, with greater leadership (Niblock, 1960).
2. They are more aggressive, with a higher need for achievement and a lower need for affiliation (Neal, 1963).
3. They are more anxious, venturesome, extroverted, and tough-minded (Malumphy, 1968).
4. They are more relaxed, scoring higher in ascendancy and lower in feelings of inferiority (Ibrahim, 1967).
5. They have higher self-concepts (Vincent, 1976).

Unfortunately, the conclusion is often expressed or implied that these differences are a result of athletic experiences. The fact is that such a conclusion about cause and effect cannot be supported by research evidence. A very small number of longitudinal studies reported in the literature indicate that differences are identifiable at least as early as upper elementary and junior high school and continue through senior high school (Schendel, 1965, 1970; Wilson, 1969). Athletes generally score higher or have more positive traits or desirable characteristics than nonparticipants in athletic programs do. These differences are more numerous and more pronounced among younger subjects and diminish with age and maturation. The fact that differences can be observed at the time of first assessment and continue throughout the period under investigation, albeit in diminishing degree, does not allow the conclusion that the differences are caused by organized athletic experiences. Apparently, whatever the causal factors are, they affect children before they reach upper elementary or junior high school. Therefore, the differences between athletes and nonparticipants at this age cannot be attributed to the presence or absence of athletic experiences during the period under investigation.

While most studies have reported that athletes tend to display more desirable personality characteristics than nonathletes, some investigators (Schendel, 1965; Johnson, Hutton, and Johnson, 1954) found the opposite at the college level. In comparisons of highly recruited athletes with nonparticipants in athletic programs at the university level, differences with respect to desirable personality characteristics tend to favor the nonparticipants. Furthermore, the more successful the athlete at the university level, the greater the tendency to reflect generally lower scores on scales that purportedly measure desirable characteristics.

One might speculate that the apparent reversal of the relative differences between athletes and nonparticipants is, at least in part, a function of maturation in physical growth and social development. Differences in physical growth and social development among individuals of the same chronological age are greater at the upper elementary and junior high school level than during any other maturation period. For children at this level, one of the most important ways to gain acceptance, recognition, and social reward for achievement is successful performance of sports skills. Children who are advanced in physical growth during early adolescence are often somewhat advanced in social maturity as well. They are given recognition and social reinforcement for their physical appearance and achievements and for their more "grown-up" behavior patterns, which may fulfill the perceived expectations of peers and adults. Consequently, these children are more likely to be successful in sports competition and in receiving opportunities for leadership than their less mature, less successful (in socially important activities) chronological age-mates. Assessment of desirable social-psychological characteristics in young adolescents is likely to reflect these differences in physical and social maturation.

As the subjects get older and approach physical maturity, however, differences in physical and social maturity begin to disappear. Many young people find other means than sports for fulfillment of their achievement needs. As these needs are satisfied and as they gain recognition and social reinforcement for success in a variety of endeavors, the measurable differences between nonparticipants and their athletic classmates begin to diminish. Students who have the ability and opportunity to go to college, and who succeed in meeting the academic and social challenges it involves, reach a level of development and maturation at which their achievement motivation is worked out in ways that afford social recognition and rewards. They develop confidence and poise and come to accept themselves as socially mature and capable of succeeding in the adult world.

In contrast, highly recruited athletes lose the advantages of accelerated growth and maturity, which previously distinguished them from their nonparticipant age-mates. That is, they lose the advantage they had held for fulfillment of their needs for achievement, social recognition, and positive reinforcement. Their college experiences, instead of contributing to the development of their abilities to succeed in a wider variety of academic and social situations, may in fact demand a restriction of interests and involvements to focus attention on athletic achievement. Thus, college athletes' physical maturity is matched by that of nonparticipants, but the breadth and extent of their academic and social experiences may be more restricted than those of their nonparticipating classmates. Consequently, it seems reasonable to expect that standard personality tests would reveal higher levels of development of some social-psychological characteristics among nonparticipants in athletics, compared with athletes.

High-Skilled and Low-Skilled Performers

Differences in personality characteristics have been observed between high-skilled performers and low-skilled performers of various kinds of physical activities (Flanagan, 1951; Kane, 1970; Merriman, 1960; Sperling, 1942; Wilson, 1969). These groups have usually been identified on the basis of their relative success in athletic pursuits. If involvement in organized athletic programs and success are taken out of consideration, however, some identifiable differences remain.

Since the studies that have reported these differences have used public school students as subjects, the differences may be a function of the relative satisfaction of achievement needs. That is, during the preadolescent and early adolescent years, skilled physical performance is recognized as highly desirable. Children who possess high levels of skill gain recognition and positive reinforcement for their successes, while children who are low in skill do not receive recognition and may experience negative reinforcement (rejection) because of their failures. Once again, these differences in skill levels may result, in part, from differences in rate of physical growth and maturation, which have wide-ranging impact on social-psychological development and maturation.

Consequently, standard personality tests that focus attention on desirable social-psychological characteristics are likely to reflect different levels of growth and maturation among adolescents, which are identifiable in both the physical and the social-psychological dimensions. These dimensions are factors in skill achievement and the satisfaction of achievement motivations, and at the same time they are related to performance on personality assessment instruments.

There is no evidence to indicate whether the differences between high-skill groups and low-skill groups continue into the adult years. If these early differences in personality characteristics can be explained on the basis of growth and maturational differences, then one would expect them to disappear when adult status is reached.

Different Sports

Researchers have looked at athletes in different sports and on different teams to see whether their personalities differ. For example, Thune (1949) and Henry (1941) reported that weight lifters are more concerned with health, body build, and manliness. Rasch et al. (1967) and Rasch and Mozee (1963), however, found no differences among weight trainers, wrestlers, and nonathlete university students. Kroll (1967) observed that wrestlers' ratings on the 16PF differ from the test norms for tough-mindedness, self-reliance, and masculinity.

Kroll and Petersen (1965) observed some personality differences between members of winning football teams and members of losing teams. Differences among members of baseball, basketball, football, swimming, and wrestling teams were reported by Slusher (1964). Differences in the personalities of boxers, wrestlers, and cross-country runners were described by Husman (1955), using projective testing techniques. Malumphy (1968) and O'Connor and Webb (1976) found differences in the personality profiles of female athletes in different sports.

Ibrahim and Morrison (1976) reported that female high school athletes and male college athletes do not differ from their nonathletic counterparts in self-concept and self-actualization; male high school athletes differ somewhat in both traits, and female college athletes differ in self-actualization, compared with their nonathletic counterparts.

Such differences are frequently reported, but the meaning of these findings is unclear. Lakie (1962), for example, reported differences in the personalities of athletes attending different colleges and universities, but the differences disappeared if the athletes were grouped by sports without regard to which school they attended. Further, Werner and Gottheil (1966) found no evidence that participation in college athletics has any effect on personality structure. It may be that those who succeed in team sports are more dependent on group identification and social interaction, while athletes in individual and dual sports are more independent in their thinking and actions and have a greater need to develop individual identity. This hypothesis is far from being proved, however. An alternative explanation is that participation in sports grows out of earlier interests or the availability of activities. Individuals who have no access to swimming, tennis, or golf facilities are obviously restricted in the development of abilities in these sports.

It has been suggested that differences between contact sports and noncontact sports are more important than differences between team sports and individual sports. The idea behind this suggestion is that athletes in contact sports are more aggressive and dominant and less sociable and self-controlled than athletes in noncontact sports. In either case—team sports versus individual and dual sports and contact sports versus noncontact sports—there is no evidence at present to suggest that personality differences can be explained by athletic experience.

Champion Athletes

Researchers and coaches alike have often wondered what distinguishes champion athletes from good athletes who never quite become champions. Often the differences appear to be dimensions other than physical and mechanical aspects of performance. The following studies were conceived to evaluate the psychological aspects of champion athletes.

Johnson, Hutton, and Johnson (1954) tested 12 all-American athletes from six different sports. These outstanding performers differed from test norms in showing extreme aggression, uncontrolled affect (emotions lacking strict controls), high and generalized anxiety, high levels of intellectual aspiration, and exceptional feelings of self-assurance. In a study of former British and American Olympic champions, Heusner (1956) reported that they differed from test norms for ego strength, dominance, adventurousness, and feelings of security. Using the California Personality Inventory, Crakes (1960) observed that better runners scored lower on responsibility, socialization, communality, and well-being than poorer runners did. The better runners also scored higher on flexibility. Similar results were obtained with other inventories in this study. Andersen (1973) reported that Olympic and national finalist swimmers differed from norms for sociability, conscientiousness, bohemianism, and self-sufficiency. Rasch et al. (1962), however, using a small sample (four subjects) of champion wrestlers, reported no differences in neuroticism and extroversion between them and other wrestlers.

Thus, there are apparent personality differences between champion athletes and nonchampion athletes. Champion athletes apparently have personalities that enable them to aggress freely under certain conditions, a freedom from social pressures in competition, and a strong need for competitive achievement. They also appear to have a flexibility that enables them to use unconventional approaches for competitive success. With the knowledge that such personality differences exist, the question arises, Can we select future champions on the basis of childhood personality tests? Tattersfield (1976) suggested that the answer to this question is no. There appear to be too many personality types among children who become successful. Only in adulthood does personality appear to distinguish champion athletes from those who are not outstanding.

IMPLICATIONS FOR TEACHERS AND COACHES

1. Teachers and coaches must recognize differences in individual needs at different age and maturation levels. If individual differences are to be dealt with honestly and effectively, students or athletes cannot be treated alike at any age or maturation level.

2. They must provide positive experiences and opportunities for success in physical activity. The earlier a student or athlete experiences success, the better.

3. They must encourage students and athletes to practice goal-oriented behavior in physical activity and help them select realistic yet challenging goals.

4. They must provide instructions to help students and athletes achieve their goals, and they must show interest in and approval of achievement.

5. They must provide positive reinforcement and tangible recognition for achievement of personal goals by each student or athlete.

6. They must help students and athletes modify existing goals or establish new goals in physical activity as they mature. A teacher must assist each student in developing positive feelings about achievement, with the recognition that the student's need for achievement and self-actualization can be fulfilled in a variety of ways, one of which is performance in physical activity. Teachers and coaches should encourage and recognize achievement in different types of activities (e.g., scholastic work, student government, clubs).

7. They must provide physical activities or sports situations in which students and athletes can practice behaviors that have desirable social-psychological characteristics. Recognition and support for appropriate behavior should be provided when it occurs.

8. Teachers must help students develop an awareness that personal satisfaction and a sense of achievement can be experienced in physical activity outside of highly competitive programs of interscholastic athletics.

Teachers or coaches who adopt these professional practices are likely to enhance the development of behavior patterns associated with positive, desirable personality characteristics. Care must be taken, however, to avoid claiming that observed changes in personality characteristics are caused by physical activity itself. Rather, emphasis should be placed on the social-psychological and physical environment in which the experiences take place and the interaction between the student, his or her peers, and the teacher.

GUIDING PRINCIPLES FOR THE TEACHER

1. Personality refers to the organization of an individual's physical, mental, moral, and social qualities, manifested in the give-and-take of social interaction. Personality includes character, temperament, abilities, interests, and appearance.

2. Most personality studies relating to physical education and sports participation classify personality according to types or according to traits. These studies have produced conflicting results for groups selected on the basis of such criteria as skill level, athletic ability, fitness levels, interests, and growth factors.

3. Personality differences generally exist between participants in athletics and nonparticipants. It is impossible to conclude that these differences result from athletic experiences, however. Longitudinal studies indicate that participants have more desirable personality

characteristics than nonparticipants at the upper elementary, junior high, and senior high school levels. This tendency is reversed at the college level, at which nonparticipants as a group have more desirable characteristics. Some differences between participants in team sports and participants in individual or dual sports have also been reported.

4. Personality differences also exist between high-skilled performers and low-skilled performers in various kinds of physical activity. It may be that these differences result from the satisfaction of achievement needs and variations in rates of growth and maturation.

5. Studies have not produced indications of consistent, reliable differences between persons who are physically fit and those who are unfit. Likewise, little is known about the effects of aging on the relationship between personality and performance in physical activities.

6. Teachers and coaches must be aware of individual differences in personalities. They must assist students in goal setting as they mature and must provide opportunities for personal satisfaction and achievement, both in highly competitive interscholastic athletics and in physical activity outside such programs.

SUMMARY

Relationships between personality and performance in sports and physical activity vary according to maturity level and age. Personality differences between high-skilled performers and low-skilled performers, between persons with high motor ability and those with low motor ability, and between athletes and nonparticipants in athletic programs, are not the same at the junior high school level as the differences at the senior high school and the college level.

Junior high school and senior high school students who rank high in skill, motor ability, and physical or athletic achievement generally possess desirable social-psychological characteristics to a greater extent than those who rank low in these characteristics. Compared with their age-mates, junior high school students with superior motor skills and physical abilities

1. possess greater qualities of leadership and social initiative
2. possess more of the qualities that lead to status
3. are more sociable
4. possess a greater sense of personal worth
5. have less self-doubt and fewer complaints
6. have more social maturity

7. are more conventional in their responses to social situations
8. possess greater intellectual efficiency

At the senior high level, students from the high performance group

1. are more sociable
2. possess a greater sense of personal worth
3. are more poised and self-assured
4. are more conventional in their responses to social situations
5. are more capable of achievement in situations that require conformity

College students with high scores in physical achievement are generally more conservative, composed, mature, adventurous, and sensitive and less anxious, tense, and withdrawn than those with low scores in physical achievement. Compared with athletes, nonparticipants in intercollegiate athletics generally

1. possess more of the qualities that lead to status
2. are more conscientious and responsible
3. possess greater tolerance
4. are more capable of independent achievement
5. have greater intellectual efficiency
6. are more interested in the psychological needs of other people
7. are more adaptable in their thinking and social behavior
8. have more feminine interests

It is likely that the lack of continuity in relationships between personality and performance can be explained, at least in part, by differences in maturation and growth levels, which are important during the early years but decline in importance as adulthood approaches. Furthermore, while success in performance of physical activity (notably interscholastic athletics) is important in satisfying achievement motivation during the school years, it is not a discriminating factor at the college level. As they mature, most people find a variety of ways to succeed, which are recognized and rewarded by society and which satisfy their achievement needs.

Champion athletes differ from test norms and from other athletes in dimensions that enhance their physical abilities. They are less socially dependent, more aggressive, and more flexible, and they have a greater need for competitive achievement.

Most of the data on relationships between personality and performance concern male subjects, and conclusions from them might not apply to populations of girls or women. Much work needs to be done to determine the relationships between personality and performance for females.

REFERENCES

Allport, G. W., and Odbert, H. S. 1936. Trait names: A psycho-lexical study. *Psychological Monographs*, vol. 47, whole no. 211.

Andersen, P. A. 1973. The relation of personality factors of Olympic, national finalist, and non-national finalist swimmers to unfamiliar and familiar aspiration tasks. Ph.D. dissertation, University of Toledo.

Behrman, R. M. 1967. Personality differences between non-swimmers and swimmers. *Research Quarterly* 38:163–171.

Cattell, R. B., and Eber, H. W. 1970. *Handbook for the Sixteen Personality Factor Questionnaire*. Champaign, Ill.: Institute for Personality and Ability Testing.

Cooper, L. 1969. Athletics, activity and personality: a review of the literature. *Research Quarterly* 40:17-25.

Crakes, J. G. 1960. The anatomical, physiological and psychological differences between distance runners of varying abilities. Ph.D. dissertation, University of Oregon.

DiCaprio, N. S. 1974. *Personality theories: Guides to living*. Philadelphia: W. B. Saunders.

Drever, J. A. 1964. *A dictionary of psychology*. Rev. ed., New York: Penguin.

Flanagan, L. A. 1951. A study of some personality traits of different physical activity groups. *Research Quarterly* 22:312-323.

Friedman, M., and Rosenman, R. H. 1958. Association of specific behavior patterns with increase in blood cholesterol, blood clotting time and incidence of clinical coronary disease. *Circulation* 18:721.

Gesell, A., Halverson, H. M. and Amatruda, C. S. 1940. *The first five years of life: A guide to the study of the pre-school child.* New York: Harper & Row.

Gesell, A., and Ilg, F. L. 1943. *Infant and child in the culture of today*. New York: Hayen.

———. 1946. *The child from five to ten.* New York: Harper & Row.

Gesell, A., Ilg, F. L., and Ames, L. B. 1956. *Youth: The years from ten to sixteen.* New York: Harper & Row.

Gough, H. G. 1960. *Manual for the California Psychological Inventory*. Palo Alto, Calif.: Consulting Psychological Press.

Harris, D. V. 1963. Comparison of physical performance and psychological traits of college women with high and low fitness indices. *Perceptual and Motor Skills* 17: 293-294.

———. 1965. An investigation of psychological characteristics of university women with high and low fitness indices. Ph.D. dissertation, State University of Iowa.

Hathaway, S. R., and McKinley, J. C. 1967. *Minnesota Multiphasic Personality Inventory: Manual for administration and scoring.* New York: Psychological Corp.

Henry, F. M. 1941. Personality differences in athletes and physical education and aviation groups. *Psychological Bulletin* 38:745.

Heusner, W. 1956. Personality traits of champion and former champion athletes. Unpublished research study, Physical Fitness Research Laboratory, University of Illinois.

Husman, B. F. 1955. Aggression in boxers and wrestlers as measured by projective techniques. *Research Quarterly* 26:421–425.

Ibrahim, H. 1967. Comparisons of temperament traits among intercollegiate athletes and physical education measures. *Research Quarterly* 38:615-622.

Ibrahim, H., and Morrison, N. 1976. Self-actualization and self-concept among athletes. *Research Quarterly* 47:68–79.

Jersild, A. T. 1963. *The psychology of adolescence.* 2d ed. New York: Macmillan.

Johnson, W. R., Hutton, D. C., and Johnson, G. B., Jr. 1954. Personality traits of some champion athletes as measured by two projective tests: Rorschach and H-T-P. *Research Quarterly* 25:484–485.

Jung, C. G. 1933. *Psychological types.* New York: Harcourt, Brace and World.

Kane, J. 1970. Personality and physical abilities. In *Contemporary psychology of sport: Proceedings of the Second International Congress of Sport Psychology*, ed. G. S. Kenyon. Chicago: Athletic Institute.

Kroll, W. 1967. Sixteen personality factor profiles of college wrestlers. *Research Quarterly* 37:49–57.

Kroll, W., and Petersen, K. H. 1965. Personality factor profiles of collegiate football teams. *Research Quarterly* 36:433–440.

Lakie, W. L. 1962. Personality characteristics of certain groups of intercollegiate athletes. *Research Quarterly* 33:566–573.

McKeachie, W. J., and Doyle, C. L. 1966. *Psychology.* Reading, Mass.; Addison-Wesley.

Malumphy, T. 1968. The personality and general characteristics of women athletes in international competition. *Research Quarterly* 39:610–620.

Maslow, A. H. 1970. *Motivation and personality.* 2d ed. New York: Harper & Row.

Merriman, J. B. 1960. Relationship of personality traits to motor ability. *Research Quarterly.* 31:163–173.

Murray, H. A., Barrett, W. G., and Homburger, E. 1938. *Explorations in personality.* New York: Oxford University Press.

Neal, P. 1963. Personality traits of United States women who participated in the 1959 Pan American Games as measured by the EPPS. Master's thesis, University of Utah.

Niblock, M. W. 1960. Personality traits and intelligence level of female athletes and non-participants from McNally High School. Doctoral dissertation, Pennsylvania State University.

O'Connor, K. A., and Webb, J. L. 1976. Investigation of personality traits of college female athletes and non-athletes. *Research Quarterly* 47:203 210.

Rasch, P. J., et al. 1962. Neuroticism and extraversion in United States intercollegiate wrestlers. *Journal of the Association for Physical and Mental Rehabilitation* 16: 153–154.

Rasch, P. J., and Mozee, G. 1963. Neuroticism and extraversion in weight trainers. *Journal of the Association for Physical and Mental Rehabilitation* 17:55 56.

Rorschach, H. 1942. *Psychodiagnostics: A diagnostic test based on perception.* Translated by P. Lemkau and B. Kronenburg. Berne: Haber. Originally published in German, 1921.

Ruffer, W. A. 1965. A study of extreme physical activity groups of young men. *Research Quarterly* 36:183–196.

Schendel, J. S. 1965. Psychological differences between athletes and non-participants in athletics at three educational levels. *Research Quarterly* 36:52 67.

———. 1970. Psychological characteristics of high school athletes and non-participants in athletics: a three-year longitudinal study. In *Contemporary psychology of sport: Proceedings of the Second International Congress of Sport Psychology*, ed. G. S. Kenyon. Chicago: Athletic Institute.

Sheldon, W. H., and Stevens, S. S. 1942. *The varieties of temperament.* New York: Harper & Row.

Sheldon, W. H., Stevens, S. S., and Tucker, W. B. 1940. *The varieties of human physiques.* New York: Harper & Row.

Slusher, H. S. 1964. Personality and intelligence characteristics of selected high school athletes and non-athletes. *Research Quarterly* 35:539–545.

Sperling, A. P. 1942. The relationship between personality adjustment and achievement in physical education activities. *Research Quarterly* 13:351–363.

Tattersfield, C. R. 1976. Developing personalities of successful and unsuccessful sports competitors. In *Physical education, sports and the sciences*, ed. J. Broekhoff. Eugene, Oreg.: Microform Publications.

Thune, J. B. 1949. Personality of weightlifters. *Research Quarterly* 20:296-306.

Tillman, K. 1965. Relationship between physical fitness and selected personality traits. *Research Quarterly* 36:483-489.

Vincent, M. F. 1976. Comparison of self-concept of college women: Athletes and physical education majors. *Research Quarterly* 47:218-225.

Watson, R. I. 1965. *Psychology of the child*. 2d ed. New York: John Wiley and Sons.

Werner, A. C., and Gottheil, E. 1966. Personality development and participation in college athletics. *Research Quarterly* 37:126-131.

Whiting, H. T. A., and Stembridge, D. E. 1965. Personality and the persistent non-swimmer. *Research Quarterly* 36:348-356.

Wilson, P. K. 1969. Relationship between motor achievement and selected personality factors of junior and senior high school boys. *Research Quarterly* 40:841-844.

Young, R. J., and Ismail, A. H. 1976. Personality differences of adult men before and after a physical fitness program. *Research Quarterly* 47:513-519.

———. 1977. Comparison of selected physiological and personality variables in regular and non-regular adult male exercisers. *Research Quarterly* 48:617-627.

10 Motivation

Life is a series of choices. We choose different professions, participate in different activities, and perform with different intensities. People engage in similar activities but for different reasons. Human behavior is goal-directed, as we strive to achieve certain ends, and we vary our behavior considerably if particular means become ineffective. From observations of behavior—of what people do and say—we infer that motives exist. Several hundred words in ordinary language refer to motives: among the more common are *wish, want, aspiration, aim, ambition, striving, hunger, thirst,* and *love*. The discussion in this chapter frequently refers to motives in terms of *needs, goals,* and *drives*. The study of motivation deals with the conditions that determine goals and the behaviors that are used to attain them.

THE NATURE OF MOTIVATION

Motivation is the energizer of behavior. It cannot be observed directly but is revealed in activity. Most studies of motivation look at behavior to see whether motives are present and to attempt to identify goals. Typically, an experimenter observes behavior, introduces a new variable (or eliminates an old one), and then observes any changes in behavior. According to Brown (1961), four criteria are used to identify a motivational variable:

1. It facilitates or energizes a wide variety of responses.
2. The learning of new responses appears to depend on appropriate manipulations of the variable.
3. Changes in the variable lead to a weakening of certain responses.
4. Occasionally, no other designation seems appropriate.

The first criterion is probably more widely accepted than any of the other three. Of course, motivation is not the only factor that is responsible for improvement in performance. Learning, perception, personality, and other factors also cause changes in behavior.

Motivated behavior occurs in a cycle with three components: a motivating state, motivated behavior, and a satisfying condition (Morgan and King, 1966). Motivating states can arise from either internal or external conditions. Internal conditions include physiological needs (such as thirst, which may cause one to search for something to drink) and psychological needs (which may cause one to seek companionship). External conditions, for example, on a very hot day, may cause a person to seek a cooler place. Getting something to drink, seeking companionship, and moving to a cooler place represent motivated behavior. Drinking some water, finding companionship, and

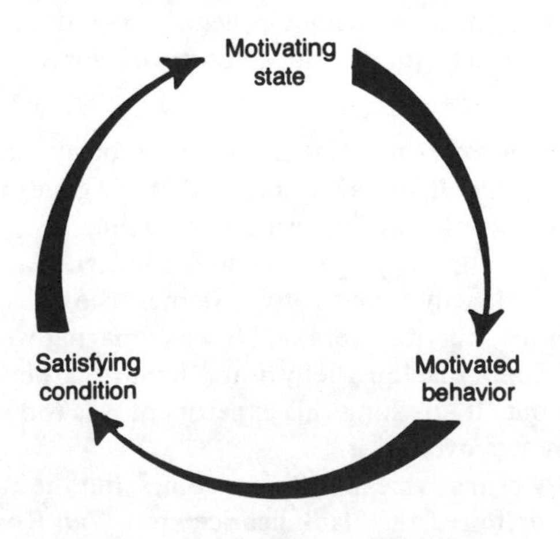

Figure 10.1. The cycle of motivated behavior. (Modified from Morgan and King, 1966.)

locating a cooler place represent the third stage of the cycle—the satisfaction of a need or the attainment of a goal—which terminates the behavior (and the cycle) until the need builds up again.

Goals

The goals of motivated behavior therefore depend on motives. If one is motivated by thirst, his or her goal is something to drink. Goals can be described as either positive or negative. Those that a person strives to reach, such as membership on a varsity athletic team, are called positive goals. Negative goals include escape from and avoidance of unpleasant or painful situations.

Rethlingshafer (1963) described goals as "learned to-be-attained effects." That is, through our past experiences we are able to symbolize satisfying conditions that have occurred previously, and we can express our desire to reattain the same effect in the future. Anticipated events may become influential as goals. Symbolic and abstract goals—money and intangibles such as power, status, and achievement—are learned in the process of psychological development. Young children strive for concrete, immediate goals, but as they become older, their goals become more abstract and satisfaction can be deferred. Goals can be learned through experience or learned vicariously, that is, through verbal and nonverbal communication and from books, movies, and television. In fact, symbolic goals can influence behavior before the individual has learned how to attain them.

The following anecdote, about collegiate swimming coach Don Van Rossen, illustrates the abstract nature of goals (University of Oregon, 1966, p. 26):

> The jelly bean experiment was . . . ludicrously simple but captivating. After all, any swimmer could have gone out to buy a bag of jelly beans, but that wasn't the point.
>
> With 15 pounds of jelly beans in his locker, Van Rossen awarded a single jelly bean to any swimmer who did 100 yards in less than his practice average. "It was amazing what those kids would do for one lousy jelly bean," he says. "They'd knock themselves out. If anything this experiment was too effective. Some swimmers overdid it."
>
> The jelly beans came in different colors, but the swimmers universally preferred the black licorice kind. Van Rossen was cagey, however. He held the black ones in reserve for what came to be called the "Jelly Bean Meet."

That was the swimming meet with the University of Washington. Washington was heavily favored to win, but its coaches had failed to reckon with the power of a black jelly bean. On the day of the meet, Van Rossen entrusted the coveted black pellets to the care of a comely young lady, the Dolphin Queen. He told her to pass out one bean for each point a swimmer made in competition.

That was all Oregon's underdog swimmers needed to explode into action. They wanted to beat Washington, but they seemed equally interested in scoring points for the privilege of running up to a pretty girl for five jelly beans for a first place, three for a second, and one for a third.

"It was comical to watch," says Van Rossen. "These guys were fagged out after swimming an event, exhausted, white from nausea. But the first thing they'd think of was those jelly beans. It was amazing."

The final result of the experiment was even more amazing. The underdog Oregon squad consumed exactly 62 jelly beans and beat Washington, 62 points to 33.

What made the jelly beans such an effective motivational force? They were important in a symbolic rather than a real, tangible sense. Significantly, the jelly beans were important to the swimmers themselves, and it made little difference how the coach viewed them. The coach capitalized on the swimmers' feelings. In fact, goals need not be verbalized or even raised to the level of awareness to be effective motivators (Rethlingshafer, 1963).

Determiners of Behavior

According to Birch and Veroff (1966), goal-directed behavior is determined by four factors:

1. availability
2. expectancy
3. incentive
4. motive

Availability refers to the extent to which a particular course of action is possible under given conditions. Structural aspects of a situation impose some constraints on types of behaviors that are available. Activities that are permitted in a football stadium are not available in a library, and available activities in a swimming pool are different from those on a tennis court. In a like manner, a person's past experiences and abilities also determine the availability of activities. Participation may be restricted according to one's ability to walk, run, swim, or perform other motor skills. Past experiences and anticipations of future effects may favor some courses of action and rule out others.

Expectancy links behavior to its consequences. It refers to the feeling that engaging in an activity will lead to a particular goal. People who go swimming expect certain things to occur at the pool—social interactions, relief from the heat, and so forth. Expectancy depends on inferences, based on one's perception of the usual consequences of similar behavior in the past.

Incentive is the attraction or repulsion of the consequences of a particular course of action. Attractive or rewarding consequences provide positive incentive: a person responds in ways that establish and maintain satisfying consequences. Negative incentive refers to situations in which a person attempts to escape from or avoid undesirable consequences. Some activities have both positive and negative incentive values. Conflict results in these cases, especially if the positive and negative values are equal, and the person may vacillate. Many athletic events offer both types of incentives—achievement and status on the one hand and pain and potential failure on the other. The relative strengths of positive and negative incentive are important determiners of participation in sports.

Motive, the fourth factor, is more general in that motives are modifiers of incentives. Motives are a general class of determiners, which interact with specific incentives to direct one's response in a given situation. An individual's past experiences shape his or her motives. For example, people with high achievement motives generally want to be evaluated with respect to the excellence of performance. The incentive value of interscholastic swimming might be low because of the time and discomfort it involves, but its attraction may be great for a person with high achievement motives.

MOTIVATION AND PERFORMANCE

Learning and performance are not influenced by motivation in the same manner or degree. Stellar (1960) reported that learning is more effective with weak motivation and low incentives than with strong motivation and highly effective incentives. A similar conclusion was expressed by Zajonc (1966), who noted that motivation causes people to perform the dominant response, or the response that they have usually made under similar conditions in the past. Consequently, strong motivation can impair the learning of new responses. That is, a highly motivated, dominant response interferes with the acquisition of new behavior. After a new response has been learned, it becomes dominant, and then performance is enhanced by motivation.

It is sometimes assumed that if a little motivation is good for performance, a lot is better. The relationship between the two is not linear, however, but curvilinear, as displayed in Figure 10.2. The best performances are achieved with optimal levels of motivation, but poor performance results if the level is either too low or too high. It may be that some excellent sports teams never win a national championship or play an undefeated season because the team members' motivation grows so strong that it interferes with their performance. One of the arts of coaching is the ability to determine the level at which players are optimally motivated and to resist the temptation to increase motivation beyond that level.

The Hawthorne effect (discovered in a series of studies of worker productivity at the Western Electric Company's Hawthorne plant in the

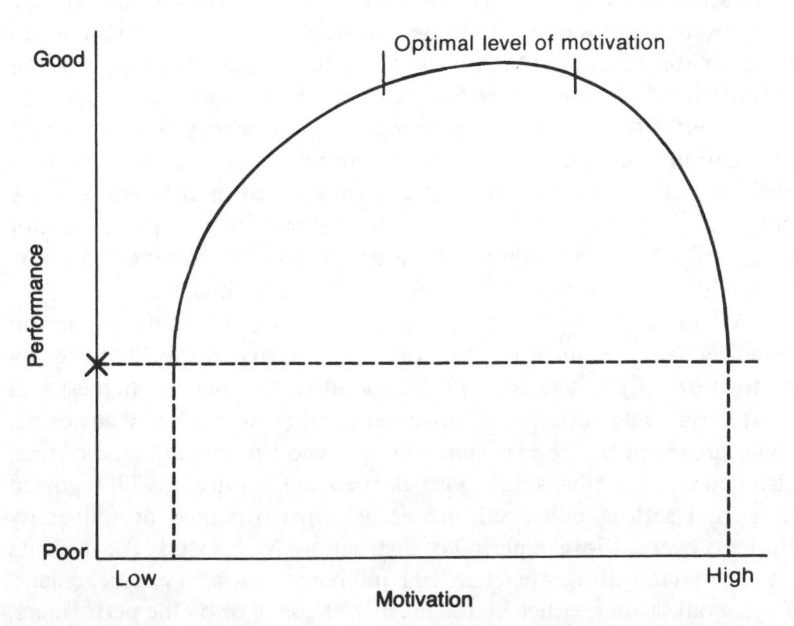

Figure 10.2. The inverted U curve showing the relationship between performance and motivation.

1920s and 1930s) indicates that social forces, as well as material incentives, can raise motivation and thus affect performance (Hanson, 1967). Researchers at the plant introduced changes in physical variables—lighting, rest periods, hours, and economic incentives—and found that productivity did indeed increase among experimental groups of workers. The productivity of control groups, however, also increased. The researchers concluded that the increase in both cases was due to social forces that affected the workers' motivation. It appears that the fact of being chosen for participation in the experiment, of being an insider rather than an outsider, raised the workers' morale and gave each group a common purpose.

Clarke (1966), in a summary of studies of muscular strength and endurance, indicated that different factors produce varying levels of motivation. Muscular endurance was tested in 10 motivational situations, distinguished by such factors as group competition, verbal encouragement, obtainable goals, presence of an observer, and instructor interest. The distance subjects could lift an ergometer load, strength decrement, and rate of strength recovery were used to classify the 10 situations according to low, high, or moderate levels of motivation (see Table 10.1). Different amounts of variability were recorded in the different situations. The standard deviation in Situation 5 (obtainable goal) was the smallest of the 10, but the standard deviation in Situation 4 (group competition) was one of the largest, although both situations fall within the moderate motivation category. The important implication of this study is that no two motivational situations produce identical effects. Further, individuals are affected in different ways by different situations, so that what may be best for one person is not necessarily best for others. This conclusion is evident from the variability and overlap of scores in Clarke's ten situations.

A later study by Nelson (1978) reinforces Clarke's work. Nelson observed that endurance performance is greatly influenced by motivation. High false norms were found to produce the highest and most variable performances, but other conditions, such as true norms, goals suggested by the experimenter, and ego-threatening false norms, also had marked effects. Likewise, Barnett and Stanicer (1979) reported that goal setting enhanced the archery performance of university students over a 10-week period of instruction. In this study the students set their goals during a teacher-led conference on archery achievement. Thus, goal setting, either by the teacher or coach or by the performers, can be an important tool in developing improved performances.

Table 10.1. Mean Strength Decrement Indices (SDI) and Rate of Strength Recovery of Subjects in 10 Motivational Situations

	MEAN DISTANCE LOAD MOVED	SDI 30 SEC.	GAIN	SDI 2½ MIN.	GAIN	SDI 7½ MIN.
Low groups						
Situation 1, Normal instructions	1157.0	34.8	17.4	17.4	4.7	12.7
Situation 7, Instructor interest	1185.3	35.9	17.2	18.7	5.6	13.1
Situation 2, Verbal encouragement	1190.0	37.7	19.0	18.7	5.5	13.2
Pastor's study	1014.0	33.3	17.7	15.6	3.7	11.9
High groups						
Situation 8, Ego involvement	1419.8	51.5	11.9	39.6	8.7	30.9
Situation 9, Air Force space program	1361.0	45.2	9.7	35.5	8.7	26.8
Situation 3, Individual competition	1321.9	42.4	9.1	33.3	7.2	26.1
Moderate groups						
Situation 5, Obtainable goal	1289.9	46.7	9.8	36.9	9.7	27.2
Situation 6, Observer's presence	1241.4	44.9	11.7	33.2	8.4	24.8
Situation 4, Group Competition	1284.5	43.1	11.2	31.9	8.0	23.9
Situation 10, Competition with Russians	1311.9	42.7	12.8	29.9	7.9	22.0

From H. H. Clarke, *Muscular strength and endurance in man,* Englewood Cliffs, N.J.: Prentice-Hall, 1966, p. 108. Used with permission.

Realistic goals set for students by teachers are probably better overall than unrealistic goals, as they generally lead to better performances.

CLASSIFICATION OF MOTIVES

Many forces influence behavior. McTeer (1972) cited such diverse factors as geography, social influences, physiological needs, mental influences, stages of psychological development. Local geographic characteristics, such as temperature, rainfall, altitude, and population density, place limitations on the availability of activities.

Social influences, either direct or indirect, have great impact on behavior. Direct social influences are interpersonal and therefore are generated whenever two or more people get together. Indirect social influences from our parents and others are integrated into our habits, expectations, and attitudes. Physiological needs are operative in the body's attempts to maintain homeostasis. Mental factors include subjective experiences stored in memory, insights, and skills.

Finally, psychological development appears to occur in stages, or developmental periods, which introduce a temporal factor in the classification of motives. The needs of an infant are different from those of a child, a teenager's needs are different from those of a young adult, and so on. In terms of Maslow's personality theory, one must first fulfill the highly potent, instinctual needs before he or she can move up the ladder of development to self-actualization. Similar approaches have been used by Erikson (1950) and Sheehy (1977). Erikson proposed that childhood is characterized by successive stages of basic trust versus mistrust, autonomy versus shame and doubt, initiative versus guilt, and industry; adolescence by the stage of identity versus role diffusion; and adulthood by stages of intimacy, generativity, and integrity.

Because each of us is the product of a unique interaction of diverse influences, there are great individual differences in our goals and purposes. Differences in motivation are reflected not only in our physical actions but also in our use of symbols and our tendencies to focus on some particular problems and particular solutions rather than others. In spite of individual differences, however, distinct types of motives can be identified, and psychologists have devised various systems of classification as aids in the study of motivation.

Psychologists have classified drives and motives into two categories, primary and secondary. Primary motives are unlearned drives, which emerge during the course of maturation. They are further distinguished into physiological needs, having their origin within the body, and general drives, which are not apparently physiological but do not appear to be learned (Fuller, 1962). Secondary motives are learned; at least, the goals and symbolic aspects of situations involving them are learned. Social needs are prime examples of these acquired motives.

Primary Motives

Primary motives differ from secondary motives in that they are not learned, but seem to be products of normal development, which appear relatively early in life. The primary drives that are physiologically determined arise from tissue needs and from hormonal levels in the blood. Internal states, such as salt levels, may stimulate one's drive to drink. External conditions, such as extreme noise or heat, can also stimulate behavior. Other important physiological drives are hunger, elimination, fatigue, and oxygen needs. Some of these, such as fatigue and oxygen requirements, fall under the control of the physical educator, but others, such as hunger, must be also recognized as affecting performance and classroom behavior.

Physiologically motivated behavior has survival value because it contributes to homeostasis, or the maintenance of the individual's internal environment (Stellar, 1960). The concept of homeostasis, originated by Cannon (1932), sees internal physiological states as being controlled much as a thermostat controls the operation of a furnace to maintain a constant temperature in a house. If the internal balance necessary for survival is disturbed, homeostatic mechanisms begin to operate to bring conditions back within the normal range. For example, if one's body temperature becomes too high, the surface blood vessels dilate and the sweat glands secrete perspiration, to create a cooling effect. Self-regulation of this sort is important, but it is only one of many factors that contribute to the control of motivated behavior, including neurological factors, sensory stimuli, feedback from motivated behaviors, and the organization of behavior patterns (Stellar, 1960).

Besides physiological needs, primary motives include general drives, which have no apparent physiological basis and yet are not learned. These include the need for affection, the need for activity, curiosity, and fear. Morgan and King (1966) indicated that many of these general motives involve competence, that is, the process through which a person learns to interact effectively with the environment. Affection, or love, is a powerful motive in human affairs. It involves relationships with one's family and with one's friends and sexual partners. It probably has both a learned and an unlearned basis. The need for affection becomes evident in the course of normal development, but pleasing experiences with our families and other people can facilitate its development.

The drive for bodily activity seems to be present in almost every species. People spend a great deal of time moving about for no apparent reason, like to manipulate novel objects, and are curious about novel stimulation, apparently simply for the sake of exploration. Fear is another motive that seems to be present from birth. It is evidenced by withdrawal from or avoidance of fear-provoking stimuli.

Secondary Motives

Secondary motives, also called acquired motives or social motives, are learned. One indication of the influence of learning is that the motives of adults differ from those of children. Adults are motivated to a much greater degree by symbolic, abstract goals, such as money, power, status, and achievement. We learn to recognize these as goals through secondary reinforcement in classical and instrumental conditioning. For example, food is a primary goal (that is, it satisfies a primary drive, namely, hunger); money, which we learn to associate with the ability to obtain food or other primary goals, thereby acquires significance as a secondary goal. From the fact that we learn secondary goals, we infer the existence of learned, secondary motives. One such motive is achievement need, or the motive for success in performance. An athlete may therefore find satisfaction in excellent performance on the playing field. He or she may also find it, however, in pregame activities, if they satisfy the player's need for belonging or recognition.

Since behavior is a product of primary and secondary motives, directed toward primary and secondary goals, it is difficult to predict an individual's performance at any given time. Two people could make the same response and attain the same performance level for vastly different motives. The variety of motives is suggested by the following categories of secondary psychological needs of adolescents (Horrocks, 1962):

1. acceptance—the need for approval; the need to feel that others hold favorable attitudes towards oneself and that they regard one as an equal
2. achievement—the need for attainment of goals, respect, knowledge, or tokens of status, evidenced through acquisitions, winning, and other forms of striving
3. affection—the need to feel loved, cherished, and wanted unconditionally and for one's own sake
4. approval—the need to feel that one is a satisfactory person and that the things one does are satisfactory; the need to avoid blame, criticism, and punishment
5. belonging—the need to feel that one is a part of a group or institution, or the feeling of identification with a person, group, institution, or idea
6. conformity—the need to be like others and to avoid being different in dress, behavior, attitudes, or ideas

7. dependence—the need to depend on others for emotional support, protection, encouragement, help, and forgiveness
8. independence—the need to be self-determining, self-sufficient, and free of external control by friends, family, and others
9. mastery-dominance—the need to be in control; to lead, manage, and govern; to overcome people, problems, and obstacles; and to influence others
10. recognition—the need to be recognized as a unique individual, to be noticed and known, and to have found one's place
11. self-realization—the need to function, learn, understand, and perform with the best of one's ability and to accomplish goals within the limits of one's capacity
12. understanding—the need to have sympathetic rapport with friends, parents, and others and to be able to express personal thoughts and problems without loss of affection or personal status

Goal-directed behavior is a complex system based on primary and secondary motives (see Figure 10.3). Because of the heavy impact of past experience, motivated behavior is highly individualistic. In some cases, people attempt to satisfy motives that are in opposition, such as dependence and independence or conformity and recognition. The heavy influence of social settings and our nature as social creatures are also evident in the list developed by Horrocks. This list is by no means all-inclusive. Other theorists have listed additional secondary motives, such as power (the need to control others), security (the need to fare well in the future), prestige (the need to feel better than others), and anxiety (a learned fear). Regardless of the label, learned motives are powerful influences on behavior.

Motives reflect either intrinsic influences, which arise from within a person, or extrinsic influences, which include such factors as peer pressure (McTeer, 1972). According to Weinberg and Jackson (1979), people exhibit more intrinsic motivation after success than they do after failure. These authors reported that success is related to high ability, high effort, good luck, and high intrinsic motivation. Conversely, failure is associated with low ability, low effort, bad luck, and low intrinsic motivation. Changes in intrinsic motivation were found to be most closely related to ability and effort. Thus, effective teaching, which improves performers' ability and increases the effort spent in accomplishing a task, can have an effect on motivation.

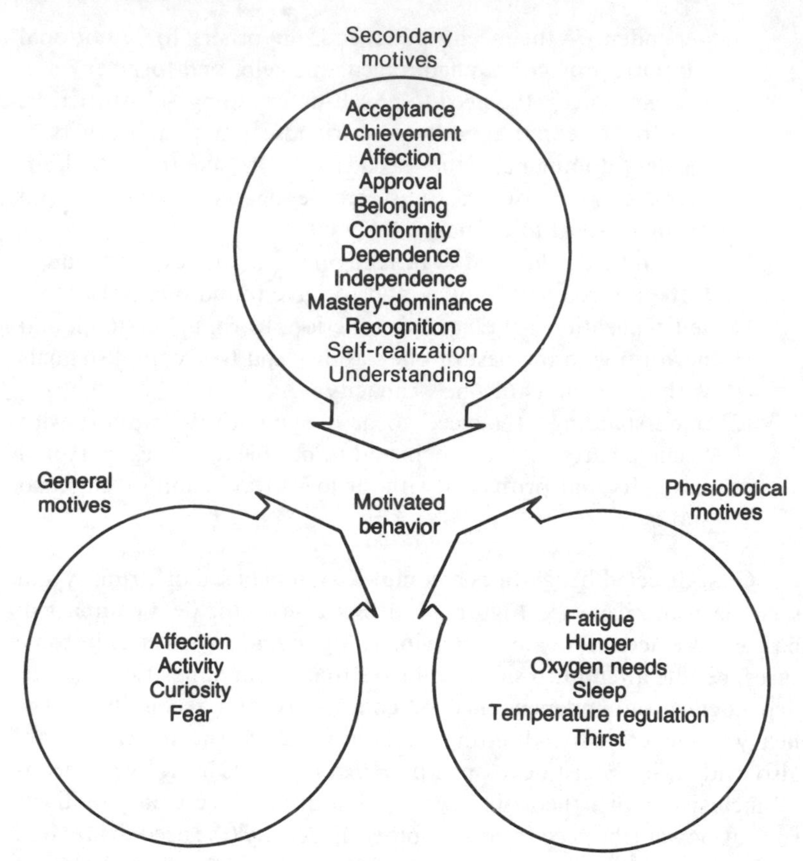

Figure 10.3. The interaction of primary motives (general and physiological) and secondary motives produces motivated behavior.

ANXIETY

The motivation of athletes before, during, and after performance has been of considerable concern and interest to coaches and sports psychologists. Basler, Fischer, and Mumford (1976), investigating arousal and anxiety among members of a college women's gymnastic team, found few and limited relationships between the actual performances and measures of anxiety. Martens and Simon (1976) obtained low and moderate correlations between measures of state anxiety and competitive performance by female high school volleyball and basketball players; the measures were better predictors of precompetitive states than of competitive states. One further finding was that coaches' ratings had little or no relationship to the other instruments.

In a review of psychological considerations in sports, Morgan (1974) summarized research on competitive anxiety and emphasized several points. First, exercise reduces state anxiety. Therefore, benefits that accrue from elevated anxiety levels prior to competition are short-lived. Next, many factors change precompetitive anxiety states. Wrestlers' practice of "making weights" decreases anxiety levels. Levels of anxiety experienced before difficult competition differ from those experienced before easy competition. Opposing teams tend to experience similar levels of anxiety. Performances may relate differently to anxiety according to whether team sports or individual sports are involved. Football players apparently need moderate anxiety on the day of a game, but better wrestlers appear to experience low state anxiety before competition. Thus, Morgan indicated that the common practice of attempting to enhance performance by changing precompetition anxiety is questionable at best. Finally, there is frequently a disparity between athletes' stated desires and their unconscious attitudes. Coaches must look beyond athletes' past performances and verbalized goals to understand the motives that direct their behavior.

LEVEL OF ASPIRATION

The concept of level of aspiration was introduced by Dembo in a study of goal setting and factors associated with changes in goals (Lewin et al., 1944). Level of aspiration (LOA), or how much a person expects (or, in some cases, wishes) to achieve, has come to be regarded as an integral aspect of personality. This concept is used to express the degree of change in one's goals when he or she evaluates past performance or is provided with some performance norm. In an LOA task, an individual predicts his or her future performance on the basis of his or her previous performances or a performance norm. The individual then performs the task, and his or her psychological reaction to the new performance, including new goal setting, is observed.

Usually, an individual's goal differs from his or her previous performance or from a performance norm. This difference is called the goal discrepancy (GD). The difference between the stated goal and the ensuing performance is called the attainment discrepancy (AD). GD scores are used in studies of the nature of goal setting and goal-directed behavior. AD scores are used to evaluate reinforcers and to study behavior in which attainment of the immediate goal constitutes a reward.

Several investigators have shown a relationship between performance or ability and LOA. For example, Locke (1966) observed that persons who set high goals perform better than those who set low goals and those who receive only knowledge of their score without setting any goals. Clarke and Clarke (1961) found that 9-year-old boys who expressed higher levels of aspiration were superior in size and physical strength. Smaller and weaker boys generally chose lower aspiration levels, which appeared to ensure some measure of success. Andersen (1973) found that highly skilled swimmers set goals with low positive GDs for familiar tasks but large negative GDs for unfamiliar tasks. These large negative values quickly change to low positive GDs as the tasks became more familiar. Frank (1935*a*) reported that aspiration levels are relatively permanent characteristics, which do not depend on the type of ability required by a task; rather, they appear to depend on persistent individual differences.

The level of performance on one task influences one's LOA on other tasks (Frank, 1935*b*). This observation has been supported by Gardner's (1938) finding that success and failure cause adjustments in one's LOA. In addition to self-appraisal, one's view of his or her relationship to the social group is a factor in aspiration. Thus, an individual always has two reference points for setting goals—one's feelings about his or her own current performance and one's views of his or her status in a social group. Hilgard, Sait, and Margaret (1940) reported that group pressure influences private goal setting if the desire for social conformity has become internalized. They noticed a tendency for estimates to regress slightly toward the mean of the social group on both easy tasks and hard tasks. Aspiration may be a useful tool for studying some factors involved in social change (Gould, 1941). Satisfaction with the present situation produces small GDs, while dissatisfaction results in large GDs. The level of aspiration may be set so low that failure is impossible, and thus goal setting can provide a means for a person to avoid failure.

Another important consideration is whether the situation is realistic or artificial. Leshner (1961) found that people experience greater muscular tension in realistic situations than they do in hopeful situations. Success produces a decrease in muscular tension, and failure produces an increase. The importance of instructions was stressed by Festinger (1942): if asked to set a goal that he or she expects to reach, a person reacts more realistically than one who is asked to set a goal that he or she would like to reach. Festinger reported that shifts in discrepancy scores are accompanied by changes in the meaning of the situation. Feelings of success and failure are one of the factors producing changes in discrepancies.

Ostrow (1976) reported that students with high achievement needs set more realistic goals and perform better under competitive conditions than those with low achievement needs. The effect of achievement need is only temporary, however, as the differences between the two groups were observed only in their first tournament contest. Since individuals with high achievement needs may have more experience in competitive situations than others do, this finding may reflect a typical change in goal setting as the conditions of competition become more familiar.

There is some support for the idea that goal setting and risk taking are related to sex roles. According to Wallach and Kagan (1959, 1961), males and females both tolerate high risks if the activity is considered appropriate for their sex. For tasks with neutral sex roles, women are more cautious than men (Roberts, 1975). Further, need achievement was found to be related to risk taking in both males and females; both men and women who strive to achieve success prefer more risk than those who strive to avoid failure.

Levels of aspiration are determined by realism; past experience; standards of the social group; goal structure of the activity; and wish, fear, and expectancy (Lewin et al., 1944). By observing the goals expressed by students, teachers can become aware of students' motivation and self-image. Students who express goals that are within their capabilities have a realistic, strong self-image. Students who consistently set goals that are extremely high or extremely low to protect themselves from failure need special attention. Aspirations can be changed from these extremes if students are placed in situations that mostly provide success, with only occasional failure. Both constant success and constant failure can produce difficulties for students. Level of aspiration, which is accessible to observation and does not require sophisticated testing to be detected, is one factor that teachers can use to determine students' needs.

GUIDING PRINCIPLES FOR THE TEACHER

1. Motivation is the energizer of behavior. It causes the dominant response to be emitted. A motivational variable meets one of the

following criteria: (*a*) it energizes a wide variety of responses; (*b*) new responses appear to depend on it; (*c*) changes in the variable weaken certain responses; and (*d*) no other designation seems appropriate.

2. Motivated behavior occurs in a cycle with three components: a motivating state, motivated behavior, and a satisfying condition. Goals determine motivated behavior and depend in turn on the motives that are active.

3. Symbolic, abstract goals are learned as a part of the process of psychological development. Young children strive for concrete, immediate goals, but as they become older, their goals become more abstract and satisfaction can be deferred.

4. Goal-directed behavior is determined by four factors: availability, expectancy, incentive, and motive. All these are influenced by an individual's past experience.

5. Optimal levels of motivation enhance performance, but poor performance results if motivation is too low or too high. The effect of motivation on learning is different from its effect on performance. Motivation impairs learning, but at optimal levels it enhances the performance of activities that have already been learned.

6. Motives are classified as primary motives, which are not learned, and secondary motives, which depend on learning. Primary motives include physiological needs and general drives. Social needs are examples of secondary motives.

7. Level of aspiration is a form of goal setting in which an individual estimates his or her future performance on the basis of past performance or some kind of norm. It is regarded as an integral part of personality, which remains consistent from task to task.

8. Level of aspiration is determined by the realism of the situation, past experience, standards of the social group, goal structure of the activity, and wish, fear, and expectancy.

9. Satisfaction produces a low discrepancy score (realistic aspiration); dissatisfaction results in a large discrepancy score. Aspirations may be set unrealistically high, so that the person protects himself or herself from failure with the knowledge that the goal could never be met, or they may be set so low that failure is impossible.

SUMMARY

Motivation is the energizer of behavior: motives direct our behavior and determine the goals we set. It involves a three-stage cycle of motivating state, or need; motivated behavior; and a satisfying condition, which eliminates the need. Behavior that is used to obtain satisfying conditions can vary considerably, depending on availability, expectancy, incentive, and motive. In all cases, the past experiences of the individual are important. Motivation causes a person to perform the dominant response. Therefore, if students are learning new material for which their dominant response is not the correct one, motivation interferes with learning. Once the correct response has been established as dominant, optimal levels of motivation enhance performance. If the level is too low or too high, however, it detracts from performance.

Motives have been classified as primary and secondary. Primary motives are not dependent on learning. They include physiological needs (such as thirst, sleep, hunger, temperature regulation, fatigue, and oxygen needs) and general drives (including the need for affection, the need for bodily activity and manipulation, curiosity, and fear). Secondary motives are symbolic factors that have been learned through past experience. These learned drives include needs for achievement, approval, acceptance, independence, self-mastery, security, and power. Anxiety is another learned drive. Motives become more complex and abstract as a result of learning.

Level of aspiration is a concept used in the study of goal setting. In most cases, there is a discrepancy between an individual's goals and his or her actual performance or between the goals and performance norms. People sometimes set discrepancies, either too low or too high, to protect themselves from failure. An individual's level of aspiration is consistent from task to task. It is influenced by the realism of the task, past experience, standards of the social group, goal structure of the activity, and wish, fear, and expectancy.

The wide range of individual differences, the variety of past experiences, and the multitude of drives make the prediction of motivated behavior difficult at best. Predictions for groups are impossible, and no single technique affects all persons in the same way. Dealing with motivated behavior on an individual basis is the only method for changing it. If a teacher is to modify motivated behavior, the first step is to identify the motivating state and the satisfying conditions. Only after these factors are known can the behavior be changed.

REFERENCES

Andersen, P. A. 1973. The relation of personality factors of Olympic, national finalist, and non-national finalist swimmers to unfamiliar and familiar aspiration tasks. Doctoral dissertation, University of Toledo.

Barnett, M. L., and Stanicer, J. A. 1979. Effects of goal setting on achievement in archery. *Research Quarterly* 50:328 332.

Basler, M. L., Fisher, A. C., and Mumford, N. L. 1976. Arousal and anxiety correlates of gymnastic performance. *Research Quarterly* 47:586 589.

Birch, D., and Veroff, J. 1966. *Motivation: A study of action.* Monterey, Calif.: Brooks/Cole.

Brown, J. S. 1961. *The motivation of behavior.* New York: McGraw-Hill.

Cannon, W. B. 1932. *The wisdom of the body.* New York: W. W. Norton.

Clarke, H. H. 1966. *Muscular strength and endurance in man.* Englewood Cliffs, N.J.: Prentice-Hall.

Clarke, H. H., and Clarke, D. H. 1961. Relationship between level of aspiration and selected physical factors of boys aged nine years. *Research Quarterly* 32:12 19.

Erikson, E. H. 1950. *Childhood and society.* New York: W. W. Norton.

Festinger, L. 1942. Wish, expectation, and group standards as factors influencing level of aspiration. *Journal of Abnormal Psychology* 37:184-200.

Frank, J. D. 1935*a*. Individual differences in certain aspects of level of aspiration. *American Journal of Psychology* 47:119-128.

———. 1935*b*. Influence of the level of performance in one task on the level of aspiration in another. *Journal of Experimental Psychology* 18:159 171.

Fuller, J. L. 1962. *Motivation: A biological perspective.* New York: Random House.

Gardner, J. W. 1938. Individual differences in aspiration level in a standard sequence of objective success and failure situations. *Psychological Bulletin* 35:521.

Gould, R. 1941. Some sociological determinants of goal strivings. *Journal of Social Psychology* 13:461-473.

Hanson, D. L. 1967. Influence of the Hawthorne effect upon physical education research. *Research Quarterly* 38:723-724.

Hilgard, R. E., Sait, E. M., and Margaret, G. A. 1940. Level of aspiration as affected by relative standing in an experimental social group. *Journal of Experimental Psychology* 27:411-421.

Horrocks, J. E. 1962. *The psychology of adolescence.* 2d ed. Boston: Houghton Mifflin.

Leshner, S. S. 1961. The effects of aspiration and achievement on muscular tensions. *Journal of Experimental Psychology* 61:133 137.

Lewin, K. T., Dembo, L. Festinger, L., and Sears, P. 1944. Level of aspiration. In *Handbook of personality and the behavior disorders*, ed. J. McV. Hunt. New York: Ronald Press.

Locke, E. A. 1966. A closer look at level of aspiration as a training procedure: A reanalysis of Fryer's data. *Journal of Applied Psychology* 50:417 420.

McTeer, W. 1972. *The scope of motivation.* Monterey, Calif.: Brooks/Cole.

Martens, R., and Simon, J. A. 1976. Comparison of three predictors of state anxiety in competitive situations. *Research Quarterly* 47:381 387.

Morgan, C. T., and King, R. A. 1966. *Introduction to psychology.* 3d ed. New York: McGraw-Hill.

Morgan, W. P. 1974. Selected psychological considerations in sport. *Research Quarterly* 45:374-390.

Nelson, J. K. 1978. Motivating effects of the use of norms and goals with endurance testing. *Research Quarterly* 49:317 321.

Ostrow, A. C. 1976. Goal-setting behavior and need achievement in relation to competitive motor activity. *Research Quarterly* 47:174 183.

Rethlingshafer, D. 1963. *Motivation as related to personality.* New York: McGraw-Hill.

Roberts, G. C. 1975. Sex and achievement motivation effects on risk taking. *Research Quarterly* 46:58-70.

Sheehy, G. 1977. *Passages: Predictable crises of adult life.* New York: Bantam.

Stellar, E. 1960. Drive and motivation. In *Handbook of physiology.* Sec. 1, vol. 3, ed. H. W. Magoun. Washington, D. C.: American Physiological Society.

University of Oregon, Alumni Office. 1966. Red-blooded world of intercollegiate athletics. *Old Oregon* 45 (May June): 17 32.

Wallach, M. A., and Kagan, N. 1959. Sex differences and judgment processes. *Journal of Personality* 27:555 564.

. 1961. Aspects of judgment and decision-making: Interrelationship and changes with age. *Behavioral Science* 6:23 36.

Weinberg, R. S., and Jackson, A. 1979. Competition and extrinsic rewards: Effect on intrinsic motivation and attribution. *Research Quarterly* 50:494 502.

Zajonc, R. B. 1966. *Social psychology: An experimental approach*. Belmont, Calif.: Wadsworth.

11 Practice Conditions

Instructors have little control over factors that shape motor learning. They cannot change one's age, sex, or past experience. Nor can they change the principles that govern the way we learn. Teachers can, however, use principles of feedback and can control factors that influence timing as they organize the material that is presented in class. Knowledge of changes that take place during learning and of types of organization that facilitate learning or performance forms the basis of teaching skill and progression.

Practice conditions used in physical education classes or in athletic training should enable teachers and coaches to carefully direct performers' progress in the acquisition of motor skill. Grouped instruction can be used to help individual learners acquire skill in stages.

Learning has been described as having three phases (Fitts, 1964; Fitts and Posner, 1967). During the early or cognitive phase, the learner develops a cognitive image of the task to be acquired. According to Fitts and Posner (p. 11), "a good instructor will call attention to important perceptual cues and response characteristics and give diagnostic knowledge of results" in this phase. Correct responses are shaped through a series of successive approximations. In the second period, the intermediate or associative phase, responses are learned and become readily available. Practice allows old responses to be tried out and new patterns to emerge. Errors become less frequent as they are gradually eliminated. The final or autonomous phase is characterized by skills that require less cognitive control and are less subject to interference and distractions. Since they require less processing by the central nervous system, a person can perform them while he or she is learning new activities or engaging in other tasks. Speed or efficiency of responses continues to improve during this phase, but at a decreasing rate.

Practice conditions influence the efficiency of learning in the associative phase. They should be instituted according to answers to questions such as the following. Should practice trials be massed into a single unit, or should they be distributed about a series of rest periods? Should learners practice the skill in its entirety, or is it better learned in parts? Does a knowledge of underlying principles improve acquisition of a skill? How should learners receive knowledge of their performance? Does mental rehearsal of a skill aid acquisition? What is the effect of practice in social settings? The remainder of this chapter is addressed to these questions. The discussion that follows should help teachers and coaches develop practice conditions under which skills can be acquired more effectively.

MASSED PRACTICE AND DISTRIBUTED PRACTICE

The distribution of practice involves the relationship between work periods and rest periods. *Massed practice* is carried out in one long session, in which practice is continuous, with no provision for rest. *Distributed practice* is carried out in several shorter sessions interspersed with rest periods. The practice-rest relationship can be organized in many ways—long practice sessions with infrequent rests, short practice sessions with frequent rests, long or short rest periods, and rest periods of increasing or decreasing length. Therefore, the question is not merely whether rest periods should be allowed during practice, but what relationship between work and rest is best.

Early studies of the distribution of practice were conducted at the beginning of this century. Murphy (1916) reported no significant effect of spaced practice on the acquisition of skill in javelin throwing. The work of Snoddy (1935), however, probably stimulated most of the research in this area. After a series of investigations of mirror tracing, Snoddy concluded that there are two types of "mental" growth processes. He believed that primary growth, which occurs early, is facilitated by distributed practice and appears to increase as the length of rest periods increases. Secondary growth, which occurs later in the learning process, seemed to Snoddy to be enhanced by reducing the distribution of practice. He believed that secondary growth is maximized if practice is massed, or continuous. In response to these findings, Dore and Hilgard (1937), after a study of pursuit rotor tasks, argued that distributed practice is more advantageous, but they neither supported nor disproved the existence of primary and secondary growth. A later investigation by Cook and Hilgard (1949) found no support for Snoddy's prediction that massed practice is harmful early in training and beneficial late in training. They also found no differences between practices with decreasing rest periods and those with increasing rest periods.

Other research supports the view that there are no long-term differences between performance after massed practice and performance after distributed practice. Ammons (1947) and Ammons and Willig (1956) reported that the lower performance level observed after massed practice on the pursuit rotor represents a temporary work decrement, which reaches a maximum after 8 minutes of continuous work and is dissipated after 20 minutes of rest. A companion study by Ammons (1950) also pointed out the temporary nature of the decrement after massed practice. Further, this research indicated that optimal times exist for the intertrial rest periods: 50-second and 2-minute rests were found to be superior to 5-minute and 12-minute rests. Franklin and Brozek (1947) reported no differences between effects of massed practice and effects of distributed practice on gross reaction time, pattern-tracing performance, and retention. Fleishman and Parker (1962) found that retention depends on specific task habits rather than on practice conditions.

Abrams and Grice (1976) evaluated the effects of practice and position of the task. They observed that different practice schedules are apparently optimal for tasks performed in different positions. Distributed practice is better for tasks performed overhead or in a vertical position, apparently as a result of task complexity, since the tracking task they used is more difficult in those positions. They also suggested that the selection of massed practice or distributed practice is highly dependent on other factors.

It is difficult to use the results of studies of simple psychomotor tasks, such as pursuit rotor tracking, to generalize about practice schedules for complex skills. Austin (1975) indicated that distributed practice is more effective than massed practice for elementary school girls learning to increase throwing velocity. Although the massed-practice group improved initially, the distributed-practice group showed superior results over a 6-week period.

There is some evidence that the effects of massed practice and distributed practice depend on mental ability. Jones and Ellis (1962) observed a larger buildup of inhibition with normal subjects in massed practice than with educable retardates under the same conditions. Using trainable subjects in massed practice and two schedules of distributed practice, Drowatzky (1970) observed that some trainable children were unable to learn a tracking task in massed practice. He also reported that trainables are not affected the same as normals by different distributions of practice and that the decrement associated with massed practice is temporary. Barnett and Cantor (1957), using retarded subjects, also recorded temporary decrements. That is, manipulation of the distribution of practice produces changes in performance rather than changes in learning.

The performance curves shown in Figure 11.1 are typical of those reported in studies of massed and distributed practice. There is little or no initial difference in performance, but as the number of trials

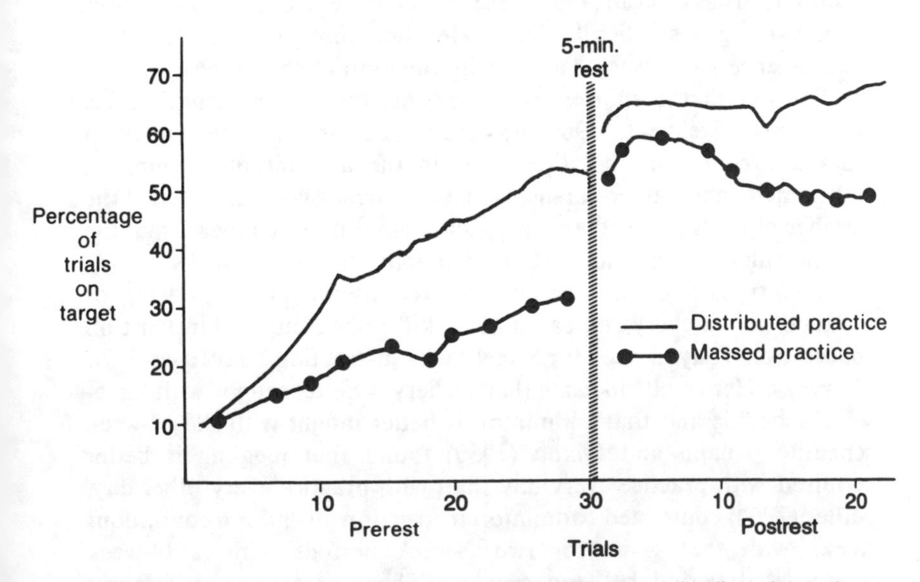

Figure 11.1. Performance curves for massed practice and distributed practice. (Data from Jones and Ellis, 1962.)

increases, distributed practice produces increasingly superior performances. If a rest is provided, any significant difference between the conditions is eliminated. The differences reappear when practice sessions are resumed. These differences are produced by some type of inhibition. Most psychologists believe that the inhibitory factors are fatigue, boredom, decreased motivation, or combinations of these and similar factors.

The choice between massed practice and distributed practice is mainly one of economy; the total time for distributed practice plus rests may preclude its use. Distribution of practice might be critical if the performance requires accuracy during its acquisition, and this consideration may eliminate massed practice. Kleinman (1976) reported no difference between massed practice and distributed practice in learning gymnastic skills; rather, such variables as pacing and complexity of the task are the determining factors. These are the types of considerations that instructors must use in their decisions about the distribution of practice.

In practical terms, the organization of the school day usually imposes distributed practice, and the question arises, What distributed schedule is most conducive to learning gross motor skills? Using a stabliometer task, Ryan (1965) observed no difference in performances with varying rest distributions. He did observe, however, that reminiscence gains were a decreasing function of the prerest practice distribution; that is, shorter rest periods produced more reminiscence. In contrast, Stelmach (1969) observed a performance decrement in massed practice but no differences in the amount of learning in stabliometer and ladder-balancing tasks. Learning was a function of the number of trials rather than any practice condition. It appears that the general rules for fine motor skills also apply to balance tasks.

Two types of distributed practice were used by Young (1954) for instruction in archery and badminton skills. She compared instruction spaced over 4 days a week for 5 weeks with instruction 2 days a week for 10 weeks. Her results indicate that archery is better taught with the 5-week schedule and that badminton is better taught with the 10-week schedule. Knapp and Dixon (1950) found that juggling is better acquired with practice every day than with practice every other day. Miller (1964) contrasted badminton instruction given for 6 continuous weeks with that given for two 3-week periods with a 14-week interpolated period between sessions. She reported no differences between the two instructional organizations. Unfortunately, few other studies have looked at the organization of instructional units. The findings of Young and of Knapp and Dixon suggest the need for a series of studies to investigate the optimal spacing of instructional periods.

Retention of skills represents another aspect of instruction that needs further study. Lynn (1971) found that massed practice produces higher performance levels in a lacrosse skill immediately after practice, but that distributed practice produces higher retention levels after 35 days. Using a novel basketball skill, Singer (1965) found no significant differences between massed practice and distributed practice conditions after a 5-minute rest, but after 1 month the distributed practice conditions produced better retention. Once again, these studies suggest needs for research on the optimal organization of instructional materials. There are more questions than answers about practice conditions for gross motor and sports skills.

As indicated in chapter 3, learners frequently adopt the most economical speed of performance, so that self-pacing is the preferred rate, if it is practical. But what is the best rate of practice if a motor task must be performed at a criterion speed? Sage and Hornak (1978) reported that continuous motor skills can be acquired as efficiently through practice with gradual, progressive increases in speed as they can through constant practice at the criterion speed.

Adaptive training has also been suggested as an effective training procedure (Lintern and Gypher, 1978). Adaptive training individualizes the schedule by varying the task difficulty through a graded series of steps at a rate that is related to the performer's speed of learning. This regimen is based on the assumption that a demanding task can be learned more efficiently if it is presented throughout training at a level of difficulty that is optimally matched to the performer's current ability (Kelly, 1969). Adaptive training is similar to programmed instruction for cognitive skills. Perceptual variables and response variables are carefully manipulated to guide subjects to performance at the criterion level.

WHOLE INSTRUCTION AND PART INSTRUCTION

Whole instruction and part instruction are distinguished by the size of the unit that is presented to the learner. The *whole method* involves the presentation of large units at one time, as opposed to the introduction of instructional materials in smaller units. If the whole method were used in teaching swimming, for example, the entire crawl stroke would be presented at once to the beginner. The part method would present smaller components of the stroke, such as the kick, the arm stroke, and breathing. If a *progressive-part method* were used, the parts would be presented in a planned sequence and combined as they were mastered. In swimming, a student would learn to float and then to kick, and the prone float would be combined with the kick before the presentation of the next instructional part; then the arm stroke would be taught and combined with the previously learned float and kick. Another alternative is the *whole-part method,* which begins with whole instruction, shifts to part instruction when students experience difficulty, and then returns to whole instruction. In light of these various options, instructors must be aware of guidelines to use in making their decisions. The following studies provide information on which such decisions can be based.

It appears that no one method is appropriate in all situations, as the complexity of the situation is one factor determining whether the whole method or the part method is most effective. For example, Cross (1937) looked at whole, whole-part, and progressive-part instruction to find the most effective method of teaching basketball to ninth-grade boys. His results indicate that the whole method is best suited for simpler skills, the progressive-part method for skills of intermediate difficulty, and the whole-part method for complex skills. Similar results were obtained by Niemeyer (1958*a*, 1958*b*). He observed that swimming is best taught with the whole method and volleyball with the part method, and that both methods are equally effective for badminton instruction. Niemeyer concluded that individual activities are best taught by the whole method, dual activities by the whole-part method, and team sports by the part method.

These conclusions have been supported by the findings of Briggs and his coworkers. Using a relatively simple lever-positioning skill, Briggs and Brogden (1954) found that whole learning is markedly superior to part learning. They believed that this superiority would disappear with complex skills, however. In a second study, Briggs and Naylor (1962) reported that the part method is more efficient with complex skills and that the whole method and the progressive-part method produce more transfer than either the pure-part method or a simplified whole (large parts) method. Finally, Naylor and Briggs (1963) reported a relationship between task complexity and instructional method. They found that the progressive-part method is best for tasks of low organization.

Hall (1959) observed no differences between the whole method and the part method in bowling classes. Shay (1934) found that the whole method is superior to the part method in learning the horizontal bar upstart. A later study by Wickstrom (1958), however, comparing the effectiveness of these two methods for eighteen gymnastic and tumbling skills, found a difference between methods in only one case; his results indicate that the back roll–snap-down is better learned by whole instruction. Juggling skills have also been observed to be better learned through the whole method (Knapp and Dixon, 1952).

Unfortunately, few studies have considered the influence of student characteristics in the effectiveness of whole and part instruction. McGuigan and MacCaslin (1955), looking at the intelligence of army recruits in learning rifle marksmanship, reported a relationship between intelligence and the type of instruction. In some respects, the whole method was better than the part method for recruits with above-average intelligence. Murray (1979) reported that students can be classified as sequential learners and holistic learners: the former learn more efficiently by the part method, the latter by the whole method.

These studies indicate that neither method is superior in all situations. The part method appears to be better suited for more complex skills, and the whole method for less complex skills. Both must involve skills that are meaningful. Thus, part instruction should use skills that are easily separated from the whole, such as the lay-up in basketball. The part method might be used to advantage in avoiding problems of fatigue or boredom, which may arise from long practice sessions in the whole method. It may also give more rapid feedback and reinforcement. The whole method appears to be better if the material is so meaningful that it hangs together well and if the students are intelligent enough to learn quickly. In fact, the whole method appears to be better in most learning situations. The notable exception is team games.

Probably the best recommendation is that the teacher should follow a flexible plan, beginning with materials organized in larger units but moving to smaller units of instruction when students experience difficulty in learning. If the part method is used, the instructor must plan for the parts to be combined into a whole, since integration cannot be expected to occur through incidental learning.

KINESIOLOGICAL INSTRUCTION

One method of instruction is the kinesiological approach, in which students are taught mechanical principles that explain how a skill is performed, in addition to instruction in techniques. The supporters of this method believe that it enables students to acquire a basic understanding of movement, more versatility in dealing with the environment, a deeper appreciation of body mechanics, and greater efficiency during skilled motor performance.

The classic study in this area was conducted by Judd (1908). He compared the performances of fifth- and sixth-grade boys in hitting a submerged target with a dart. One group was given explanations of refraction, but the others worked out the problem on their own. He found no difference between the groups in the initial phase, but when the depth of the target was changed, the boys who had been instructed in refraction showed superior performances. This study was replicated by Hendrickson and Schroeder (1941), using eighth-grade students as subjects, and the groups that received instruction in refraction again performed significantly better.

Using intermediate-grade students, Werner (1972) observed that knowledge of principles of levers aids in the acquisition of the softball throw for distance but makes no difference in a soccer kick for distance. Stanton (1968) found that instruction in principles of stability helped his third-grade students to apply the sprinter's start in situations other than those presented in the instruction. According to Broer (1958), instruction emphasizing problem solving and mechanical principles also produces superior performance in seventh-grade girls. Likewise, Daughtrey (1945) reported that junior high school boys who received kinesiological instruction improved their performance in five sports skills more than boys who received traditional instruction. All of these studies, conducted with elementary and junior high school students, indicate that instruction in mechanical principles enhances the students' later performances.

Studies conducted with college students have not provided such clear-cut findings. Barrett (1959) and Mohr and Barrett (1962) reported that a knowledge of mechanical principles aids in the acquisition of swimming strokes and intermediate swimming skills. Nessler (1961) reported that instruction in mechanical principles related to basic movement patterns facilitates performance in elementary games. Zuber (1957) found that students who are instructed in the laws of motion learn gymnastic stunts more rapidly.

Success in shooting the one-hand push shot after receiving kinesiological instruction was evaluated by Halverson (1949). She reported no overall difference between the kinesiological approach and other methods. It should be noted that the kinesiological group in her study practiced without a basket. Her results suggest that low-ability students would benefit from a kinesiological approach more than other students.

A number of studies have indicated that college students do not benefit from a kinesiological approach. Dehnert (1963) found that this method has no effect on ability to shoot free throws. According to Colville (1957), knowledge of mechanical principles has no effect on performance in archery and ball rolling and catching. Evaluating the performances of women with low motor ability, Frey (1947) found that knowledge of the reasons for correct form does not improve their skills in tennis, volleyball, and rhythms. Kearns (1960) reported that knowledge of principles makes no difference in the acquisition of bowling skills, and Mikesell (1962) reached the same conclusion for instruction in badminton. In tennis instruction, Cobane (1959) observed that knowledge of principles makes no difference in performance but does improve the students' performance on written tests.

How can the disparities in these findings be explained? One explanation may lie in problems of experimental control. If kinesiological instruction is accomplished at the cost of a great loss of practice time, the study could be reporting the effect of varying amounts of practice rather than differences between instructional methods. It is hard to determine the consistency of practice times from the reports of these studies. A second explanation may be found in the acceptance of the procedure by the students. Younger students may more readily accept instruction in mechanical principles. Further, some skills may be more dependent on an understanding of principles than others. There is a lack of research relating to the analysis of skill level and instructional method. Lawther (1968) noted that, although experimental evidence does not establish the value of kinesiological instruction for advanced performers, the data do suggest that persons with high levels of skill may benefit more from it.

KNOWLEDGE OF RESULTS

Knowlege of results (KR) refers to the process through which a performer receives information about his or her performance, either directly through the senses or in a modified or supplemented form, and which thereby is a factor in determining subsequent actions. A more extensive discussion of this process was presented in chapter 4. This section summarizes the importance of KR in teaching methods.

According to Bilodeau and Bilodeau (1961), KR is the strongest and most important variable controlling performance and learning.

There is no improvement without it. Progressive improvement accompanies KR, and deterioration occurs after KR is removed. Some researchers identify these roles for KR: a reward role if it strengthens habits, an informational role if it provides cues to evoke already established habits, and a motivational role if it provides incentive for performance.

Information can come from any of three primary sources. First, it can come from an external source, that is, from the configuration of the sensory environment, which appears to activate an intrinsic feedback loop. This intrinsic loop works in concert with a second, internal proprioceptive loop, which also provides information to control responses. The third source, a supplementary loop provided through the presence of extra information, may or may not be present.

Welford (1972) has noted that little learning occurs without the knowledge of one's actual overt response, which allows a performer to adjust biases and correct future responses. He appears somewhat skeptical about the value of supplemental feedback, as performance often deteriorates quickly if it is removed. Welford believes that training is effective only if it teaches performers to observe and use inherent feedback.

Three situations, in which KR was presented with varying degress of precision, were evaluated by Shapiro (1977). She reported no difference among the three groups' performances, but with more precise KR, subjects tended to make fewer errors. Since the accuracy of the KR controls the accuracy of the response, teachers must provide learners with accurate information about their performance. Feedback is effective in all stages; it sustains performance early in practice just as much as it does later (Bilodeau and Bilodeau, 1961).

Knowledge of results alone can enable performers to acquire a skill. With the addition of knowledge of performance (KP), however, which is feedback that supplies information about the quality of performance, they can attain a higher level of skill (Wallace and Hagler, 1979). For such feedback to be effective, learners must either establish in memory an internal model of performance or be provided with an external model. One method to provide an external model uses a videotape recorder, with which the teacher shows a model and then replays it side by side on a split screen with a student's response (Posner and Keele, 1973). The instructor would still have to ensure that the performer can perceive the critical differences between the two.

Teachers' primary task in providing KR is to present ways in which learners can recognize and use inherent feedback. The inherent cues usually involved in a learner's feedback system are the external, usually visual, characteristics of the environment and the internal cues arising from proprioceptive sensations of movement. Any supplemental KR must emphasize these inherent aspects of the task and help the learner incorporate inherent KR into his or her performance. Teachers must emphasize KR at all stages of performance, as it is equally important in each phase of practice. In tasks requiring accuracy of performance, KR must also be precise and accurate.

MENTAL PRACTICE

Mental practice is a teaching method that does not require an overt response on the part of the learner. Rather, the learner sits quietly, usually with the eyes closed, and mentally (covertly) experiences the motor skill to be learned. This method has been used in a variety of ways: to learn new skills; as a preperformance review of a skill; in combination with physical practice; and to review or develop strategy. Many investigators have studied mental practice for one or more of these uses. Their results show that the efficacy of this method depends on the purpose for which it is used and the skill involved.

Results from a number of investigations have shown mental practice to be as effective as physical practice in the acquisition of skills. For example, Maxwell (1968) and Kelly (1965) found no difference between physical practice and mental practice in acquiring the overhand volleyball serve. Wills (1965) reached a similar conclusion for passing the football for accuracy. Studies of various ball-throwing skills also indicate that performances after mental practice are equally good as performances after physical practice (Stephens, 1966; Luebke, 1967; Vandell, Davis, and Clugston, 1943). Rawlings (1972) concluded that mental practice is as effective as physical practice in acquiring a tracking skill. Mental practice is also effective in improving the performance of a simple eye-hand coordination task (Smith and Harrison, 1962). Jones (1965) found that it improves performance of the hockswing upstart, but this study did not present any comparison with a physical practice condition.

Another group of studies indicate that, although some improvement does occur, mental practice is not as effective as physical practice. The skills involved in these studies include a basketball push shot (Halverson, 1949), tennis forehand and backhand drives (Wilson, 1960; Surburg, 1968), muscular endurance (Steel, 1952; Kelsey, 1961), ring tossing (Twining, 1949), and hitting a projected ball with a tennis paddle (Egstrom, 1964).

Studies that used various combinations of mental practice and physical practice have reported these conditions to be as effective as physical practice alone in improving performance. In some cases, a combination has been the most effective practice condition. Waterland (1956) found that a combination of kinesthetic perception and mental practice facilitates the acquisition of bowling skills. Similar results were observed with accuracy in ball throwing (Stebbins, 1967); improvement in jumping ability (Wills, 1966); juggling ability (Trussell, 1952; Howe, 1968); dart throwing (Burns, 1962); complex gymnastic skills (Whiteley, 1962; Gilmore, 1972); and pursuit rotor tracking, a soccer kick for accuracy, and a modified jump shot (Oxendine, 1969). A combination of physical practice and mental practice was reported by White, Ashton, and Lewis (1979) to be more effective than either mental practice or physical practice alone in learning the competitive swimming start. They also reported no difference between mental practice and physical practice.

Finally, another group of studies either show that mental practice is ineffective or explain the improvements observed in other studies as results of factors other than practice conditions. Using a task that required subjects to project a ball and catch it in a socket, Gilmore and Stolurow (1951) found that persons who conducted mental practice did more poorly than those who received no practice of any sort. This study has been replicated twice with the same results both times. Shick (1970) observed that, in performing volleyball serving and wall volley tasks, persons with mental practice did not improve more than those with no practice. Mental practice on a unique want-tossing task also proved ineffective in improving the performance of subjects (Corbin, 1967*a*).

Mental practice was found to be as effective as physical practice in some studies; it improved performance somewhat in others; and it was of no value in still others. The basic reason for these differences lies in the subjects' relative familiarity with the task at hand. For example, Clark (1960) studied high school basketball players, classified as novice, junior varsity, or varsity performers on the basis of their ability, and found that, for the more skilled performers, mental practice is about as effective as physical practice. For the novice performers, however, physical practice led to greater improvement (see Figure 11.2). In a

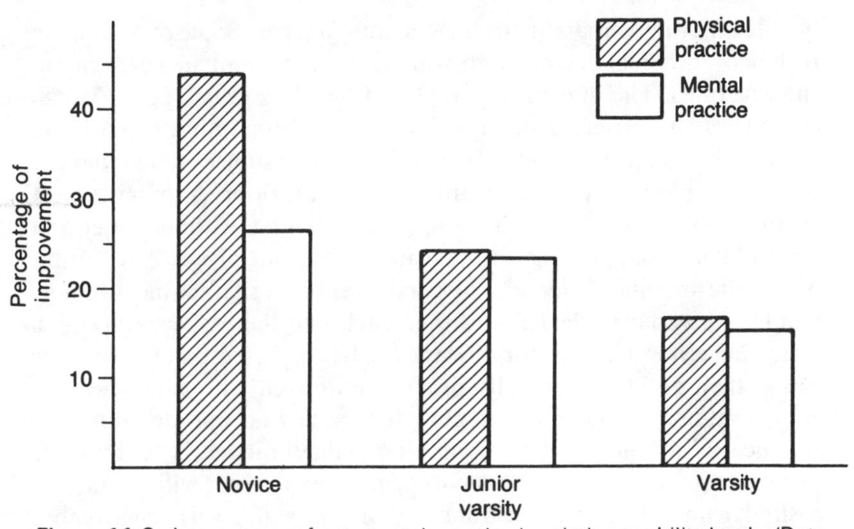

Figure 11.2. Improvement from mental practice in relation to ability levels. (Data from Clark, 1960.)

follow-up to his previous study, employing the same unique wand-tossing task, Corbin (1967*b*) also found that experience with the task or a similar task enables learners to benefit from mental practice.

Two further studies suggest that the type of task may affect the value of mental practice. Brumbach and Beckow (1968), using the short and long badminton serves and the golf putt, found that only the group involved in the short serve improved through mental practice. Consequently, they concluded that mental practice is more effective with skills requiring restricted and precise muscular control (such as a short serve) than for those involving more gross and dynamic movements (such as a putt). The effects of mental practice on skills of varying difficulty were investigated by Phipps (1968). He found that mental practice improves performance in the simplest skill (the hockswing mount) but not the more complex skills (the jump-through and the soccer hitch kick) unless a physical session is interjected between mental practice bouts. Phipps concluded that the effectiveness of mental practice without prior physical practice is specific to the skill and is more pronounced for simpler skills. These findings may not be directly supported by the summary of research presented in this chapter, but few studies have specifically investigated this problem.

Imagery may also play a role in one's ability to benefit from mental practice. Children can form mental images more easily than adults, and people differ in their ability to form mental images. Some of us think in technicolor, others in black and white, and some think in words rather than pictures. The illustrations reported by Clark (1960, pp. 567–568) emphasize the variety of mental imagery. In attempting to mentally bounce the ball in preparation for shooting, one subject stated that the ball would not bounce and became stuck to the floor. Another subject reported visualizing the ball going into a basket without a net and immediately disappearing until it came back "out of nowhere" to hit him in the abdomen. Finally, one person reported that his mental shots would swerve far to the left and then back into the basket rather than following a normal trajectory. Clark further reported that the subjects found their ability to mentally practice improved with experience.

In summary, the following guidelines seem appropriate for mental practice as a teaching technique. If mental practice is to improve performance, learners must have some prior experience with the task or a similar task. Therefore, persons with higher skill levels benefit more from mental practice than beginners do. In the same way, combinations of mental and physical practice may be more effective than mental practice alone. It apparently is important that a learner is able to symbolize movements by words and concepts. It has also been suggested that simple skills and restricted movements can be improved through mental practice more than complex movements and gross movements can. Most subjects must be instructed in the correct manner of mental practice, and their ability improves with experience. Finally, several studies suggest that mental practice with greater freedom procedure is superior to more restricted practice; one study (Gilmore, 1972) reported contradictory findings in this regard.

GUIDED PRACTICE

A variety of instructional techniques are available for physical education. Mosston (1966) has classified these as ranging from command techniques to problem-solving techniques. Until recently, however, few systematic investigations have been conducted to assess the relative merits of each instructional style. In 1976 Singer and Pease reported on a comparison of discovery learning and guided instructional techniques on the learning, retention, and transfer of a complex motor skill. The results of this study indicate that error correction through guided discovery produces more initial learning but that the discovery technique produces superior retention and transfer of the skill.

Halverson et al. (1977) looked at the effect of guided practice on overhand-throw ball velocities in kindergarten children. No change was reported in ball velocities after 120 minutes of guided practice spread over an 8-week period. The Halverson study, however, cites investigations by Hanson (1961) and Nichols (1971), which indicate that other aspects of throwing, such as distance and general body position, improve through guided instruction.

The relative values of a teacher-directed classroom and one in which the students share the decision making was evaluated by Martinek, Zaichkowsky, and Cheffers (1977). They indicated that a teacher-directed classroom is more effective in motor skill development, and that a classroom in which students share in decision making contributes more to the development of a positive self-concept.

The type of instructional style adopted by a teacher depends on several factors. These include the developmental level of the child, the task involved, and the purpose of the instructional unit. If the primary purpose is time efficiency, then guided practice appears to be the appropriate style. If retention and transfer of the skill are the primary instructional aim, then the discovery technique should be adopted. If both time efficiency and retention are desired, a combination of guided practice and discovery techniques should be used. Finally, for any technique to be effective in producing changes, the students must have reached a developmental level at which they can benefit from the instruction. If changes in self-concept are desired, the teacher must adopt instructional strategies that facilitate such changes.

PRACTICE IN SOCIAL SETTINGS

Social settings are situations in which more than one person is present. According to Zajonc (1966), there are three types of social settings:

1. social behavior, in which the behavior of a single person is influenced by the presence of others
2. social interaction, which is the mutual and reciprocal dependence of behavior among individuals
3. group processes resulting in social behavior and interactions, evidenced by social uniformity, group structure, and group performance

A group is defined as a set of persons who have some observable set of relations and who display mutually interdependent behaviors in response to external influences. Thus, group behaviors involve characteristics of the persons composing the group; effects of the environment; community, or social context; and variables associated with the task at hand (Davis, 1969).

The social setting can also involve either individual performance or collective performance. Researchers have focused their investigations on three general areas:

- the effects of the presence of others as passive observers (an audience)
- the effect of the presence of others simultaneously engaged in the same task but working independently (coaction)
- the effect of interaction with others

Certainly, the school setting fulfills the definition of a social group, and the three areas of research represent situations that can easily be observed in any physical education classroom.

Audience Effects

An audience of one or more persons represents the simplest of the three social settings. It is the only social setting whose effects have been investigated by physical educators. Research generally indicates that the knowledge that others are or will be present has a strong effect on performance. These findings began with Menmann's (1904) observations that a student's work output on the ergograph increased whenever he entered the room where the student was working. His subsequent experiments and others, such as the one conducted by Nelson (Clarke, 1966), have shown this increase to occur in muscle endurance studies using the ergograph. Nelson indicated that the presence of a passive observer produces a moderate motivating situation. In an evaluation of pursuit rotor performance with and without an audience, Travis (1925) observed a slight improvement if an audience was present. Similar results were obtained by Bergum and Lehr (1963), using a vigilance task, in which National Guard trainees monitored a panel of lights for long periods of time. These studies all indicate that performance on tasks is improved by the presence of an audience. Contrary to these findings, Wankel (1977) and Bird (1975) reported that the mere physical presence of an audience has no effect on performance.

This facilitation effect does not appear if the learner is engaged in the acquisition of a new task. Husband (1931) found that the presence of an observer disturbed and interfered with the learning of a finger maze. Likewise, Martens (1969) found that subjects who were observed while learning a coincidence timing task made significantly greater errors than those who learned the task alone, but once the task was acquired, subjects performing in the presence of an audience did better than those performing alone.

Zajonc (1966, p. 14) concluded that "learning is impaired and performance facilitated by the presence of an audience." The presence of an audience enhances the emission of the dominant response. The dominant response during the learning process is not necessarily the correct response, and therefore acquisition is disrupted. Once the correct response becomes the dominant response, performance is enhanced by an audience. Also, simple motor skills are likely to be overlearned and not disrupted by an audience as are verbal and complex motor skills.

Coaction

Coaction is a social setting in which persons engage in the same activity but do not directly interact with each other. It is often hard to distinguish coaction from a competitive set, through which one evaluates one's own performance in connection with what others are doing. Triplett (1898) made the earliest observations, when he noted that cyclists racing against time are inferior to those racing against pacers or other competitors. He then designed an experiment in which children wound fishing reels alone and together: some did better alone, others did better together, and still others did equally well under either conditions. Subsequent research cited by Hare (1962, p. 346) has confirmed Triplett's findings.

> Some children are stimulated positively by the presence of others while some are not (Shevaleva and Ergolska, 1926). In general, children seem to find the together situation more stimulating than do adults (Feofanov, 1928). Subjects with low intelligence are less stimulated (Abel, 1938) than the more intelligent. Under social influence, subjects were observed to be more active but less accurate at the beginning of a task such as printing or putting pegs in a board (Sengupta and Sinha, 1926; Anderson, 1929; Leuba, 1933; Daskiell, 1930, 1935). A similar effect was observed when a second subject was added after the first subject was satiated with the task (Burton, 1941). Subjects

were less likely to become bored if others were working at the same task (Taylor, Thompson, and Spassoff, 1937.)

Nelson (Clarke, 1966), in his study of muscle endurance, reported that coaction provides a competitive and highly motivating situation. According to Bird (1973). subjects in coaction performed better than those in front of an audience, but the performances of both these groups were not different from a group of subjects performing alone. Nobel et al. (1958) trained persons in a group on a discrimination reaction task and a pursuit rotor task and then, after training, tested the subjects as individuals. They showed a performance decrement on the discrimination reaction task but no change in performance on the pursuit rotor. Subsequently, these investigators suggested that the effect of social competition is contingent on undetermined task factors.

Davis (1969) reported that grouping appears to improve the speed of performance, reduce the quality of work, and increase the variability of both quality and speed of performance. The effect of social stimulation appears to move from "benign to harmful" as the complexity of the task increases. Davis also reported that social situations have different effects on the acquisition of new responses and the performance of well-learned ones. Coaction appears to facilitate performance in many situations, but on the basis of Zajonc's (1966) citation of a series of animal studies, it seems to impair learning.

Coaction has also been used in disagreeable and stressful conditions as social support. For example, Seidman et al. (1957) found that soldiers could tolerate more electrical shock in the presence of others than when they were alone. Ader and Tatum (1963) found that social support in a stressful situation inhibits the acquisition of an avoidance response. Thus, regardless of whether one engages in an approach task or an avoidance task, learning is impaired, but the performance of already acquired responses in stressful situations is enhanced by the presence of others.

According to Zajonc (1966), the generalization about the impairment of learning by the presence of others does not apply in two situations. In the first situation, members of a group follow the person who learns the task first; in the second, imitation learning, members of a group learn from persons who already can perform the task. Consequently, teachers must attempt to provide opportunities for students to acquire new skills, either alone or in situations involving imitation learning.

TEACHERS' EXPECTATIONS

Rosenthal and Jacobson, in *Pygmalion in the Classroom* (1968), described the profound effects of teachers' expectations on their pupils' behavior and intellectual development. They reported how the self-fulfilling prophecy works in education. Teachers' favorable expectations benefited the children in as short a period as 4 months.

In an investigation of the effects of teachers' expectations on their students' self-concept, Martinek and Johnson (1979) reported findings similar to those of Rosenthal and Jacobson. Physical education teachers were asked to rate students on the basis of their own expectations about how the students would perform in physical achievement. The high-expectancy group received more encouragement and acceptance of ideas and more analytic questions and directions from their teachers than low-expectancy groups did. Further, in three of the five classes, expected high achievers had significantly better self-concepts than low achievers did.

Thus, teachers have a great influence over their student's behaviors, both by class organization and by their expectations about their pupils. Teachers should adopt realistic, positive expectations and support the students as they direct them toward instructional goals. What the student thinks the teacher thinks about him or her is important!

GUIDING PRINCIPLES FOR THE TEACHER

1. During the initial phase of instruction, teachers should call attention to important perceptual cues and response characteristics and provide students with a diagnostic knowledge of results.

2. A practice session with rest periods spaced throughout produces better performance than a practice period without rests. This difference is due to a temporary factor, called reactive inhibition. Although it affects performance, it does not influence the amount of learning that occurs under either massed practice or distributed practice. Reactive inhibition disappears if a rest is provided.

3. The organization of the school day imposes distributed practice on physical education classes. Few studies have been conducted to determine the best organization of instruction within this framework. Studies have suggested that activities like archery are best taught 5 days a week and skills like badminton are best taught on an every-other-day schedule. A great deal more research is needed in this area of instructional organization.

4. Whole instruction and part instruction are distinguished by the size of the unit that is presented to the learner. Neither method is always more appropriate, as the complexity of the situation determines which one is more effective. The whole method is best suited for simple skills and for skills that are meaningful as a unit. The progressive-part method is best for skills with intermediate difficulty. The whole-part-whole method is most effective for complex skills.

5. The best instructional plan appears to be one that begins with material organized in larger units, moves to smaller units if learners have difficulty, and then returns to larger units.

6. Knowledge of mechanical principles behind a skill appears to aid elementary school and junior high school students' later performances. Kinesiological instruction appears to enable a better transfer of learning from one situation to new situations.

7. Knowledge of mechanical principles does not appear to improve the performance of adults and college students who are beginners. Such instruction does appear to improve their scores on written tests.

8. Although studies have not investigated the effect of knowledge of mechanical principles on advanced students' performance, empirical evidence suggests that they should benefit more from such instruction than less skilled performers do.

9. Knowledge of results, or information about one's performance, is an important variable in controlling performance and learning. There is no improvement without KR. Progressive improvement accompanies KR, and deterioration occurs after KR is removed.

10. Some knowledge of results is always present in human performance. Consequently, supplemental KR must emphasize the inherent aspects of the task and help learners incorporate inherent KR into their performance.

11. Mental practice can be used to learn new skills, as a preperformance review of a skill, and to review or develop strategy. It is more effective with highly skilled performers than with beginners.

12. Mental practice can be an effective learning method if certain requirements are met: (*a*) learners should have prior experience with the task or a similar task, (*b*) they should be able to translate words and concepts into movements, (*c*) they should be given prior instruction in how to practice mentally, and (*d*) mental practice should be combined with physical practice in the acquisition of new skills.

13. Social settings are situations in which more than one person is present. Three types of social settings have been identified: (*a*) the

presence of others as an audience, (*b*) the coaction of others in the same task, and (*c*) the interaction of others in the same task.

14. Social settings appear to act as motivating situations. In general, they impair the learning of new responses but enhance the performance of already acquired responses. Social situations cause persons to emit the dominant response.

15. Social settings facilitate learning in cases of imitation learning, that is, if individuals follow the member of the group who learns the quickest. This is the only exception to the preceding general rule.

16. The presence of others provides social support in disagreeable and stressful situations. Social support also impairs learning but improves performance.

SUMMARY

This chapter has summarized a variety of practice situations that teachers can consider in developing an instructional plan. The distribution of practice and rest periods, in massed practice and distributed practice, appears to have more effect on performance than on learning. The influence of the size of the unit presented to students was evaluated in whole and part instruction. Generally, a flexible method, using the whole method and switching to the part method as students experience difficulty, is suggested. A knowledge of mechanical principles behind a skill appears to be more valuable with younger students and more advanced performers.

The process through which one receives information about his or her performance is referred to as knowledge of results, or KR. Some KR is always present. It is necessary during performance. Supplementary KR must emphasize the intrinsic aspects of the task to promote learning.

Mental practice can be valuable if the learner has some past experience with the task or a similar task and if it is used in combination with physical practice. If this method is used, students must be taught how to practice mentally.

Most classroom instruction takes place in a social setting, and teachers must be aware of its effect on learning and performance. The three basic social settings are the presence of an audience, coaction, and interaction with others. With one exception, in the case of imitation learning, social settings impair the learning of new responses but facilitate the performance of already learned responses. Teachers should keep in mind the characteristics of the different practice conditions in planning instructional periods, as they can work either to one's advantage or to one's disadvantage.

REFERENCES

Abel, T. M. 1938. The influence of social facilitation on motor performance at different levels of intelligence. *American Journal of Psychology* 51:379-389.

Abrams, M. L., and Grice, J. K. 1976. Effects of practice and positional variables in acquisition of a complex psychomotor skill. *Perceptual and Motor Skills* 43:203-211.

Ader, R., and Tatum, R. 1963. Free-operant avoidance conditioning in individual and paired human subjects. *Journal of Experimental and Analytical Behavior* 6:357-359.

Ammons, R. B., and Willig, L. 1956. Acquisition of motor skill: IV. Effects of repeated continuous practice before and after a single rest. *Journal of Experimental Psychology* 37:393-411.

———. 1950. Acquisition of motor skill: III. Effects of initially distributed practice on rotary pursuit performance. *Journal of Experimental Psychology* 40:777-787.

Ammons, R. B., and Willig, L. 1956. Acquisition of motor skill: IV. Effects of repeated periods of massed practice. *Journal of Experimental Psychology* 51:118-126.

Anderson, C. A. 1929. An experimental study of "social facilitation" as affected by intelligence. *American Journal of Sociology* 34:874-881.

Anderson, N. H. 1961. Group performance in an anagram task. *Journal of Sociology and Psychology* 55:67-75.

Austin, D. A. 1975. Effect of distributed and massed practice upon the learning of a velocity task. *Research Quarterly* 46:23-29.

Barnett, C. D., and Cantor, B. N. 1957. Pursuit rotor performance in mental defectives as a function of distribution of practice. *Perceptual and Motor Skills* 7:191-197.

Barnett, M. E. 1959. A study of the effect of a knowledge of mechanical principles on learning to perform specific swimming strokes. Master's thesis, University of Maryland.

Bergum, B. O., and Lehr, D. J. 1963. Effects of authoritarianism on vigilance performance. *Journal of Applied Psychology* 47:75-77.

Bilodeau, E. A., and Bilodeau, I. McD. 1961. Motor-skills learning. In *Annual review of psychology*. Vol. 12, ed. P. R. Farnsworth. Palo Alto, Calif.: Annual Reviews.

Bird, A. M. 1973. Effects of social facilitation upon females' performance of two psychomotor tasks. *Research Quarterly* 44:322-330.

———. 1975. Cross sex effects of subject and audience during motor performance. *Research Quarterly* 46:379-384.

Briggs, G. E., and Brogden, W. J. 1954. The effect of component practice on performance of a lever-positionary skill. *Journal of Experimental Psychology* 48:375-380.

Briggs, G. E., and Naylor, J. C. 1962. The relative efficiency of several training methods as a function of transfer task comlexity. *Journal of Experimental Psychology* 64:505-512.

Broer, M. 1958. Effectiveness of a general basic skill curriculum for junior high school girls. *Research Quarterly* 29:379 388.

Brumbach, W. B., and Beckow, P. A. 1968. Effectiveness of mental practice upon the learning of two types of gross motor skills. *Abstracts of research papers*. Washington, D. C.: AAHPER.

Burns, P. L. 1962. The effect of physical practice, mental practice, and mental-physical practice on the development of a motor skill. Master's thesis, Pennsylvania State University.

Burton, A. 1941. The influence of social factors upon the persistence of satiation in preschool children. *Child Development* 12:121-129.

Clark, L. V. 1960. Effect of mental practice on the development of a certain motor skill. *Research Quarterly* 31:560-569.

Clarke, H. H. 1966. *Muscular strength and endurance in man.* Englewood Cliffs, N.J.: Prentice-Hall.

Cobane, E. 1959. A comparison of two methods of teaching selected motor skills. Doctoral dissertation, Syracuse University.

Colville, F. M. 1957. The learning of motor skills as influenced by knowledge of mechanical principles. *Journal of Educational Psychology* 48:321.

Cook, B. S., and Hilgard, E. R. 1949. Distributed practices in motor learning: Progressively increasing and decreasing rests. *Journal of Experimental Psychology* 39:169-172.

Corbin, C. G. 1967*a*. The effects of covert rehearsal on the development of a complex motor skill. *Journal of General Psychology* 76:143-150.

———. 1967*b*. Effects of mental practice on skill development after controlled mental practice. *Research Quarterly* 38:534-538.

Cross, T. J. 1937. A comparison of the whole method, the minor game method, and whole-part method of teaching basketball to ninth-grade boys. *Research Quarterly* 8:49-54.

Daskiell, J. F. 1930. An experimental analysis of some group effects. *Journal of Abnormal Social Psychology* 25:190-199.

———. 1935. Experimental studies of the influence of social situations on the behavior of individual human adults. In *A handbook of social psychology*, ed. C. Murchison. Worchester, Mass.: Clark University Press.

Daughtrey, G. 1945. The effects of kinesiological teaching on the performance of junior high school boys. *Research Quarterly* 16:26-33.

Davis, J. H. 1969. *Group performance.* Reading, Mass.: Addison-Wesley.

Dehnert, A. E. 1963. A comparison of the effect of two methods of instruction upon free throw shooting ability. *Completed research in health, physical education and recreation.* Washington, D.C.: AAHPER.

Dore, L. R., and Hilgard, E. R. 1937. Spaced practice and the maturation hypothesis. *Journal of Psychology* 4:245-259.

Drowatzky, J. N. 1970. Effects of massed and distributed practice schedules upon the acquisition of pursuit rotor tracking by normal and mentally retarded subjects. *Research Quarterly* 41:32-38.

Egstrom, G. H. 1964. Effects of an emphasis on conceptualizing techniques during early learning of a gross motor skill. *Research Quarterly* 35:472-481.

Feofanov, M. P. 1928. Kvoprosu ob izuchenii strukturnykh osobennostei kollektinov [The question of investigating the structural characteristics of a group]. *Zh. Psikhol. Pedol. i Psikhotekh* 1:107-120. P.A. 3:4117. Cited by A. P. Hare, *Handbook of small group research.* New York: Free Press, 1962.

Fitts, P. M. 1964. Perceptual-motor skill learning. In *Categories of human learning*. ed. A. W. Melton. New York: Academic Press.

Fitts, P. M., and Posner, M. I. 1967. *Human performance.* Monterey, Calif.: Brooks/Cole.

Fleishman, E. A., and Parker, J. F., Jr. 1962. Factors in the retention and relearning of perceptual-motor skill. *Journal of Experimental Psychology* 64:215-226.

Franklin, J. C., and Brozek, J. 1947. The relation between distribution of practice and learning efficiency in psychomotor performance. *Journal of Experimental Psychology* 37:16-24.

Frey, B. 1947. A study of teaching procedures in selected physical education activities for college women of low motor ability. Doctoral dissertation, University of Iowa.

Gilmore, G. B. 1972. An experimental study to determine which of five different practice procedures is more effective in the acquisition of a complex motor skill. Doctoral dissertation, University of Toledo.

Gilmore, R. L., and Stolurow, L. M. 1951. Motor and "mental" practice of a ball and socket task. *American Psychology* 6:295.

Hall, M. F. 1959. A study of two methods of teaching bowling to college women of high and low motor ability. Doctoral dissertation, University of Iowa.

Halverson, L. E. 1949. A comparison of three methods of teaching motor skills. Master's thesis, University of Wisconsin.

Halverson, L. E., Roberton, M. A., Safrit, M. J., and Roberts, T. W. 1977. Effects of guided practice on overhand-throw ball velocities of kindergarten children. *Research Quarterly* 48:311-318.

Hanson, S. K. 1961. A comparison of the overhand throw performance of instructed and non-instructed boys and girls. Master's thesis, University of Wisconsin.

Hare, A. P. 1962. *Handbook of small group research.* New York: Free Press.

Hendrickson, G., and Schroeder, W. H. 1941. Transfer of training in learning to hit a submerged target. *Journal of Educational Psychology* 32:205-213.

Howe, D. P. 1968. The influence of five schedules of mental practice upon the physical performance of a gross motor skill after a criterion measure of skill had been attained. Doctoral dissertation, Texas Women's University.

Husband, R. W. 1931. Analysis of methods in human maze learning. *Journal of Genetic Psychology* 39:258-277.

Jones, J. G. 1965. Motor learning without demonstration of physical practice, under two conditions of mental practice. *Research Quarterly* 36:270-276.

Jones, W. R., and Ellis, N. R. 1962. Inhibitory potential in rotary pursuit acquisition by normal and defective subjects. *Journal of Experimental Psychology* 63:534-537.

Judd, C. H. 1908. The relationship of special training to general intelligence. *Education Review* 36-38.

Kearns, N. J. 1960. A study of an analytical and kinesiological approach to teaching bowling. Master's thesis, Women's College of the University of North Carolina.

Kelly, C. R. 1969. What is adaptive training? *Human Factors* 11:547-556.

Kelly, D. A. 1965. The relative effectiveness of selected mental practice techniques in high school girls' acquisition of a gross motor skill. Master's thesis, University of Washington.

Kelsey, I. B. 1961. Effects of mental practice and physical practice upon muscular endurance. *Research Quarterly* 32:47-54.

Kleinman, M. 1976. The effects of practice distribution on the acquisition of three discrete motor skills. *Research Quarterly* 47:672-677.

Knapp, C. G., and Dixon, R. W. 1950. Learning to juggle: A study of whole and part methods. *Research Quarterly* 21:389-401.

Lawther, J. D. 1968. *The learning of physical skills.* Englewood Cliffs, N. J.: Prentice-Hall.

Leuba, C. J. 1933. An experimental study of rivalry in young children. *Journal of Comparative Psychology* 16:367-378.

Lintern, G., and Gypher, D. 1978. Adaptive training of perceptual-motor skills: Issues, results and future directions. *International Journal of Man-Machine Studies* 10:521-551.

Luebke, L. L. 1967. A comparison of the effects of varying schedules of mental and physical practice trials on the performance of the overarm softball throw. Master's thesis, University of Washington.

Lynn, R. W. 1971. Effects of massed and distributed practice on rate of learning of a fine and a gross perceptual-motor skill. Master's thesis, University of Toledo.

McGuigan, F. J., and MacCaslin, E. F. 1955. Whole and part methods in learning a perceptual-motor skill. *American Journal of Psychology* 48:658-661.

Martens, R. 1969. Effect of an audience on learning and performance of a complex motor skill. *Journal of Personality and Social Psychology* 12:252-260.

Martinek, T. J., and Johnson, S. B. 1979. Teacher expectations: Effects on dyadic interactions and self-concept in elementary age children. *Research Quarterly* 50:60-70.

Martinek, T. J., Zaichkowsky, L. D., and Cheffers, J. T. F. 1977. Decision making in elementary age children: Effects on motor skills and self-concept. *Research Quarterly* 48:349-357.

Maxwell, J. M. 1968. The effects of mental practice on the learning of the overhand volleyball serve. Master's thesis, Central Missouri State College.

Menmann, E. 1904. Haus- und Schularbeit: Experimente an Kinder der Volkschule. *Die Deutsche Schule* 8:278-303, 337-359, 416-431.

Mikesell, D. J. 1962. The effect of mechanical principle centered instruction on the acquisition of badminton skills. Master's thesis, University of Illinois.

Miller, S. E. 1964. The relative effectiveness of high school badminton instruction when given in two short units and one continuous unit involving the same total time. Master's thesis, University of Washington.

Mohr, D. R., and Barrett, M. E. 1962. Effect of knowledge of mechanical principles in learning to perform intermediate swimming skills. *Research Quarterly* 33:574-580.

Mosston, M. 1966. *Teaching physical education: From command to discovery*. Columbus, Ohio: Charles E. Merrill.

Murphy, H. H. 1916. Distribution of practice periods in learning. *Journal of Educational Psychology* 7:150-162.

Murray, M. J. 1979. Matching preferred cognitive mode with teaching methodology in learning a novel motor skill. *Research Quarterly* 50:80-87.

Naylor, J., and Briggs, G. 1963. Effects of task complexity and task organization on the relative efficiency of part and whole training methods. *Journal of Experimental Psychology* 65:217-244.

Nessler, J. 1961. An experimental study of methods adapted to low-skilled freshmen women in physical education. Doctoral dissertation, Pennsylvania State University.

Nichols, B. A. 1971. A comparison of two methods of developing the overhand throw for distance in four, five, six and seven year old children. Ph.D. dissertation, State University of Iowa.

Niemeyer, R. K. 1958*a*. Part versus whole methods and massed versus distributed practice in the learning of selected large muscle activities. Doctoral dissertation, University of Southern California.

———. 1958*b*. Part versus whole methods and massed versus distributed practice in the learning of selected large muscle activities. *National College Physical Education Association for Men Proceedings* 61:122-125.

Noble, C. E., Fuchs, J. E., Robel, D. P., and Chambers, R. W. 1958. Social facilitation and team and individual performance. *Perceptual and Motor Skills* 8:131-134.

Oxendine, J. B. 1969. Effect of mental and physical practice on the learning of three motor skills. *Research Quarterly* 40:755-763.

Phipps, S. J. 1968. Effects of mental practice on the acquisition of motor skills of varying complexity. Master's thesis, Pennsylvania State University.

Posner, M. I., and Keele, S. W. 1973. Skill learning. In *Handbook of research in teaching*, ed. R. M. Travers. Chicago: Rand-McNally.

Rawlings, E. L. 1972. The facilitating effects of mental rehearsal in the acquisition of rotary pursuit tracking. *Psychoneurological Science* 26:71-73.

Rosenthal, R., and Jacobson, L. 1968. *Pygmalion in the classroom*. New York: Holt, Rinehart and Winston.

Ryan, E. D. 1965. Prerest and postrest performance on the stabliometer as a function of distribution of practice. *Research Quarterly* 36:197-204.

Sage, G. H., and Hornak, J. E. 1978. Progressive speed practice in learning a continuous motor skill. *Research Quarterly* 49:190-196.

Seidman, D., Bensen, S. B., Miller, I., and Meeland, T. 1957. Influence of a partner on tolerance for self-administered electric shock. *Journal of Abnormal and Social Psychology* 54:210-212.

Sengupta, N. N., and Sinha, C. P. N. 1926. Mental work in isolation and in group. *Indian Journal of Psychology* 1:106-110.

Shapiro, D. C. 1977. Knowledge of results and motor learning in preschool children. *Research Quarterly* 48:154-158.

Shay, C. T. 1934. The progressive-part versus the whole method of learning motor skills. *Research Quarterly* 4:62-67.

Shevaleva, E., and Ergolska, O. 1926. Children's collectives in the light of experimental reflexology. In *Sbornik, posvyzohennyi V. M. Bekhterevu k 40—135 nyu professorskow dyatelnosti* [Bekhterev fortieth anniversary commemorative volume]. P.A. 1:2486. Cited by A. P. Hare, *Handbook of small group research.* New York: Free Press, 1962.

Shick, J. 1970. Effects of mental practice on selected volleyball skills for college women. *Research Quarterly* 41:88-94.

Singer, R. N. 1965. Massed and distributed practice effects on the acquisition and retention of a novel basketball skill. *Research Quarterly* 36:68-77.

Singer, R. N., and Pease, D. 1976. A comparison of discovery and guided instructional strategies on motor skill learning, retention and transfer. *Research Quarterly* 47:788-796.

Smith, L. E., and Harrison, J. S. 1962. Comparison of the effects of visual, motor, mental, and guided practice upon speed and accuracy of performing a simple eye-hand coordination task. *Research Quarterly* 33:299-307.

Snoddy, G. S. 1935. *Evidence for two opposed processes in mental growth.* Lancaster, Pa.: Science Press.

Stanton, J. M., Jr. 1968. Comparison of kinesiological and traditional methods of instructing third grade pupils to perform a sprinter's start. Master's thesis, University of Toledo.

Stebbins, R. B. 1967. Comparison of the effects of physical and mental practice in learning a motor skill. *Research Quarterly* 39:714-720.

Steel, W. I. 1952. The effect of mental practice on the acquisition of a motor skill. *Journal of Physical Education* 44:101-108.

Stelmach, G. E. 1969. Efficiency of motor learning as a function of intertrial rest. *Research Quarterly* 40:198-202.

Stephens, M. L. 1966. The relative effectiveness of mental and physical practice on performance scores and level of aspiration scores for an accuracy task. Master's thesis, University of North Carolina, Greensboro.

Surburg, P. R. 1968. Audio, visual, and audio-visual instructions with mental practice in developing the forehand tennis drive. *Research Quarterly* 39:728-734.

Taylor, J. H., Thompson, C. E., and Spassoff, D. 1937. The effect of conditions of work and various suggested attitudes on production and reported feelings of tiredness and boredness. *Journal of Applied Psychology* 21:431-450.

Travis, L. E. 1925. The effect of a small audience upon eye-hand coordination. *Journal of Abnormal and Social Psychology* 20:142-146.

Triplett, N. 1898. The dynamogenic factors in pace-making competition. *American Journal of Psychology* 9:507-533.

Trussell, E. M. 1952. Mental practice as a factor in the learning of a complex motor skill. Master's thesis, University of California.

Twining, W. E. 1949. Mental practice and physical practice in learning a motor skill. *Research Quarterly* 20:432-435.

Vandell, R. A., Davis, R. A., and Clugston, H. A. 1943. The function of mental practice in the acquisition of motor skills. *Journal of General Psychology* 29:243-250.

Wallace, S. A., and Hagler, R. W. 1979. Knowledge of performance and the learning of a closed motor skill. *Research Quarterly* 50:265 271.

Wankel, L. M. 1977. Audience size and trait anxiety effects upon state anxiety and motor performance. *Research Quarterly* 48:181 186.

Waterland, J. G. 1956. Effect of mental practice combined with kinesthetic perception when the practice precedes each overt performance of a motor skill. Master's thesis, University of Wisconsin.

Welford, A. T. 1972. The obtaining and processing of information: Some basic issues relating to analyzing inputs and making decisions. *Research Quarterly* 43:295 311.

Werner, P. 1972. Integration of physical education skills with the concept of levers at intermediate grade levels. *Research Quarterly* 43:423 428.

White, K. D., Ashton, R., and Lewis, S. 1979. Learning a complex skill: Effects of mental practice, physical practice and imagery ability. *International Journal of Sport Psychology* 10:71 78.

Whiteley, G. 1962. The effect of mental rehearsal on the acquisition of motor skill. Diploma in education dissertation, University of Manchester.

Wickstrom, R. L. 1958. Comparative study of methodologies for teaching gymnastics and tumbling stunts. *Research Quarterly* 29:109 115.

Wills, B. J. 1966. Mental practice as a factor in the performance of two motor tasks. Doctoral dissertation, University of Wisconsin.

Wills, K. C. 1965. The effect of mental practice and physical practice on learning a motor skill. Master's thesis, Arkansas State University.

Wilson, M. E. 1960. The relative effect of mental practice and physical practice in learning the tennis forehand and backhand drives. Doctoral dissertation, State University of Iowa.

Young, O. G. 1954. The rate of learning in relation to spacing of practice periods in archery and badminton. *Research Quarterly* 25:231 243.

Zajonc, R. B. 1966. *Social psychology: An experimental approach.* Belmont, Calif.: Wadsworth.

Zuber, R. H. 1957. The effect of instruction in the laws of motion in learning gymnastic stunts. Master's thesis, University of Illinois.

Appendix

This book has emphasized motor learning as a process that is composed of interdependent stages. Although different authors present varying views of the number of stages involved, they all reflect the contemporary view that learning is a process. The following reprints of three articles are representative of this view.

In the first article, A. M. Gentile expresses her view that skill acquisition involves two stages. The initial stage—getting the idea of the movement—involves establishing a goal, learning the stimuli that regulate performance, developing a motor plan, and using information feedback. The second stage consists of fixation and diversification of the motor response. She also suggests ways in which teachers can use verbal communication and supplementary visual input, how they can position students, and how they can structure the learning situation to facilitate skill acquisition.

H. T. A. Whiting evaluates Gentile's model in the second paper, emphasizing his agreement with her overall approach but indicating his belief that information processing must be built into a model.

In the final paper, Sandra Hoth emphasizes the need for effective communication between instructor and pupil. Without such communication, the first stage of learning is greatly impaired.

A WORKING MODEL OF SKILL ACQUISITION WITH APPLICATION TO TEACHING

A. M. Gentile

In writing this paper, the objectives are to present some basic concepts concerning skill acquisition, loosely formulated in terms of a working model, and then to draw some practical applications to teaching. The presentation is far from complete. All possible factors that could affect motor learning are not included. Further, in making applications to teaching, there are many inductive leaps and intuitive jumps from data to general statements.

Why present such a tentative and, at times, speculative model for consideration? First, although specific details within the model undoubtedly will be revised with further investigation, the major relationships already are adequately supported and the general formulation probably represents an accurate picture of the factors involved in skill acquisition.

A second reason for presenting the model at this time pertains to its usefulness for teachers. The writer found that most motor-learning textbooks, and her own class presentations, represented a disjunctive collection of facts, largely devoid of unifying themes. The area of motor skills seemed to have a supermarket quality: a little massed/distributed practice here, feedback there, stacks of reaction time, mental rehearsal, speed/accuracy, short-term memory, and other distinct topics of interest piled about in disarray. For the novice in the skills area, especially for the teacher-in-training whose entire experience may officially terminate with one undergraduate or graduate course, there seemed to be a need to selectively integrate the material into a package which could be easily handled and serve as a basis for future study or as a guide for operations performed by the teacher of skills.

The paper is organized into three sections. In the first, the motor patterns to which the model pertains are briefly identified. The nature of skill acquisition, partioned into initial and later stages, is presented in section two. Finally, in the last section, application is made to teaching strategies.

Reprinted by permission from A. M. Gentile. A working model of skill acquisition with application to teaching. *Quest XVII* (January 1972), pp. 3-23.

DEFINITIONS AND DELIMITATIONS

The movement patterns of interest are those generally described as goal-directed, instrumental, or intentional. These are the movements characterized by forethought with reference to the consequences they produce. The outcome to be obtained is clear to the performer and determines his organization of the movement pattern. Excluded from consideration are movements which are consistently elicited from organisms within the same species, are under direct stimulus control, do not result from prior learning or modification by experience, and are usually mediated by phylogenetically older neurological structures. Generally, then, motor responses commonly called reflexes or those responses labelled "fixed action patterns" by ethologists (Lorenz, 1969) are not the movements to be examined.

Within the broad category of what we shall call goal-directed movements, there would appear to be two major types: orienting responses and adaptive motor patterns. Orienting responses are those movements used to focus, direct, or adjust the sensory apparatus so as to gather information from the environment. For example, movements of the eyes and head used to track or follow a moving object would be characterized as visual orienting responses. Similarly, head movements used to present differential patterns of input to the ears which assist in localization of sound in space would be considered auditory orienting responses.

Movements classified as adaptive differ from orienting responses in terms of the outcome to be produced. The goals for adaptive motor patterns involve changing or maintaining the position of the body in space with reference to external objects, the position of objects in space with reference to the body, or both. In contrast to direct adaptive movements, in which the individual's limb and trunk movements are used to accomplish these goals, communicative responses (facial expression, gesture, speech) are considered as indirect adaptive patterns. In this paper, the analysis of acquisition is limited to direct, adaptive motor patterns. Thus, the focus of discussion is upon how the individual learns to change or maintain his position or the positions of objects in space.

SKILL ACQUISITION

Skill learning involves at least two identifiable stages: the first sometimes is labelled as cognitive or exploratory (Fitts, 1963). In this paper, the initial phase of learning a skill is referred to as "getting the idea of the movement" (Ragsdale, 1950). The later stage of skill acquisition is to be denoted as "fixation/diversification." As an overview of the discussion of factors involved in the *initial stage,* the major areas to be recognized as important are outlined in Figure 1.

Stage I. Getting the Idea of the Movement

The Goal. The individual organizes a motor pattern in order to solve some problem which has emerged in terms of his need-reduction interaction with the external environment (Bernstein, 1967). The problem usually is clear to the individual: a particular outcome or change in the environment has to be produced (Pribram, 1963). The means-end relationship or the plan of action which will accomplish the particular goal constitutes what is to be learned (Tolman, 1932; Miller, Galanter, & Pribram, 1960).

Man is "neurologically wired" for all of his movement capabilities at birth or, through relatively rapid maturational development, shortly thereafter. What appears to be learned is the organization of this wealth of potential muscular response into patterns having delimited temporal/spatial characteristics (Lashley, 1951). Modulation of force from opposing muscle groups seems to be the basic output of higher neural structures yielding the movement's temporal/spatial specifications (Evarts, 1967). To selectively release a specific pattern of movement, the individual must learn to precisely balance inhibitory/excitatory processes subserving force outflow.

Regulatory Stimulus Subset. Within the individual's morphological limits, the motor pattern which will be effective in producing a particular outcome is determined, is restricted, is controlled by the environmental characteristics inherently related to the goal. Man must learn to mold his movements to the environment in which he lives (Luria, 1966). The child, reaching to grasp a cup, must learn to organize

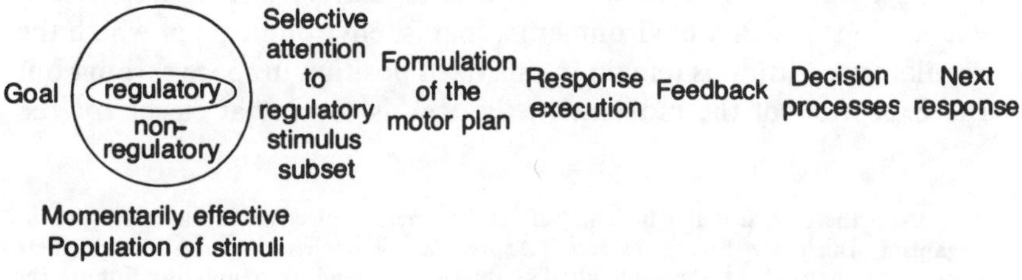

Figure 1. Initial stage of skill acquisition.

a motor pattern that conforms to the position of the cup in space, its size, and its shape (Bruner, 1968). The motor pattern which will yield effective goal attainment is, therefore, under the spatial control of the structural/positional characteristics of the cup. As another example, the movement of a football player attempting an interception is controlled by the spatial and temporal characteristics of the ball. Once he has established the "interception" goal, he is not free to choose or decide when and where he is to move. Rather, the ball and its flight pattern determine the organization of the motor pattern which will be effective.

The tolerance band for variability in the motor pattern of the football player attempting an interception is restricted to a far greater extent than in the child's reaching movement. Generally, as the number of environmental events related to the goal increases and as the associated spatial characteristics change over time, the degree of spatial/temporal control imposed upon the organization of a goal-directed movement increases.

Let us consider all energy changes in the environment at a given time, the "momentarily-effective stimulus population" (Guthrie, 1952; Estes, 1950 & 1959). Within this population, a limited subset would be established as regulatory (or relevant) whenever the individual sets a particular goal. Regulatory in the sense that the movement pattern must conform to these environmental conditions if the goal is to be accomplished. All other events in the momentarily effective stimulus population we shall consider as nonregulatory (or irrelevant).[1]

Selective Attention. In his initial attempt to find the range of motor patterns which will yield goal attainment, the learner must identify and selectively attend to the regulatory subset of the stimulus population. Only after he can identify and attend to these regulatory conditions is he able to formulate a motor plan that is effective. This is not always a simple task for the learner, especially in complex stimulus environments having a considerable number of both regulatory and nonregulatory events. In stationary environments, that is, environments in which the regulatory conditions remain in one fixed position in space throughout the execution of the movement, the task is somewhat easier for the

[1]Note there are stimuli which may affect the general arousal or emotional state of the organism which are here considered nonregulatory or irrelevant. Although these conditions may affect the individual's ability to attend to regulatory input, the organization of the motor pattern for goal attainment is not specified by these inputs.

learner than when regulatory events change or are going to change position in space. Using terms introduced by Poulton (1957), let us refer to those movements performed under stationary environmental conditions as "closed." Although there is an underlying continuum, let us dichotomize the nature of environmental control and label those movements performed under conditions in which the regulatory events are changing position in space (that is, are themselves in motion) as "open" (Poulton, 1957). It should be evident that for closed movements the individual is limited in his spatial organization of the effective motor pattern. However, as the regulatory conditions in the environment are stationary, he is quite free to select from a wide range of temporal organizations for the patterning of his motor outflow (e.g., onset, duration, offset). In contrast, the temporal and spatial characteristics of open motor patterns are concomitantly controlled by the temporal/spatial characteristics of the variable regulatory conditions in the environment.

Probably, the initial stage of acquisition is similar for open and closed skills: the learner tries to find the general motor organization that works to produce the outcome. Although this stage may be commonly summarized as getting the idea of the movement, the emphasis upon the movement can be misleading. Unless the learner recognizes the events to which his movement must conform, unless he selectively attends to the stable or variable regulatory conditions, he will not be able to consistently organize a movement that matches the environmental demands. Thus, of even greater importance than simply formulating motor output, the task for the learner is to identify and process information about the environmental conditions that control his movement.

The Motor Plan. Preceding execution, an image of the movement (James, 1950) or general plan of action (Miller, Galanter, & Pribram, 1960) seems to occur. As brilliantly discussed by Lashley (1951) the temporal organization of spatial components within the motor pattern directed toward a specific objective, that is, the syntax of movement, is preconceived and is used to guide movement execution.

The units of organization could be highly integrated patterns resulting from prior learning (Kay, 1969) or, in the case of the infant, the raw motor potential provided for by his neuromuscular apparatus. The type of unit organization may take the form of TOTEs (an acronym for "Test-Operate-Test-Exit") suggested by Miller, Galanter, & Pribram (1960). A TOTE organizational scheme can be conceived as a program that provides for the matching of outcomes with intentions.[2] Consider the image or plan of the intended movement as the "Test" component. The "Operate" phase would involve the pattern of muscular contractions which, in turn, would give rise to movement-produced feedback. By "Testing" the feedback against the image of the intended movement, a match or mismatch decision can be made leading to termination of the operations "Exit" or a modification of the operations. Using hierarchical arrangements of TOTEs, in which the "Operate" phase of a higher level plan serves as a test for subroutines of lower level plans, more elaborate movement organization can be formulated.

For our discussion, the important aspects of the TOTE concept are that (1) an image or plan of movement exists prior to execution; (2) information concerning the output is fed back to be matched against the plan; and (3) the evaluation of the "Feedback-Plan" comparison guides in the execution of the movement and determines at what point to terminate further action. The plan may or may not be amenable to alteration during execution as a function of the temporal characteristics of the movement and the complexity of the error (mismatch) signals. Modification of the output to attain congruity with the plan may only be possible on the next attempt.

Information Feedback. The aftereffects of movement-produced stimulation (kinesthetic and somesthetic) and the concurrent and terminal feedback concerning alterations produced by the movement in the external environment (predominantly visual and auditory) would be available to the performer for at least some short period of time following execution. For our discussion, we shall refer to all changes within the internal and external environment that normally occur as a

[2]The neurological substrate of the motor image could involve the activation of elementary or functionally organized units associated with a dynamic configuration of kinesthetic input ("gnostic units" of Konorski, 1967). Output would involve efferent control of the supporting structures (both intrafusal and extrafusal muscle fibers) around the muscle receptors. The hierarchical arrangement of gnostic units could result in a schemata of action releasing an exquisitely balanced force modulation affected by graded and temporally integrated contraction patterns of opposing muscle groups. When kinesthetic feedback matches the configuration associated with the gnostic units, output would terminate. In slow, precision movements, peripheral feedback could be available in time to allow for alteration of output (the "comparator" mechanism of Ruch, 1965). Even in very rapid movements, however, central feedback mechanisms from collateral outflow of descending efferent systems could provide for the "feedback-test" function (Higgins & Angel, 1970).

consequence of the movement as "intrinsic" feedback (Holding, 1965). Short-term storage of sensory input is very limited in time (Sperling, 1960). The brief interval following the movement probably involves some process whereby the intrinsic feedback is categorized and coded (verbally or nonverbally) to allow for maintenance over longer intervals, that is, to be held in short-term memory (Bartlett, 1932; Gentile, 1967). The consolidation of input after movement execution, involving the encoding process that provides for the retention of intrinsic feedback, is essential for the subsequent organization of the next response (Woodworth & Schlosberg, 1954; Gentile & Stadulis, 1970).

Decision Processes and the Next Response. How the learner utilizes information resulting from his movement to formulate his next motor plan is an area of considerable interest and one that has been relatively unexplored. Let us return and review the analysis thus far. In attempting to solve a problem in the environment by producing a particular outcome, the learner formulated a plan of action. Barring neurological impairment or marked distraction, the short-term memory of the goal and of the plan will still be available to the performer after executing the movement. In addition, the learner now has (1) "knowledge of results"—encoded, intrinsic feedback concerning the outcome produced by the movement, and (2) "knowledge of performance"—encoded, intrinsic feedback concerning the movement itself (Annett & Kay, 1957; Bilodeau, 1966). It seems reasonable to expect that some sort of comparison between goal/outcome and plan/movement would indeed occur and would provide the basis for decisions concerning the next response.

Let us examine what such a decision process may involve. The learner's initial concern may well be with the question, "Was the goal accomplished?" Secondarily, the question of whether the movement was executed as planned would occur. For simplicity, the answers to these two questions have been dichotomized into yes/no classes rather than by presenting them as they probably occur in gradations or extents. The two comparisons (goal/outcome and plan/movement) and the four possible results have been presented in Table 1.

The response and strategy of the learner after comparisons of this type are quite speculative. However, the possible alternatives can be explored. Consider the case in which the goal is accomplished by the execution of the movement as planned (the YES/YES cell in Table 1). From introspection and from casual observation of learners, it would

Table 1. Summary of Schedules of Reinforcement Used to Promote Instrumental Conditioning

Type of Evaluation		Was the Movement Executed As Planned?	
	Outcome	Yes	No
Was the goal accomplished?	Yes	Got the idea of the movement	Surprise!
	No	Something's wrong	Everything's wrong

seem that this result usually elicits a response like, "Yes, I have the idea of the movement now." The problem has been solved. The hypothesis (plan of the movement) has been confirmed (Bruner, Goodnow, & Austin, 1956). In accord with the empirical law of effect, the likelihood of the same motor plan being used for the next attempt would seem to be very high. Both classes of feedback (outcome and movement) would tend to reinforce the occurrence of the same response.

In contrast, the strategy of the learner when one question yields a positive answer and the other question a negative one would not be as obvious. In the case in which the goal is not attained but the movement is executed as planned, the immediate response would seem to be that something is wrong with the motor plan. Revision of the motor plan is one obvious strategy for the next response. If similar results were obtained, additional revision and attempts would occur. However, after initial or successive results of "YES" for the movement but "NO" for the outcome, a different strategy may be required. Perhaps there are regulatory conditions which the learner has not identified. Continued revision of plans based on selective attention to the same incomplete subset of regulatory stimuli would not be sufficient in accomplishing the goal. Rather, a reexamination of the definition of the regulatory stimulus subset is essential. Thus, the "something's wrong" outcome would seem to require the learner to determine whether his environment/movement match or his initial identification of regulatory conditions was inadequate.[3]

[3]"While the simple realization, *that* something does not work, can lead only to some variation of that old method, the realization of *why* it does not work, the recognition of the *ground of conflict,* results in a correspondingly definite variation which corrects the recognized defect. . . ." (Duncker, 1945, pp. 13–14.)

A "surprise" experience seems to result when the goal is attained but not by the movement as planned. What the learner does in organizing his next response indeed would be interesting to know. Does he attempt to repeat the successful but deviant motor plan? Does he attempt to execute the originally planned movement? Does he do both and then compare which one feels right (perhaps an efficiency evaluation)? How often this outcome occurs during initial attempts in skill acquisition, for what types of skills it is most common, and what the strategy of the learner is subsequent to such an event are all fascinating but, for the most part, uncharted domains.

The last result, "everything's wrong," could lead to several alternate strategies not the least of which would be quitting. Having failed to produce either the movement or the outcome, the motivational level of the performer would seem to be an important determinant for continued solution behavior. Given that drive conditions are sufficient to sustain further efforts, an attempt to repeat the previously planned movement might be an initial strategy. Hopefully, the result would be one of the three other cases (Table 1). If complete failure occurs again, any one of several strategies might be used by the learner: (1) try another attempt of the movement as planned, (2) revise the plan, (3) reevaluate environmental conditions, or (4) alter the goal. Again, there does not appear to be information available in the motor skills literature pertaining to the behavior of individuals when confronted with this result during early acquisition.

The second stage of skill acquisition, as defined in this paper, is entered into after one or more YES/YES outcomes following initial attempts. The number of hypothesis confirmations required before the learner shifts from stage one to stage two may be a function of personality characteristics or, although not an independent factor, the success/failure history of the individual in acquiring motor skills. However, at some point, the learner feels secure that he has a basic grasp of a movement plan that works and now proceeds to a different stage of learning.

Stage II. Fixation/Diversification

Having acquired a general concept of the motor pattern that seems to be effective, the learner progresses into a stage in which he attempts to increase the consistency or to refine some characteristic of goal attainment. Motor skill, as defined in this paper, refers to the degree of effectiveness in producing a particular outcome. In this sense, it is not synonymous with learning a motor pattern. If a relatively consistent change is observed in the movement used by the performer in a specific situation, then learning of a motor pattern is inferred. However, it is quite possible for a performer to have acquired a very consistent motor pattern which is either totally or relatively ineffectual in producing a particular outcome during stage two. The change in movement organization is a necessary but not sufficient condition for skill acquisition.

During stage one, the individual learned a general motor pattern which will be useful in accomplishing the goal. During stage two, the orientation of the learner is to reach a particular level of skill. In attempting to do so, the general motor pattern acquired during the initial stage may be (1) refined and retained, or (2) markedly altered, *depending on the nature of environmental control.* For closed skills, in which the regulatory environmental conditions remain constant, there is fixation of a motor pattern very similar to, if not the same as, the pattern acquired in stage one. However, for open skills, in which environmental conditions are quite variable, diversification of the original pattern occurs.

Let us consider closed skills first. By definition, the likelihood of change for the regulatory stimuli is close to zero. During the movement, the environmental conditions to which the motor pattern must conform are fixed, constant, stable, stationary. Thus, the performer can predict well in advance, with a probability close to one, what the conditions will be like during the movement's execution. Further, these conditions will remain relatively the same from one attempt to the next. From the entire range of possible movement patterns that could be used in this situation, the individual can select and narrow in on the most effective band width. Thus, restriction of variability in movement is evident with practice. The performer can strive for consistency in executing the motor pattern yielding the highest degree of goal attainment and, perhaps, having maximal efficiency. As the movement becomes more "habitual" (to use Knapp's term, 1964) or as the motor-kinesthetic-gnostic unit becomes more firmly established (jumping to a neurophysiological level and using Konorski's terms, 1967), the performer becomes progressively less dependent upon monitoring the external environment (Poulton, 1957). With continued practice, a highly stereotyped movement organization becomes evident. Concomitantly, a consistent level of skill (goal attainment) is achieved.

In contrast, open skills are performed under regulatory environmental conditions that change during movement execution and may vary from one attempt to the next. Each time the regulatory conditions are altered, the performer must modify his original motor pattern to match the demands of the new situation. In fact, the general motor formula acquired during stage one now will be effective only when that particular subset of regulatory environmental events occurs. For a skill like the forehand drive in tennis, consider the multitude of possible stimulus subsets that could occur during a game. If the same motor pattern was used for each of these markedly different conditions, the relative effectiveness would be exceedingly low. Each attempt to respond to the variable environment probably results in a feedback-decision process similar to the one used in the first stage of acquisition. Thus, what is required of the learner during stage two for open skills is quite different than for closed skills. Rather than fixing a particular motor pattern, the performer in an open skill situation must learn a multitude of motor patterns. Indeed, the performer must develop a response repertoire in which there are an exact number of motor patterns to match the number of possible regulatory stimulus subsets. Each specific pattern may involve a slight modification in the spatial or temporal component within a seemingly common generic formula. However, these slight or marked modifications involve the organization of a uniquely new pattern.

The performer in an open skill environment is under a time stress not present in the closed skill situation. In open skills, objects are moving through space, other performers are altering their positions, or initially stable events suddenly change. If the performer waits for the event to occur before organizing his motor plan, he is ineffectual because of the inherent time lags in his system. Information concerning the nature and extent of change must be received and processed. Additional time is lost in the internal motor organization as well as the initiation of the movement. Thus, the individual is required to predict what conditions are going to be like in the immediate future from the input of the immediate or more distantly removed past. To be coincident with an event in the present imposes both interpolation and extrapolation requirements upon the individual's information processing (Bernstein, 1967).

Within the population of possible regulatory stimulus subsets, there is a probability distribution covering the likelihood of occurrence. Imposed on the performer in acquiring an open skill is the requirement to develop a repertoire of motor patterns that not only conform to the temporal/spatial characteristics of the regulatory conditions but also have probabilistic tags determined by their likelihood of occurrence. Unlike the performer in a closed skill situation, the time between response selection and execution is limited. In some cases, the particular motor pattern must be selected from the total repertoire and executed immediately. The shortstop in baseball does not have time to evaluate leisurely which fielding motor pattern he is going to use to stop a hard-hit fast-moving ball. The rapidity of his selection will determine the degree of his effectiveness. If all motor patterns within the response repertoire are treated as equally likely events, selection and execution would be a relatively slow process. Rather, it would seem that "priming" some patterns as more likely to be used than others would facilitate the selection process. This facilitation would be a crucial determinant when marked time stress is placed on selection. Of course, there would be a "trade-off." Priming some patterns implies a lack of readiness for selecting other patterns. Unfortunately, less likely events do occur, catching the performer off guard. However, in terms of maximizing the frequency of success, matching of regulatory subsets to specific motor patterns and selective priming of patterns in accord with their probability tags would seem essential (Estes, 1964).

In summary, the nature of skill acquisition during later stages of learning will be a function of the type of environmental control under which the movement is performed. When the individual is moving in a stationary environment, there is little time stress placed upon his selection and execution of a motor plan. He can predict with very high certainty the exact nature of the regulatory events that will be effective during his execution of the movement. On successive repetitions of the response, conditions in the environment that control his movement will remain relatively unchanged. Thus, the performer can establish a highly consistent, narrowly defined motor pattern that yields the highest degree of goal attainment.

When the individual must move in accord with other moving objects or performers, the information-processing and predictive demands placed upon him are more complex. Each unique configuration of regulatory environmental conditions must be exactly matched by the temporal/spatial organization of his movement if he is to attain his goal. The time lags inherent in his system require that he plan ahead, both in terms of the likelihood of certain events occurring and in terms of which motor patterns may be required. The critical factor is that no single motor pattern will accomplish the goal under all conditions. Rather, the skilled performer in a variable environment has a repertoire of motor patterns precisely specified and probabilistically tagged in accord with the nature of spatial/temporal control and the probability distributions of the regulatory stimulus subset.

APPLICATION TO TEACHING

The basic operations a teacher can perform in an effort to facilitate the skill acquisition of the learner can be reduced to (1) verbal communication, (2) providing supplementary visual input (including nonverbal communicative responses and various forms of demonstrations), (3) direct movement or positioning of the student by the teacher, and (4) structuring the environmental conditions under which the movement is performed. How the teacher utilizes these tools as he takes various roles and assumes different responsibilities during the learning process is discussed with reference to the phases of skill acquisition: Stage I, getting the idea of the movement, and Stage II, fixation/diversification.

Stage I. Initial Skill Acquisition

The Goal. One of the important differences between skill learning as it normally occurs in the individual's interaction with the environment and skill learning as it occurs under the guidance of a teacher pertains to the clarity of the goal. For the individual confronted with a problem in his everyday environment, there is an obvious need to move in some way in order to produce a particular outcome. The goal immediately is evident. In attempting to provide instruction in a skill, however, the goal of the movement frequently becomes obscured. It would seem obvious that the initial task of the teacher would be to specify what is the problem or what is the nature of the outcome to be produced. Having a clear understanding of the goal, the teacher often assumes that the student has the same understanding. Thus, in his initial presentation, the teacher may progress quickly to a description of the movement itself. The rapid shift from some vague mention of purpose to a verbal description of the movement, a description purportedly helpful to the student's formulation of an effective motor plan, seems to result in *goal confusion.* The student's view of the outcome to be produced may be to move in the manner described by the teacher. Thus, the style of movement, as specified by the teacher, and not the consequence of the movement, in terms of the nature of environmental change, becomes the student's goal.

The suggestion offered in this paper is that there are two very important tasks for the teacher to perform early during skill acquisition: (1) creating a specific environmental problem, and (2) establishing an adequate motivational level. The nature of the teaching/learning situation determines the extent of teacher responsibility in these areas. Individuals who voluntarily seek tennis instruction in order to improve their game performance usually have adequate motivation and generally understand the problem situations which emerge and require specific skills. Individuals who are being taught tennis not by choice but because of an imposed requirement are a group requiring considerable teacher involvement. These students may not be motivated toward learning to play tennis nor do they necessarily understand the kinds of environmental demands placed upon them during the game.

A very simpleminded tenet of learning seems to be: without sufficient drive to sustain behavior, little behavioral change will be evident. The teacher has several means available to produce a drive state: (1) force, which would include appeals to grades, vague or specific punishment, disapproval, et cetera, (2) incentive motivation, which would appeal to the pleasures to come in the future by acquiring these skills, or (3) maintenance of a play environment, which would appeal to immediate pleasures obtained through the movement or game, or both.

It has always been a source of wonderment to the author that within a few minutes to perhaps an hour, children can teach each other all there is to know about the conduct of a game: the basic idea, rules, scoring, how to play, some strategy, et cetera. The level of skill in the game performance after such a rapid initial exposure usually is not very high; but some things are evident. The participants seem to recognize the outcomes that have to be produced for success in the game and, therefore, understand what skills have to be learned and why. Further, there appears to be some immediate pleasure evident on the part of the participants, even if inversely related to degree of skill.

In contrast to this play environment, in which individuals are immediately involved in the total situation, physical education class instruction seems to be based on an inductive model: one skill, artificially removed from the normal game environment, is taught at a time, progressing from simple to complex. It may be a matter of weeks or months (or never) before the learner gets to play the game. Little wonder there are motivational difficulties. Beyond sustaining the drive state, it is difficult to imagine how the instructor can create an awareness of the environmental/movement match that must occur under the actual game conditions, that is, how he can make the student aware of the problems to be confronted in the game situation.

Given that the teacher has found some means to "drive" the student, the important point of this discussion can now be summarized in terms of goal clarification. The learner must recognize that the task is to produce a particular outcome. The learner must realize that the means through which the outcome is produced are his responsibility. Under the requirements imposed by the goal to be attained, the student must organize a specific movement that matches environmental demands and for which there is no exact teacher specification. How the teacher makes this clear to the learner has not been adequately explored. Certainly, one teacher strategy may be to "tell'em," that is, to verbally describe the problem as it is going to occur in the actual encounter with the environment, to specify what the outcome is that must be produced. A second strategy could involve setting up the environmental conditions, artificially or as they naturally occur. In doing so, the teacher could attempt to structure a microcosm of the total game in which a particular skill would be required or could wait for the situation to emerge during normal game play. These and alternate teacher strategies would be interesting areas for research. At the present time, the choice appears to be under the best judgment of the teacher. However, if the teacher hopes to affect skill development, there is no choice with reference to goal clarification. The purpose for moving must be made known to the student.

Regulatory Stimulus Subset. To organize an effective response, the student must be confronted with the environmental conditions that control his movement. The teacher is responsible for how these conditions are arranged. The teacher must, therefore, identify the regulatory stimulus subset governing the movement and make several decisions as to how to structure the environment. Are the conditions under which the student acquires the skill going to be structured in the same way as the environment under which the movement eventually must be performed? Obviously, *all of the regulatory stimuli must be evident during initial student attempts.* However, the number and extent of nonregulatory stimuli present during this early stage is an area of teacher choice.

The teacher may decide to simplify conditions by reducing nonregulatory inputs. The disadvantage of such a strategy might be the distraction provided by irrelevant cues when the learner is placed in the actual situation. The teacher may decide to exaggerate normal figure/ground relationships or to make the regulatory stimuli more distinctive with similar "trade-off" disadvantages occurring later. Here, again, is another area ready for systematic inquiry, especially with reference to the type of skill involved, open or closed.

In structuring the environment during the learning of closed skills, the teacher's decisions relate primarily to the possible enhancement of constant regulatory conditions and the absence or presence of nonregulatory ones. When the conditions under which the movement is to be performed are variable, as in open skills, more complex decisions are required. Should the teacher structure the environment using a "mode" strategy: select the most frequently occurring set of events? Should the conditions yielding early success be chosen, given that the teacher can identify what these are? Perhaps, those conditions providing for maximum transfer to other situations should be the ones used initially; this may involve a progression from difficult to easy situations (Bartlett, 1947).

Let us use the skill of baseball batting to exemplify the nature of decisions confronting the teacher. All the regulatory stimulus conditions must be provided in the learner's *initial* environment: the bat, a pitched ball (not an artificial batter's tee), a batter's box, the plate, et cetera. Now, the teacher must decide how many nonregulatory stimuli are to be present: other players in the field, spectators, et cetera. In addition, as this is an open skill, the teacher must decide on the type of pitched ball to be used during initial attempts: its speed and flight pattern. First the teacher strategy and then the type of pitch is selected. For example, using a "mode" strategy, the most frequently occurring pitch in a game situation would be selected. In choosing other strategies, the teacher has less guidance in the choice of pitch. For example, an early success strategy may seem to require a moderate to moderately slow pitched ball. However, from preliminary laboratory information (Stadulis, 1970), faster pitched balls may be easier to hit. The point to be made is that the conditions yielding early success or greater transfer in an open skill situation are not always known.

Regardless of the extent of our present knowledge concerning open skills, the teacher must determine the strategy he will employ and then structure conditions in accord with his best judgment. For all skills, the teacher is responsible for "rigging" the environment, that is, setting up those stimulus conditions to which the learner's movements must conform.

Selective Attention. The goal is clear to the student. The environment has been structured. Now, the teacher's task is to help the student identify and attend to the regulatory stimulus subset. The relative effectiveness of various teacher strategies for providing this assistance is not known. The choices available include straightforward verbal instruction, "guided discovery" or verbal problem solving by the student.[4]

In helping the student to attend selectively to particular inputs, the teacher should recognize that instruction pertaining to orienting movements may be required. For example, to gather visual information from the environment, the student may need guidance in terms of where to position himself with reference to other objects, where to scan the environment to pick up relevant cues, and the usefulness of peripheral vision in providing certain types of information.

For open skills, there is another area of teacher responsibility. As the student is required to anticipate or predict the nature of enviromental change, some prior description of these events by the teacher or a demonstration of the type of change to occur would seem essential. Otherwise, the effectiveness of the student undoubtedly will be hindered by the inherent time lags in his information processing of unforeseen conditions.

Formulation of the Motor Plan. It is the student's responsibility to organize a plan of action that, within his morphological limits, will be effective in producing the specific outcome. At most, the teacher can provide guidance of a very general nature. Given the unique structural configurations of each individual and diversity in units of movement available through prior learning, it is naive to assume that one form of movement organization, precisely delineated by the teacher, will yield goal accomplishment for all performers. Rather, considerable variability should be expected.

There is only one occasion in which an exact form of the movement is important: when the *goal* is to move in accord with externally imposed standards, as in gymnastic events or diving. The outcome to be produced in these situations is a particular *movement.* The usual means to an end has become an end in itself. Under these circumstances, the teacher's involvement in the student's formulation of a

[4]Throughout this paper, there is no extended discussion of teaching styles. This does not seem necessary in terms of Mosston's (1966) very fine, general analysis and other similar attempts.

motor plan is quite active, indeed, is required. Supplementary inputs to the learner to clarify the goal (the movement) probably would be beneficial, i.e., visual aids and demonstrations.

For all other skills in which the movement is only the means by which an outcome is produced, the teacher should recognize that undue emphasis upon a particular form may result in the goal confusion discussed previously. The teacher should accept that any movement organization that effectively and consistently matches the environmental conditions under which it is to be performed is, by definition, a skill. If this concept of skill can be accepted, then pseudo-issues, such as speed/accuracy instructional sets (Solley, 1952), teaching by wholes or parts, and form/outcome "trade-offs" (Del Rey, 1970), would not confound the teaching-learning process.

Response Execution. The student is about to initiate the movement. He is focused upon the outcome to be produced. The plan of movement is formulated: the units within the motor pattern are activated, the organizational schema is clear. At this point, it would seem best for the teacher to reduce distracting elements in the environment including any further verbal comments or suggestions. Before this point, however, the teacher may be able to facilitate the decision process that follows the response by providing certain types of instructional sets.

Based upon the information he is to receive, the student is going to evaluate the effectiveness of the movement he used. Appropriately, the focus of the student is upon the intrinsic feedback related to goal attainment. There is a need, however, for concomitant attention to the intrinsic feedback resulting from the movement itself. To maintain the availability of kinesthetic/somesthetic stimuli for utilization in the decision-making process, active organization (encoding) of this input must occur.

How the teacher can facilitate this stage of acquisition is not known. These are some interesting possibilities which may be fruitful areas of investigation. First, what would be the effect of informing students about the nature of the decision processes purported to occur subsequent to the response? Second, although not an independent factor, what would be the effect of giving an instructional set to the student which directs his attention to the intrinsic feedback resulting from the movement?

The points in time at which these teacher behaviors occur would seem to be an important consideration. Too close to the actual performance could be a source of interference. However, some discussion prior to movement execution concerning the nature of feedback-decision processes might be helpful to the student. It may be that the "learning to learn" phenonmenon (Harlow, 1949) is a function of acquiring strategies for approaching the problem-solving aspects of the task (Levine, 1965). In learning to learn motor skills, the performer may have acquired a strategy for attending to and utilizing different classes of input (regulatory and feedback information) at different times during his initial attempts, thus facilitating the decision processes subserving the organization of his next response. Identifying important sources of information and discussing strategies for utilizing information may be important responsiblities of the teacher.

Feedback and Decision Making. Any information concerning the movement or the degree of goal attainment that is provided in addition to intrinsic feedback is referred to as artificial or augmented (Holding, 1965). The need for additional information beyond that which normally occurs as a consequence of the movement is not entirely clear. Simple redundancy would seem to have little value unless the performer (1) failed to attend, encode, or retain input, or (2) was unable to determine degrees of goal accomplishment. Some indication from the student should be evident before the teacher provides supplementary information.

In any case, the student should not be subjected to conditions which may interfere with consolidation processes that take place immediately following the movement. Teacher comments should be delayed for a brief interval of time so that the student can process and encode the information he obtained during and after the movement.

Perhaps the most efficient way for the teacher to proceed after this delay is to assist the student in the decision-making process. If the student is unable to make goal/outcome or plan/movement comparisons, then the teacher could provide augmented feedback. If the student can determine the degree of goal attainment and whether he moved as planned, the teacher could be available to help the student in his decisions about the next response.

When the results of the two comparisons are of the YES/YES type (Table 1), the teacher should be prepared to guide the student into stage two of skill acquisition. When the comparisons yield results of "something's wrong" or "surprise" (Table 1), the teacher should assist the student in recognizing what alternative strategies he may use in organizing his next response. The "everything's wrong" result requires the most teacher involvement both in terms of helping the student analyze the situation and in providing additional support and motivation to maintain the student's drive level (Burke and Meyer, 1970). Hopefully, all students will eventually attain one or more YES/YES results and be ready to move into the second stage of skill acquisition.

Stage II. Fixation/Diversification

Once the student has the idea of the movement, the two most important areas requiring continued teacher involvement would seem to be (1) structuring conditions of practice, and (2) providing feedback and assisting in decision processes. There are other possible types of teacher behaviors during Stage II. However, they are assumed to be less crucial to skill development.

Conditions of Practice. Structuring the environmental conditions for the practice of a *closed* skill is relatively easy for the teacher. The regulatory conditions are stable or stationary during the performance of the movement. Thus, the teacher's responsibilities are (1) to have the performer practice under the same conditions as well as will prevail under test circumstances (e.g., actual competition in a sport), and (2) to try to hold constant all regulatory stimuli while providing for the normal variation of nonregulatory inputs.

The task of structuring the environment for the practice of *open* skills is more complex. The teacher's objective is to vary systematically the regulatory conditions, thus enabling the performer to acquire the repertoire of motor patterns that match the total number of possible stimulus subsets. How to proceed in varying the environment has not been investigated to any great extent.[5] One possible outcome of an obviously poor procedure would seem evident, however. Prolonged practice under one or a very limited number of possible subsets of regulatory conditions could result in a probability distribution within the individual's response repertoire which may not be in accord with the probability of those conditions actually occurring. Thus, restricting variability in the environment may result in the development of one or a few motor patterns when the actual conditions under which the movement is to be performed require a multitude of motor patterns. Perhaps the safest procedure for the teacher would be to allow the total range of possible variation in regulatory conditions to occur. In practical terms for the physical educator, this means that once the student has the basic concept of an open skill, he is placed into the actual

[5]Although at a preliminary stage, research is presently underway in this area for skills involving body and limb transport in three-dimensional tracking (Schwartz, 1970).

game conditions or under the conditions as they would normally occur. The alternative teacher strategy would involve (1) identifying all possible regulatory subsets, (2) determining the probability of their occurrence under actual conditions, (3) structuring the environment, systematically introducing variation covering the total range of possibilities in accord with their probability of occurrence, and (4) avoiding prolonged practice under any one environmental variation.

Feedback and Decision Processes. The teacher can provide augmented feedback of two types: (1) information concerning the movement's execution (knowledge of performance) or (2) information about the degree of goal attainment (knowledge of results). During the fixation stage for closed skills, the student is trying to increase the consistency with which the effective movement is produced. The student is striving to eliminate ineffectual and, perhaps, extraneous components within his motor pattern. Therefore, if augmented feedback seems warranted, the most appropriate type of information the teacher could provide for closed skills seems to be knowledge of performance. Providing additional information about how the movement was performed could take several forms, for example, verbal description, demonstration, instant-replay video tape, or polaroid graph-check sequences (Del Rey, 1970; Hampton, 1970). When the information should be administered is not clear. As discussed previously, additional information should not be given immediately after the response to avoid interference with consolidation of intrinsic feedback. Perhaps, augmented feedback would be most usable if administered just prior to the next response during the time in which the individual is formulating his next motor plan. Here is a potentially fruitful area of research.

In the second stage of acquiring an open skill, when the performer is trying to develop as many diverse motor patterns as required, the environmental conditions from one attempt to the next will probably change. If augmented feedback seems necessary, providing information about the outcome produced (knowledge of results) or even about the regulatory conditions that were effective during the movement seems most appropriate. The learner's task in acquiring an open skill is not to move in one prescribed fashion but to consistently produce a particular outcome under variable environmental conditions. Giving information to the student about how he moved during his last attempt will be of little assistance when he will probably have to move differently for his next attempt. If the student needs additional information in order to evaluate his previous response, it would seem helpful (1) to review the environmental conditions that were effective at the time he selected a particular motor pattern and (2) to provide for greater specificity of information concerning the degree of goal attainment. As there is a time stress between the selection and the execution of the motor pattern in the performance of open skills, one of the difficulties of the learner relates to which of the many motor patterns that could be used *should* be selected to match the conditions on that attempt. Restructuring the conditions, if possible, so that the learner can identify the important elements requiring a particular modification of the basic motor plan could be an important feedback function of the teacher. If an instant-replay video tape device is available, the environmental conditions could be recorded from the performer's point of view. Similarly, information concerning the nature of the outcome produced by the performer's movement could be augmented through the teacher's verbal description or through some graphic recording (e.g., video tape).

Each attempt of an open skill during stage two probably will involve decision processes similar to those in the initial stage until the performer identifies the total range of motor patterns required. Further, the ability to predict or anticipate the occurrence of particular conditions will be slowly developed. The type of teacher involvement in the on-going decision making and in the prediction processes is an area in which research seems essential if we are going to understand how to facilitate acquisition of open skills.

SUMMARY: APPLICATION TO TEACHING

All the operations a teacher performs in an attempt to facilitate skill learning are directed toward helping the student match his movement to the environmental demands. The nature of environmental requirements, therefore, affects not only the performer but the strategies employed by the teacher.

During early stages of skill acquisition, the type of movement involved (open or closed) affects some aspects of teacher behavior, such as the added complexity of structuring open skill environments. Other areas of teacher behavior during this first stage may involve very similar operations for both open and closed skills. However, during stage two, the nature of teacher behavior is very much determined by the type of movement to be learned. What may be an appropriate teacher strategy during acquisition of a closed skill may be inappropriate for, and even detrimental to, the acquisition of an open skill. Effective teaching thus requires analysis of the nature of the skill to be learned.

REFERENCES

Annett, J. & Kay, H. Knowledge of results and "skilled performance." *Occupational Psychology*, 1957, 31, 69.

Bartlett, F. C. *Remembering, A study in experimental and social psychology*. Cambridge: Cambridge University Press, 1932.

Bartlett, F. C. Some problems of "display" and "control." In A. Michotte (Ed.), *Miscellanea psychologica*. Louvain: Libraire Philosophique, 1947.

Bernstein, N. *The co-ordination and regulation of movements*. Oxford: Pergamon Press, 1967.

Bilodeau, I. M. Information feedback. In E. A. Bilodeau (Ed.), *Acquisition of skill*. New York: Academic Press, 1966.

Bruner, J. S. *Processes in cognitive growth: Infancy*. Clark University: Press-Barre Publishers, 1968.

Bruner, J. S., Goodnow, J. J., & Austin, G. A. *A study of thinking*. New York: Wiley and Sons, 1956.

Burke, T. & Meyer, J. Accuracy of overhand throwing behavior under different conditions of information feedback and incentive motivation. In *Proceedings of the Second Canadian Psycho-Motor Learning and Sports Psychology Symposium*, University of Windsor, October, 1970.

Del Rey, P. The effects of video-taped feedback and environmental certainty on form, accuracy and latency during skill acquisition. Unpublished doctoral dissertation. Teachers College, Columbia University, 1970.

Duncker, K. On problem-solving. *Psychological Monograph*, 1945, 58, No. 270.

Estes, W. K. Toward a statistical theory of learning. *Psychological Review*, 1950, 57, 94.

Estes, W. K. Component and pattern models with Markovian interpretations. In R. R. Bush & W. K. Estes (Eds.), *Studies in mathematical learning theory*. Stanford: Stanford University Press, 1959.

Estes, W. K. Probability learning. In A. W. Melton (Ed.), *Categories of human learning*. New York: Academic Press, 1964.

Evarts, E. V. Representation of movements and muscles by pyramidal tract neurons of the precentral motor cortex. In M. D. Yahr & D. P. Purpura (Eds.), *Neurophysiological basis of normal and abnormal motor activities*. New York: Raven Press, 1967.

Fitts, P. M. Factors in complex skill learning. In R. Glaser (Ed.), *Training research and education*. Pittsburgh: University of Pittsburgh Press, 1963.

Gentile, A. M. Short-term retention of simple motor acts. Unpublished doctoral dissertation, Indiana University, 1967.

Gentile, A. M., & Stadulis, R. Short-term motor memory and consolidation. In *Proceedings of the Second Canadian Psycho-Motor Learning and Sports Psychology Symposium*, University of Windsor, October, 1970.

Guthrie, E. R. *The psychology of learning*. New York: Harper and Row, 1952.

Hampton, G. E. The effects of manipulating two types of feedback, knowledge of performance and knowledge of results, in learning a complex motor skill. Unpublished doctoral dissertation, Teachers College, Columbia University, 1970.

Harlow, H. F. The formation of learning sets. *Psychological Review*, 1949, 56, 51.

Higgins, J. R. & Angel, R. W. The correction of tracking errors without sensory feedback. *Journal of Experimental Psychology*, 1970, 84, 412.

Holding, D. H. *Principles of training*. Oxford: Pergamon Press, 1965.

James, W. *The principles of psychology*. Vol. 2. New York: Dover Press, 1950.

Kay, H. The development of motor skills from birth to adolescence. In E. A. Bilodeau (Ed.), *Principles of skill acquisition*. New York: Academic Press, 1969.

Knapp, B. *Skill in sport*. London: Routledge and Kegan Paul, 1964.

Konorski, J. *Integrative activity of the brain*. Chicago: University of Chicago Press, 1967.

Lashley, K. S. The problem of serial order in behavior. In L. A. Jeffries (Ed.), *Cerebral mechanisms in behavior*. New York: John Wiley and Sons, 1951.
Levine, M. Hypothesis behavior. In A. M. Schrier, H. F. Harlow, & F. Stollinitz (Eds.), *Behavior of nonhuman primates*. Vol. 1. New York: Academic Press, 1965.
Lorenz, K. Innate basis of learning. In K. H. Pribram (Ed.), *On the biology of learning*. New York: Harcourt, Brace and World, 1969.
Luria, A. R. *Higher cortical functions in man*. New York: Basic Books, 1966.
Miller, G. A., Galanter, E. G. & Pribram, K. H. *Plans and the structure of behavior*. New York: Holt, Rinehart and Winston, 1960.
Mosston, M. *Teaching physical education*. Columbus, Ohio: Charles E. Merrill, 1966.
Poulton, E. C. On prediction in skilled movements. *Psychological Bulletin*, 1957, 54, 467.
Pribram, K. H. Reinforcement revisited: A structural view. In M. Jones (Ed.), *Nebraska symposium on motivation*. Lincoln: University of Nebraska Press, 1963.
Ragsdale, C. E. How children learn the motor types of activities. In N. B. Henry (Ed.), *The forty-ninth yearbook (Part 1: Learning and instruction)*, National Society for the Study of Education. Chicago: University of Chicago Press, 1950.
Ruch, T. C. Basal ganglia and cerebellum. In T. C. Ruch, H. D. Patton, J. W. Woodbury, & A. L. Towe (Eds.), *Neurophysiology*. Philadelphia: W. B. Saunders, 1965.
Schwartz, S. The reliability characteristics of a projection device. In *Proceedings of the Second Psycho-Motor Learning and Sports Psychology Symposium*, University of Windsor, October, 1970.
Solley, W. The effects of verbal instruction of speed and accuracy upon the learning of a motor skill. *Research Quarterly*, 1952, 23, 231.
Sperling, G. The information available in brief visual presentations. *Psychological Monograph*, 1960, 74, No. 11.
Stadulis, R. Coincidence-anticipation in children. Unpublished doctoral dissertation, Teachers College, Columbia University, 1970.
Tolman, E. C. *Purposive behavior in animals and men*. Berkeley: University of California Press, 1951.
Woodworth, R. S. & Schlosberg, H. *Experimental psychology*. New York: Henry Holt & Co., 1954.

THEORETICAL FRAMEWORKS FOR AN UNDERSTANDING OF THE ACQUISITION OF PERCEPTUAL-MOTOR SKILLS

H. T. A. Whiting

The student of perceptual-motor skill acquisition is concerned with the study of the development of highly organized, complex human behavior involving the whole organism working as a coordinated unit. At this stage of knowledge of the processes involved, any framework which will aid in understanding such a complex phenomenon, which will prove of heuristic value and which is in itself not so oversimplified as to prove facile is to be welcomed.

Reprinted with permission from H. T. A. Whiting. Theoretical frameworks for an understanding of the acquisition of perceptual motor skills. *Quest XVII* (1972), pp. 24 34.

Every sympathy can be felt with Gentile's (1972) dissatisfaction at the "disjunctive collection of facts, largely devoid of unifying themes" in many of the existing motor-learning textbooks. A similar situation existed (and continues to exist in places) in the U.K. in relation to academic courses concerned with skill acquisition—particularly at the B.Ed. degree level. This state of affairs prompted me to present a unified conceptual framework within the context of ball-skill acquisition (Whiting, 1969). This model, classified as a systems analysis of perceptual-motor performance, is closely allied to the communication models outlined by Fitts (1964) in an article in which he proposed three broad categories of framework for the study of perceptual-motor skill. At the same time, it draws on concepts which are utilized in what he designates as control system models.

One of the limitations of the model I put forward was the fact that textbook presentation necessitated a static two-dimensional form whereas the conception I had in mind was that of a three-dimensional adaptive-system model elaborating and integrating over time. This limitation prompted me to comment:

> One of the difficulties in presenting two-dimensional models of this kind on paper is that they give the reader the idea of a static system. The nervous system of the human body is constantly active (in terms of the firing of nerve cells), the environment (both internal and external) is continually changing, attention fluctuates and man is never still. The components of the model while maintaining their overall basic structure and function are in a continuous state of change, of elaboration and sophistication. The model must be conceived as a dynamic one.

Gentile would appear to be presenting a similar model to the one I have outlined (Fig. 1) and, moreover, to be aware of both its usefulness and limitations.

The basic emphasis in both our approaches is to consider man as an information-processing system. While the working analogy with more mechanical communication systems to which information theory is normally applied is a useful one, particularly as a first stage, it also is a narrow one. Although a consideration of the human organism as an information-processing system with limited channel capacity (Welford, 1968) has been of considerable value, the fact that difficulties have been encountered in generalizing from a theory developed in the context of more mechanistic communication systems is perhaps not surprising.

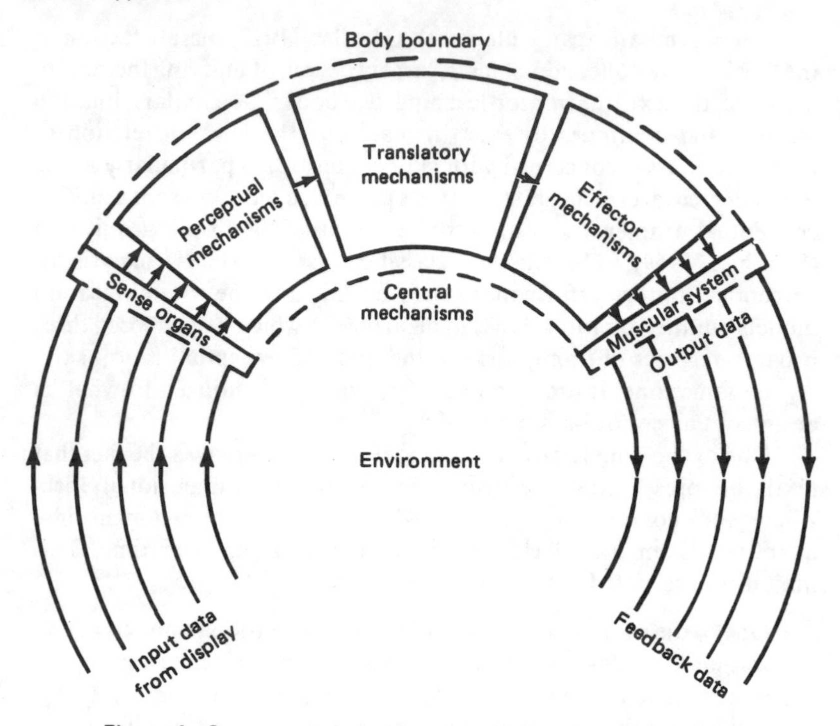

Figure 1. Systems analysis of perceptual-motor performance.

While information from the display is necessary for performance decisions to be made, it is not true that such decisions are dictated solely by such information and thus a pure information theory model is incomplete[1]. As Meredith (1964) has pointed out:

> Any day you can witness men exposed to information who make decisions manifestly not necessitated by the information and often indeed incompatible with it. It is information *selected*

[1]Gentile fails to stress this point although it will not have escaped her notice. But at the same time on page [274] she argues that a football player wishing to intercept the ball is not free to choose or decide where and when he is to move once he has established the interception goal.

She continues, "Rather the ball and its flight pattern determine the organization of the motor pattern which will be effective." But, there will be variation in how the player uses this input—the stimulus itself does not account for the end result (Bartley, 1970). He could, for example, intercept early or late. As Gentile suggests, he has a "tolerance band" and this point will need to be returned to later in discussing open skills.

and often *transmuted* and further *augmented* from our internal source, which shapes the decision.

While decision-theorists look to the current situation for evidence of the variables that control decision-making, it is clear that the display alone cannot account for the response produced by the individual. Information both from the display and from memory stores is only the starting point of a decision: "Preference and belief are the other two factors. Preference expresses taste and temperament and it influences both the selecting of information and the felt relevance of particular beliefs [Meredith, 1964]."

Dynamic decision-theory, which needs to be incorporated into any comprehensive model of perceptual-motor skill performance,[2] deals with variables in the current situation which affect decision-making as well as those which are due to past experience (Edwards & Tversky, 1967). While the impact of information-processing on decision-making assumes a central role in decision theory, it will be appreciated that the *value* of the stimulus subset—its *utility* value—will influence decision-making, as will the *probability* of the outcome of a particular event. It also will be appreciated that different kinds of information may have different utility values for different persons, or for the same person on different occasions, and such values may affect the strategies adopted.

In all acts of behaviour, it is neccessary to process information from the display. Gentile rightly stresses the importance of *selective* attention to those stimulus subsets in the display which are pertinent (Norman, 1969).[3] For some skills, such information will be of primary

[2] I am not criticizing Gentile's model on this account, since in my own approach I have avoided such elaboration for the sake of simplicity.

[3] It is difficult to understand Gentile's usage of "identify and selectively attend" (page [274]) which surely should be reversed in order? A related difficulty appears on page [275] when the statement "identify and process information" is used as though they were distinct and sequential stages in analysis. It would seem more logical to suggest that selective attention leads to the processing of information from the display which in turn leads to identification.

Later (page [285]), in relation to the teaching situation, Gentile makes the comment that ". . . obviously all of the regulatory (relevant) stimuli must be evident during initial student attempts . . ." Whichever way one interprets "evident," i.e., obvious, perceptible or present, available, this statement is a truism. But, the stimuli that are relevant will entirely depend on the conditions created. The relevant stimuli in a game situation will be different from those pertaining when a subskill is removed from the game.

A qualification is also necessary to the "regulatory (relevant) stimuli," since consideration of progression hypotheses (Fitts & Posner, 1967; Whiting, 1969) cautions against the assumption that the beginner utilizes the same information as the expert. The teacher and learner, therefore, must be aware of what the regulatory stimuli are at various stages of learning a particular skill.

importance, while for others, its purpose may simply be that of indicating to the person performing the skill where or when it is to be carried out (e.g., in a shot-put circle; at 06.30 hours precisely sound the bugle call), its use in actual ongoing control of the movement being minimal.

Adams (1966) makes the point that attention is always "to" something. In his case, toward a stimulus subset of a general stimulus field. The major difficulty, as he implies, is in deciding upon how a particular stimulus subset becomes instrumental in producing a response. Difficulties similar to those encountered in discussing attention, arise with respect to the concept of orientation. As indicated in the following quotation from Fellows (1968), the difficulty is further enhanced in restricting the concept to the classical orienting-reflex.

> These reflexes involve such overt receptor-adjusting R's as turning the head and eyes towards the source of an S, pricking up the ears, etc. These R's together with their recently discovered covert accompaniments (EEG changes, physio-chemical changes in sense organs, muscle tonus) are now usually referred to as the 'orientation reaction' (Lynn, 1966). This has two main features: (1) it serves to increase the organism's capacity to extract information from the environment; and (2) it prepares the organism to respond on the basis of what it receives (Berlyne, 1960).

Such a limited conception developing from the early work of Pavlov (1927) is not accepted by current Russian developmental psychologists. Fellows (1968), for example, notes that Zaporozhets has made the distinction between

> . . . *executive behavior* (e.g., pressing a key, pushing a toy car along a maze) upon which the goal is contingent, and *orienting-investigatory activity* (e.g., touching the keys, feeling the paths of the maze with the fingers, turning the head towards signals, following the movements of the experimenter during a demonstration), which prepares the subject for the executive actions.

Gibson (1968) elaborates this idea further in discussing the senses as perceptual-systems. He suggests at one stage, that such systems are oriented in the appropriate way for the assimilation of environmental information and that such a procedure depends upon the general orientation of the whole body. The generality of such a process is further reflected in his statement that perceptual systems ". . . serve to explore the information available in sound, mechanical contact, chemical contact and light." In a more specific way he contends that "... the animal adopts temporary orientations to events and objects whenever he attends to them."

Given the kind of interpretation above (which Gentile seems to have in mind) I find it difficult to understand the exclusion of orienting responses from the category of movements classified as adaptive. While there is orienting behavior which is primarily innate (Fantz, 1967; Salapatek & Kessen, 1966; Kessen, et al., 1965), in the main this would seem to fall into the category of learned behavior. Such orienting responses would then be considered as skills in themselves and could be interpreted by a similar kind of model to that currently being discussed.[4] It might well be that an early stage in skill-learning is getting the idea of the *orientation* required in order to be capable of picking up the appropriate information! Such an idea might apply particularly in the case of social skills. Argyle (1969) makes the point that, "In general it can be said that the relationships between people are reflected in the way they are positioned and oriented—as can be seen in a courtroom or a debating hall."

Gentile's Stage 1, "Getting the idea of the movement," is I think of such importance as to deserve particular emphasis, although it does seem unnecessary for her talk about need-reduction. In any skill-learning situation, we are faced as teachers with an *individual*—an individual who has more or less highly developed abilities and skills at his disposal. We do not expect the learner to produce highly adapted motor patterns at the first attempt (although our task will probably be easier the nearer such initial attempts are to the required terminal performance). I have summarized (Whiting, 1969) this procedure previously as follows.

> Newell, Shaw & Simon (1959) talk about 'plans' in describing the general strategy of a performance before the details have been worked out. It would appear that a similar viewpoint would suit the present situation. The coach is trying to get across to the player a procedure—a rough outline of what follows what in performance of the skill in question. He is not really intending that the player should reproduce the skill in the

[4]Gentile seems to recognize this, since on page [287] she talks about "instruction pertaining to orienting movements."

way that he has demonstrated it (he is probably incapable of doing so anyway). He is trying to get him to reproduce a rough approximation to the skill in order that his behavior may be 'shaped' towards the final required performance. It would appear that models for so-called 'imitation' might better be considered as being used for the purpose of 'social facilitation' (Thorpe, 1956). This term developing from animal psychology would imply, not that the person is imitating in the sense of copying exactly but is being made aware that a particular movement is both feasible and desirable. What this really amounts to, is getting the player to discriminate an appropriate action as against all the other possible actions which he might have carried out in the situation.

What we are attempting to do, is to get the person to produce a movement pattern which is as near as possible to that required, in order that we may shape such patterns by the use of feedback of one form or another. We may use a number of artifices for this purpose—demonstration, manual guidance, visual aids, or verbal mediation. But, even in this simple analysis we have to be careful. Once again, a consideration of progression hypotheses would cause us to question the assumption that the information utilized by the learner in the early stages is similar to that which is utilized by the expert performer. Such information may in fact differ both in quality as well as quantity, and it may be necessary for the learner to go through the initial stages in order to be able to achieve optimal performance at some later date.

Gentile touches upon a fundamental issue in relation to skill learning and to the learning of so-called "open" skills in particular. So fundamental, in fact, that superficial treatment can be misleading. The crux of the problem is implicit in the statement made (page [275]) relating to the learning of open skills: "Thus, of even greater importance than simply formulating motor output, the task for the learner is to identify and process information about the environmental conditions that control his movement." Here, a value judgment is being made in favor of learning appropriate stimulus subsets as compared with learning the appropriate motor output. There does not appear to be adequate experimental evidence which would support such a statement. Further elaboration would perhaps be helpful at this stage.

From a theoretical viewpoint, Knapp (1961), extrapolating from the work of Poulton (1957), has proposed a skill classification on a continuum ranging from open to closed depending upon the extent to which control of the skill is determined by exteroceptive rather than interoceptive information. While such a classification is useful at an everyday level for categorization purposes, the analysis cannot be pushed too far. Many skills involve what have been termed "ballistic" movements which take place over such a short period of time that it must be assumed information from the external environment can have no regulatory function. Therefore, many skills classified on Knapp's continuum as being open may include components which in themselves are closed skills (controlled by proprioceptive feedback at lower levels or preprogrammed in the brain as a whole). Thus, they are open in the sense that it is necessary to monitor information from the display for the purpose of determining when to trigger off a movement, but the movement itself is a closed skill (e.g., a push-pass in a game of football or hitting a nail into a piece of wood). For this reason, I have referred to such tasks as "closed skills in an open situation" (Whiting, 1969).

From the practical point of view, the decision to be made by the teacher in such situations is whether to teach such ballistic actions outside the more complex total skill situation and then put the relatively sophisticated closed-skill performer into the situation to learn to fit such actions to the appropriate open stimulus subsets or, alternatively, to structure the situation in such a way that the learner acquires the ballistic action within the complex skill situation while he is learning the appropriate stimulus subsets to which to attend. Such a dilemma relates to the concept of whole-part learning and I know of no firm evidence supporting either viewpoint. It is likely that such decisions will be based on the nature of the task and considerations of optimal motivation for the learner. I have speculated upon this issue (Whiting, 1969) in the following way.

> If anything, there has been a discernible move towards methods which span those outlined in sections 2 and 3[5] such that skills

[5]Section 2 presents a development which proceeds from the specific to the general. Ball games are broken down into a series of skills, subskills, and tactical situations. These are then practiced in isolation or in small groups and the game is gradually built up from the isolated skill level to the composite game. As progress is made, more complex skill sequences involving groups of players may be taken out of the game situation and practiced as a unit with the idea that when later fitted back into the game there will be a carry-over from the practice situation.

Section 3 presents an almost reverse procedure which progresses from the general to the specific. In this situation, the players are introduced to the game more or less immediately and specific skills are acquired during the game itself. Any coaching which takes place is always in the game situation and it is considered unnecessary to abstract patterns of play for practice in isolation.

> considered to be too complex to be acquired during a game are practised in isolation while the more simple skills are acquired during play. It must still be recalled that when skills are learned outside the game situation itself, there is still the necessity for experiencing the perceptual cues which are necessary for bringing the ballistic (or other) action into play at the *right* time. There is no reason to suppose that this aspect of the learning is any easier or quicker to be acquired than the effector action itself and it may well be that acquisition is delayed by practising the two in isolation.

The differentiation made by Gentile between "knowledge of results" and "knowledge of performance" is a useful one, particularly in relation to the TOTE concept of Miller, Galanter, & Pribram (1960). Gentile develops this concept at some length—often in a speculative fashion. I was rather more cautious (Whiting, 1969), which does not always help progress!

> The player samples the internal and external feedback from his own attempts at the skill, often together with additional feedback information from the coach—and will usually make some form of discrimination on this basis between his own performance and that of the model.

The quotation above emerged from a discussion of the "image of the movement" as a representational image (Posner, 1967) conjured up by one or another of the artifices previously described. What kind of feedback does the learner use in order to modify his response if it is unsuccessful? Does he utilize another representational image of his own performance and, if so, what criteria are used for comparing one representation with another? Does the initial representation lead to a form of verbal coding explicit to the movement, such as, do this and then this and then this, etc.? If the latter, to what extent does verbal ability contribute to the success of this kind of mediation? Are there stages in development where this kind of mediation is possible and, if so, what forms of representational imagery are used in the absence of verbal ability? Whichever method is utilized, the learner, having made a relatively unsuccessful attempt at the skill, may, on the basis of feedback, be aware that he did not carry out the action as coded. Alternatively, he may be reasonably sure that he carried out the action as coded and suspect that his representation of the desired performance was awry. He may then ask for another demonstration. On the other hand, he may pay little attention to any model of the skilled act that is presented to him and just "play about" with similar actions until he achieves something approaching the desired result and then home in on that action in much the same way a child will do in learning a novel skill in the absence of a teacher. The relationship between learning and teaching is of fundamental importance and one that has been ignored by learning theorists over the years (Whiting, 1971).

Gentile touches on most of the points raised above utilizing a simple model of combinations of success and failure. However, what is apparent in the breakdown of any perceptual-motor skill is that the difficulty may lie in one or more of the subsystems outlined in Fig. 1 or their coordinated functioning. One of the advantages of this kind of systems-analysis of perceptual-motor skill performance is that it focuses attention on such possibilities. It would have been useful for this to have been emphasized in Gentile's article.

I find it difficult to understand Gentile's (page [279]) discussion of a "surprise" experience in which the goal is achieved but "not by the movement as planned." If all attempts at a skill are goal-orientated by definition, then the outcome is always planned. True, the learner may be "surprised" to get so near at the first attempt. In a similar way, I wonder if there can ever be something designated a "complete failure." Presumably any attempts at the skill bear some resemblance to the required action and "shaping" can be taken from there.

Part of this difficulty is a semantic one related to Gentile's use of the word "plan." This is not at all clear from her discussion and there would appear to be inconsistencies from time to time. On page [277], for example, she states, "Secondarily, the question of whether the movement was executed as planned would occur." Here she uses the term "planned" presumably to imply intention with all its subjective connotations. On page [278], a similar usage may be meant, but the statement is ambiguous. Thus, "In the case in which the goal is not attained but the movement is executed as planned the immediate response would seem to be that something is wrong with the motor plan." Does the second phrase mean the movement is executed as intended and, if so, does the last phrase mean something is wrong with the motor intention?

Since in the main Gentile's discussion revolves around Miller, Galanter, & Pribram's (1960) TOTE concept, it might have been appropriate to have retained their usage of the word "plan." They propose that, "A Plan is any hierarchical process in the organism that can control the order in which a sequence of operations is to be performed," and "Thus, we are reasonably confident that 'program' can be substituted everywhere for 'Plan' . . ."

I find it very difficult to go along with Gentile's discussion on the development of open skills (page [281]). Particularly when she suggests that, "Indeed, the performer must develop a response repertoire in which there are an exact number of motor patterns to match the number of possible regulating stimulus subsets." True, this is qualified by the comment, "Each specific pattern may involve a slight modification in the spatial or temporal component within a seemingly common generic formula. However, these slight or marked modifications involve the organization of a uniquely new pattern." I am not sure in this context just how one would want to define "unique."

It seems unlikely that the performer has a vast array of motor patterns available to fit every possible stimulus subset. The implication here would be that each stimulus subset fires off a corresponding motor pattern. Shades of S-R psychology! Imagine the difficulties which would ensue in games-playing as teams or individuals moved from one pitch or court to another where the whole stimulus backcloth may differ in almost every detail. True, one may argue that the stimulus backcloth represents the "non-regulatory stimulus subsets" as Gentile has so very well (page [281]) in relation to the teaching situation. It must, however, be remembered that the ball is perhaps the major regulatory stimulus subset in a ball game and it is always to be discriminated against the backcloth.

There is much evidence available to indicate how such figure-ground differentiations can affect perceptual performance (Alderson, 1971). It is also true that changes of ground, court, etc., do affect a player's performance and he has to learn to adjust to modifications in the display. Is it to be assumed, therefore, that he learns a "uniquely different pattern" for every movement carried out in this new environment? Again, since no stimulus subset is ever the same from one occasion to another, it must be assumed on Gentile's argument that every motor pattern is a one-off attempt to match such a stimulus subset. The motor pattern can then be allowed to decay because it will never be needed again since an identical stimulus subset will never occur! I think it also is important to remember in most open skills that there is a considerable margin for error, although this probably decreases, for example, in very fast ball games. There are in consequence a whole family of possible motor patterns which will do, more or less, in response to any stimulus subset. Furthermore, much can be achieved by varying the orientation of the body in the environment prior to what is being designated as the executive response in the open skill in question.

I would like to be able to produce further evidence in support of speculations about the output characteristics of skill performance. While we have work under way in our own perceptual-motor skills unit, results are not yet available. Much of the current work on skill has been concerned with input characteristics, for the historical reason that these were largely ignored in earlier work. It would seem now that it is the output side which is being neglected.

I do not wish to enter into any further critique about Gentile's discussion of the applications of the model to teaching situations. I have discussed the relationship of learning to teaching in another article (Whiting, 1971) and this to some extent overlaps Gentile's work. I found the rest of her discussion speculative but nevertheless very interesting and thought-provoking. I feel that she has raised a large number of potential research areas which would merit attention.

In conclusion, I would like to say how much I am in agreement with Gentile's basic premises and discussion. For the student reader, I find that the discussion is not helped by the overelaboration which occurs from time to time and the use of jargon like "the individual can select and narrow in on the most effective band width" grates with me. Nevertheless, I feel sure that her model will prove to be a great stimulus to motor skill teaching theory and practice. If at times I have been overcritical of omissions from the model as presented, it should be remembered that learning the theory underlying perceptual-motor skill acquisition is a progression in much the same way as acquiring a skill. The learner goes through a number of stages of development hierarchically structured. The concepts of selective attention, feedback, etc. are just as important here. It would seem logical for the progression to be made via simple models based on information processing to which can be added at a later stage the more complex understanding which is brought about by the inclusion of signal detection theory and other decision-making processes in the system.

REFERENCES

Adams, J. A. Mechanisms of motor responding. In E. A. Bilodeau (Ed.), *Acquisition of skill.* New York: Academic Press, 1966.

Alderson, G. J. K. The perception of velocity in sports situations. In H. T. A. Whiting (Ed.), *Reading in sports psychology—1971.* Longon: Henry Kimpton, 1971.

Argyle, M. *Social interaction.* London: Methuen, 1969.

Bartley, S. H. Some misconceptions concerning perception. *Am. J. Optom. Arch. Am. Acad. Optom.*, 47(4), 259–266.

Berlyne, D. E. *Conflict, arousal and curiosity*. New York: McGraw-Hill, 1960.
Edwards, W., & Tversky, A. *Decision-making*. Hardmondsworth: Penguin, 1967.
Fantz, R. L. Visual perception and experience in early infancy. In H. W. Stevenson, E. H. Hess, & H. L. Rheingold (Eds.), *Early behaviour, comparative and developmental approaches*. New York: Wiley, 1967.
Fellows, B. J. *The discrimination process and development*. London: Pergamon, 1968.
Fitts, P. M. Skill learning. In A. W. Melton (Ed.), *Categories of human learning*. New York: Academic Press, 1964.
Fitts, P. M., & Posner, M. I. *Human performance*. Belmont: Brooks/Cole, 1967.
Gentile, A. M. A working model of skill acquisition with application to teaching. *Quest*, 1972, XVII.
Gibson, J. J. *The senses considered as perceptual systems*. London: George Allen & Unwin, 1968.
Kessen, N., Haith, M. M., & Salapatek, P. The ocular orientation of newborn infants to visual contours. In R. N. Haber (Ed.), *Contemporary theory and research in visual perception*. New York: Holt, Rinehart & Winston, 1968.
Knapp, B. A note on skill. *Occup. Psych.*, 35, 76–78.
Lynn, R. *Attention, arousal and the orientation reaction*. Oxford: Pergamon, 1966.
Meredith, G. P. *Decision theory in the light of recent research*. Unpublished paper, Dept. of Psychology, University of Leeds, 1964.
Miller, G. A., Galanter, E., & Pribram, K. H. *Plans and the structure of behaviour*. New York: Holt, Rinehart & Winston, 1960.
Newell, A., Shaw, J. C., & Simon, H. A. A report on a general problem solving program. *Proceedings of the International Conference on Information Processing*, Paris, 1959.
Norman, D. A. *Memory and attention: an introduction to human information processing*. New York: Wiley, 1969.
Pavlov, I. P. *Conditioned reflexes*. Oxford: University Press, 1927.
Posner, M. I. Short-term memory systems in human information processing. *Acta Psych.*, 27, 267–284.
Poulton, E. C. On prediction in skilled movements. *Psych. Bull.*, 54(6), 467–478.
Salapatek, P., & Kessen, W. Visual scanning of triangles by the human newborn. *J. Exp. Child Psych.*, 3, 155–167.
Thorpe, W. H. *Learning and instinct in animals*. Cambridge: Harvard University Press, 1956.
Welford, A. T. *Fundamentals of skill*. London: Methuen, 1968.
Whiting, H. T. A. *Acquiring ball skill: A psychological interpretation*. London: Bell, 1969.
Whiting, H. T. A. Learning motor skills. In J. Kane (Ed.), *Readings in the psychology of physical education*. London: Routledge & Kegan Paul, 1971.
Zaporozhets, A. V. The development of voluntary movements. In B. Simon (Ed.), *Psychology in the Soviet Union*. London: Routledge & Kegan Paul, 1957.

THE LANGUAGE OF MOTOR LEARNING

Sandra Hoth

Just as a native-speaking German uses a language that is nearly incomprehensible to a first-year German student, professional physical

Reprinted with permission from Sandra Hoth. The language of motor learning. *Quest XXIII* (January 1975), pp. 68-73.

educators too often speak a language that the novice performer cannot grasp. Some teachers are excellent practitioners of organizational technique and have a good understanding of what constitutes a valuable curriculum, but never become great, or even good, teachers because they are unable to communicate with students in terms that are meaningful. The verbal cues they use are like a foreign language to the neophyte, and teacher and student alike feel frustration and disappointment when the desired motor response is not forthcoming.

As relatively proficient athletes, long familiar with the language of the gymnasium, we assume that certain expressions we use are universally crystal clear. The beginning student is uninitiated in our nomenclature and slang and, if we are to communicate with him, it must be in a manner that is meaningful on the basis of his background and understanding. For instance, we can well expect confusion if we tell a novice tennis player to "put his body" into a forehand drive. He is trying very hard simply to get the racket head to make contact with the ball. The closest connection he has had to putting his body into anything, other than the bathtub, was "putting his back" into moving a piano or pushing a car. Now he is asked to make a connection between that gross motor activity and the precise task of contacting a very small ball.

A teacher attempting to get a six-year-old to float on his back may repeatedly tell the youngster to arch his back. "Arch" means little or nothing to a child of this age. The verbal cue must be tied to something familiar to him. Every child knows how to stick out his stomach and a meaningful cue will quickly produce desired results.

To use meaningful, descriptive cues, an instructor should first determine the kinesthetic and mental conceptual cues for the movement he is attempting to elicit. Oxendine (1968) explains that participation in a wide range of motor activities appears to help develop a more accurate kinesthetic sense. If we accept this contention, physical educators, who could be expected to have such a wide range of experiences, should be able to interpret kinesthetic sensations into meaningful verbal cues. But how, in fact, does one transform experience and sensation into a truly communicative language?

PRE-PERFORMANCE VERBALIZATION

The greatest importance is normally placed on the pre-performance or direction-giving phase of verbal instruction. The first step in approaching any motor learning situation is to define specifically the task involved. What are the performance objectives for the student with this particular background?

As well as understanding the nature of the task, the student and teacher should be clear on the quantity of the task that is to be accomplished. This allows the student to pace himself and find satisfaction in approximating the objective. Unless the terminal goals are established by both parties, the teacher may have one goal in mind and the student another. This can create only frustration for both. In determining a common terminal goal, the student should first be given the opportunity to verbalize the goal as he sees it. The teacher's responsibility then is to accept that goal or to make modifications that will make the goal possible. When the goal has been established, the teacher and the learner have begun to communicate.

In determining specific pre-performance instructions, several factors should be considered. First, this is the phase during which formal instruction is most successful. Trial and error learning will be more valuable after the student has some mastery of the task. Second, recent research indicates that initial instruction should be devoted to the gross framework or the general idea rather than to details of the movement. The beginning student is not prepared to deal with too many specifics. He will learn more quickly if he is allowed to spread his attention over the total act, with specific consideration to the major features of the task. He should be given such checkpoints as the initial position, the general direction of the movement, and the final position.

There is not complete agreement among motor learning experts on the value of knowledge of mechanical principles in the learning process. Some teachers use kinesthetic and mechanical principles either to attempt to clarify or to attempt to impress students, instead of using everyday terms which are more meaningful to the student. The nature of the learner must certainly be taken into consideration, but in general Singer's (1968) conclusion appears very sound, that "it is a mistake to assume the students wish to understand what lies behind a process that they consider simply a tool. They want to know how to use the tool to reach a goal but well may not have the curiosity that a teacher does [p. 231].

Directions to the learner should never exceed his comprehension either in language or complexity. Learning can be slowed or disrupted from the outset if excessive mental review is demanded by the nature of the verbal instructions. Problems in motor learning are frequently problems of sorting out complex stimuli rather than inadequacy in motor capacity. Singer (1968) notes the many sensory channels through which the outer world signals to a person, stating that "The amount of sensory information yielded in any situation is more than any one person can perceive [p. 82]." Yet man has basically a single-channel system of reception and interpretation. When bombarded by many signals or tasks, the execution process slows down and the chance of error increases. The responsibility of the teacher, then, is to help the student learn to deal with one element or sub-routine at a time. Cues should be carefully sequenced to conform to the main features of the task. It might be helpful to consider teaching a skill in terms of writing a programmed learning guide. Basically, such a program is successful because it is simple and explicit, sequential, multiple and varied in explanation, and successful in getting and keeping the learner's attention.

Whether or not a student or a class understands and learns depends on how he or they interpret the instructions. Pre-performance directions are seldom given to one student at a time. Therefore, the instructions should reach as many students as possible through diversity of language and multiplicity of cues. Cues should be tied to something meaningful yet should whenever possible be themselves unique or novel.

Pre-performance verbalization for advanced performers should emphasize cues consistent with their stage of skill acquisition. It is generally recognized that verbal instructions are more meaningful for the advanced learner, partially because he has learned the language and has associated certain movement patterns with certain verbal symbols. Also, he is less likely to be distracted by extraneous stimuli. With the language problem lessened, verbalization for advanced students (Lawther, 1968) becomes a "means of: (1) tying together sequential simpler tasks, (2) tying specific cues to specific responses, (3) learning which acts and what variations of previous acts are appropriate for present purposes [p. 72]." Situation cues as well as movement pattern cues become important to the advanced learner.

In summary, pre-performance verbalization should (*a*) involve the student in establishing what the task is to be and, in so doing, build a language bridge between student and teacher, (*b*) define the general task with simple, explicit, sequential, and novel word cues, and (*c*) be consistent with the skill acquisition level of the student.

PERFORMANCE VERBALIZATION

Little verbal instruction occurs during the performance phase of motor learning. The question has been raised as to whether or not students should be trained, in the pre-performance phase, to analyze their own performance on the basis of visual and kinesthetic cues. Although use of kinesthetic training may aid skilled performers in mental rehearsal, the importance of kinesthesis in motor learning has not been firmly established. Research seems to indicate that much kinesthetic feedback and response operate at levels below consciousness. The theory that man is capable of perceiving only vague or gross kinesthesis is consistent with research findings (Brown, 1969) that indicate that subjects more accurately assess movements of large joints than of small distal ones. Robb (1972) found that the enforced use of proprioceptors was not superior to conventional methods in learning specific motor patterns. Visual and tactile feedback appear to have a greater effect on the individual's total perception, and when in conflict with kinesthetic feedback, the kinesthetic feedback is diminished.

Kinesthetic perceptual training may be of value for the advanced level learner, and may be achieved by repeated emphasis on specific performance phase cues. However, beginning level performers do not have a vivid awareness of body position. The sensations they experience are those involving large joints and gross movement patterns. While emphasizing a gross framework sensation may be valuable, special notice to a specific proprioceptive sensation may hinder rather than help the learner.

POST-PERFORMANCE VERBALIZATION

Practice doesn't always make perfect. Performers do not improve if they have no knowledge of results of their actions. Knowledge of results can ensue from internal or external feedback.

> Feedback can be concurrent or terminal. It can evaluate, compare, prescribe or affect performance. It can serve to motivate, to reinforce, and to change performance. Feedback can give information about an entire movement sequence, a sub-routine, an executive program, a temporal error, or a sequential error [Robb, 1972, p. 151].

To be most effective feedback should be available immediately following the performance, should be meaningful to the performer, and should be specific. Internal feedback is immediate but may be difficult for a beginning student to interpret. There are certain activities in which a performer will have only a vague notion of the quality of his performance. In these cases, the teacher is the only significant source of feedback and the real key to the student's learning.

It is, therefore, very important to determine the language of meaningful feedback. What makes feedback cues significant to the learner? First, the verbal cues should supply a positive correction, not merely a restatement or an analysis of the inaccuracies. A comment like "You let your forward get past you" gives a performer no constructive means of correcting the mistake but simply reiterates the obvious. Telling a swimmer that his straight arm pull results in a disadvantageous body position, which increases drag and consequently slows his progress, gives him a nice mechanical analysis but doesn't get him any closer to a bent arm pull. Positive instructions give a causal reason for obvious success or failure *and* a means of changing the results.

Second, as emphasized previously, corrections should center on adjustments in gross movements and on strategy rather than on specific movements. A tennis player who finishes a stroke with the racket face parallel to the ground may find it very difficult to concentrate on eliminating that specific wrist flip movement. He might be told to "Finish with your elbow pointed down." This is a larger joint, a slower movement, and an easier correction.

One of the greatest mistakes an eager instructor can make is to deluge the student with a running commentary on everything he is doing wrong. The beginning student, in particular, is hindered by this lack of sensitivity on the part of his instructor. The multiplicity of stimuli is already overwhelming. The teacher's role is to simplify, not complicate. Major errors that violate known principles of mechanics or substantially deviate from the task objectives should be corrected. However, minor errors should not be allowed to upset either instructor or learner. As the learner develops skill, the movement patterns and speed will change and minor errors will automatically disappear and be replaced by others which will in turn disappear.

There is a point during early exposure to an activity (Cratty, 1968) when the student needs to be left alone to ". . . permit the various neurological mechanisms over which he has relatively little control to smooth and retain the coordinated act [p. 119]." During this time he will gain little from augmented feedback, because he is not prepared to process it. Verbalization is extraneous and even distracting. The teacher would do well to force himself to keep quiet and let the student practice until such time as he has questions or until major errors make interruption necessary.

In dealing with the skilled student, teachers should carefully consider the corrections they suggest. Although more specific adjustments must be made to change responses at a higher skill level, the suggested correction should be for a developing incorrect pattern and not just for some minor mistake that will be automatically corrected. Too many students suffer the "paralysis-by-analysis" syndrome because their instructors feel compelled to say something, anything.

Post-performance cues should follow the basic language laws. They should be explicit and simple; they should show the learner, positively and constructively, what to avoid and how better to approximate his objective; and above all, they should be verbalized only if they are absolutely necessary to the learning process.

It would doubtless be helpful if the specialists writing in their own areas of expertise would include verbalizations they have found helpful. Further research, invention, and imaginative innovation could be shared. However, the responsibility for effective verbalization rests with each individual teacher. He should be acutely aware of every word that he utters. Verbalization can be extremely significant in relaying and refining motor patterns, but only if teachers are willing to acknowledge the problems involved and concentrate their efforts on making their language meaningful.

REFERENCES

Brown, R. C. (Ed.) *New perspectives of man in action*. Englewood Cliffs, N.J.: Prentice-Hall, 1969.

Cratty, B. J. *Psychology and physical activity*. Englewood Cliffs, N.J.: Prentice-Hall, 1968.

Lawther, J. D. *The learning of physical skills*. Englewood Cliffs, N.J.: Prentice-Hall, 1968.

Oxendine, J. B. *Psychology of motor learning*. New York: Appleton-Century-Crofts, 1968.

Robb, M. *The dynamics of motor-skill acquisition*. Englewood Cliffs, N.J.: Prentice-Hall, 1972.

Singer, R. N. *Motor learning and human performance*. New York: Macmillan, 1968.

Index